Wildlife on your
DOORSTEP
THE LIVING COUNTRYSIDE

A Reader's Digest selection

WILDLIFE ON YOUR DOORSTEP

First Edition Copyright © 1986
The Reader's Digest Association Limited, Berkeley Square House,
Berkeley Square, London W1X 6AB

Second reprint 1990

Copyright © 1986
Reader's Digest Association Far East Limited
Philippines Copyright 1986
Reader's Digest Association Far East Ltd

Front cover picture: Uninvited guests – starling chicks in a
nest built beneath the roof of an old house.

Wildlife on your
DOORSTEP
THE LIVING COUNTRYSIDE

PUBLISHED BY THE READER'S DIGEST ASSOCIATION LIMITED
LONDON   NEW YORK   MONTREAL   SYDNEY   CAPE TOWN

Originally published in partwork form
by Eaglemoss Publications Limited and Orbis Publishing Limited

Consultant

Robert Gibbons

Contributors

George Barker	Paul Freeman	Keith Porter
Stephen Blackmore	Martin Gardner	Bob Press
David Carter	Stephen Harris	John Sankey
Michael Chinery	Charles Hilton	Keith Snow
David Corke	Jack Laundon	David Squire
Steve Downer	Roger Lovegrove	Bob Stebbings
Euan Dunn	Chris Mead	Roger Tabor
Deborah Elton	Barbara Midgley	WG Teagle
Chris Feare	Anne Miller	Michael Tweedie
John Feltwell	Pat Morris	Graham Twigg
Jim Flegg	Stephen Nicholls	John Waters
Pamela Forey	Jane Ponti	Roger Whiteway

Contents

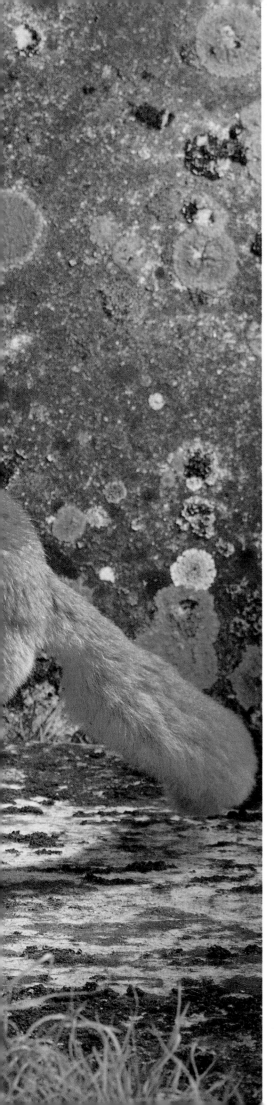

Wildlife on your
DOORSTEP

Introduction

At first sight our towns and cities seem extremely inhospitable to wildlife. It is indeed true that the more timid or demanding species shun urban areas, but many others thrive in cities, which are surprisingly green places and offer diverse habitats.

Some plants and animals have simply followed their natural foodplants or nesting situations into towns wherever they have occurred, adapting to the increased level of disturbance. There is no shortage of plants in towns. For example, a survey in Edinburgh revealed over one million trees in the city, at a considerably higher density than in the surrounding countryside. Similarly, there are over a million acres of gardens in Britain, most of them in towns and cities, and most mature gardens contain two to three hundred species of plants. So, many plant-eating or tree-dwelling animals, whether they are moths and butterflies, or goldfinches nesting in an apple tree, can feel as much at home in towns as in the country.

Other plants and animals have found a completely new niche for themselves in the urban environment, and some species are now almost completely dependent on town and city life for survival. The Oxford ragwort is one, and the house martin is another. Several sea-birds, especially in northern cities, are now nesting on buildings, and kestrels are following suit in London. Bats, too, have switched from their natural roosts and breeding sites in caves and hollow trees to house lofts. When you add these urban 'invaders' to those animals – particularly the insects and rodents – that have always lived in close conjunction with man and his dwellings, it becomes clear that the urban habitat, far from being hostile to wildlife, actually supports an increasing number and variety of species.

Left: A young fox investigates the possibility of finding a few scraps of food in a dustbin.

WILDLIFE COMES TO OUR CITY CENTRES

The majority of people live in towns, most of which have developed since the Industrial Revolution. Dense Victorian terraced housing and factories, larger suburban homes that sprang up in the interwar years, and modern high rise blocks all provide a home for assorted species of wildlife.

It is a common misconception to think of large cities, with all their inherent problems of noise and congestion, as a 20th century phenomenon. As long ago as the third century AD Rome had a population of about a million people, with associated difficulties of noise and traffic. Since urban habitats have been available for so long, it is not surprising that many animals and plants have established themselves in towns and continue to do so as towns expand and change.

Man-made cliffs One of the most obvious features distinguishing a city from the countryside is its buildings. These may be offices or homes to their original builders, but are regarded as good substitutes for a variety of natural habitats by other species. Tall offices or warehouses make ideal inland 'cliffs' and are treated as such by a number of birds. The ubiquitous town pigeon, for example, is

Above: Herring gulls, which normally nest on cliffs or isolated cliff-top grasslands, are now adapting readily to the abundance of flat and sloping roofs of factories and high rise flats. Although they are a relatively recent arrival on the urban scene (before 1940 urban nesting herring gulls were comparatively rare) they are now a major problem in some coastal towns. The chicks in this picture have hatched on a roof in the centre of Aberdeen. Here and in other towns and cities one of their favourite sources of food will be the municipal rubbish dump, where they often gather in noisy flocks.

descended from the rock dove, an inhabitant of wild, rocky coasts, so it is not surprising that this species does well in towns and cities. Herring gulls find roofs an ideal habitat – the proof is that urban gulls often breed more successfully than their more traditional relatives, quite possibly because of the abundance of food from refuse tips.

Another, somewhat more unusual gull to move into some towns is the kittiwake. It is generally one of the gulls least associated with man, spending the entire winter far out at sea, only returning to land in spring to breed in cliff-ledge colonies. However, in cities such as Newcastle-upon-Tyne, it is beginning to use ledges on deserted warehouses as substitutes for cliffs.

Although gulls may be relatively recent newcomers to towns, other birds have been associated with man's dwellings for so long that in some cases this relationship is reflected in their common names. The house martin is a familiar nesting bird in towns, plastering its mud and spittle nests under eaves or against rafters in outhouses and garages. It is quite likely that the abundance of nest sites provided by the development of towns has allowed its population to expand.

Wall life A great variety of plants have taken a roothold in the crumbling mortar of old buildings and walls. Ferns, such as the rustyback, and flowering plants, such as ivy-leaved toadflax, are common while the curious wall pennywort grows on shaded walls in the south west. Many introduced species have become naturalised on walls. Nor is it just relatively recent walls that are invaded: the tiny fairy foxglove, a favourite alpine of gardeners, is established in places along Hadrian's wall. A more widespread introduction to walls and old buildings is

Above: The grey squirrel is a common mammal in many town parks and is sometimes seen in larger suburban gardens, particularly those that were built in the interwar years which now have tall, mature trees.

Below: Badgers are becoming more common in some cities, although animals as tame as this one are unusual. Many travel quite long distances between a town and the surrounding countryside.

buddleia, a native of China. Despite its size, it can cling to the narrowest of ledges. By providing a copious supply of nectar for red admirals, peacocks, small tortoiseshells and brimstones it is now a welcome and integral part of our urban ecology.

Walls are also a home to a wide variety of different insects and other invertebrates. Many are there for the foodplants, while others are merely using the physical features of the wall. The mid-summer generation of holly blue butterfly feeds on ivy which clothes many walls in suburban areas. Underneath the ivy are insects, woodlice, springtails and spiders, many living just as they would if they were under ivy cover in woodlands.

Snails too are widespread, especially on walls of limestone. Here they derive shelter and food from the plants and calcium carbonate for shell-building from the wall itself. Snails will also rasp away whitewash to obtain this chemical. On sunny, new and sparsely covered walls the highly active, black and white striped zebra spider roams in search of prey. It uses its keen eyesight to locate its prey then, like a miniature cat, stalks it, covering the last couple of centimetres in a rapid leap. It is of course a member of the jumping spider family, Salticidae. One of its relatives, *Segestria florentina,* an introduced species originally from southern Europe, is now well established on walls in a number of ports. It lives in crevices or holes which it lines with a silken tube. At its open end the tube splays out in a fan of threads over the wall. As the tripwires are triggered, the spider darts out of the tunnel to seize its hapless prey.

Inner city life As cities grow at the edges, so the central areas often fall into disrepair. Here and on other derelict ground many urban plants and animals do well. For instance, unlike the woodland-dwelling common red-

Left: Today's distribution of urban foxes reflects the development of our towns. They are most common in southern England in affluent dormitory towns. In the north and Midlands they are least common in industrial cities where housing density is high with small gardens. For example, in the West Midlands conurbation foxes are common in Solihull and parts of West Bromwich, Birmingham and Dudley, but much rarer in the industrial parts of Dudley and the heavily industrialised areas of Walsall and Wolverhampton. You are probably less likely to see an urban fox in areas where there are large numbers of stray dogs.

start, the black redstart is very much a creature of open rocky ground. It was quite common on blitz-damaged sites in London and is now found on derelict city sites throughout Europe.

These areas soon develop a characteristic flora. The stinging nettle, for example, favours rich soils, particularly those that were well fertilised in the past. It is an important species in the ecology of urban environments and is well known as the foodplant of a number of attractive insects. Rosebay willowherb, ragwort, daisies and dandelions are speedy colonizers of any patch of land, and along with numerous garden escapes soon brighten abandoned areas.

Below: Some species of wildlife cannot penetrate further than the city suburbs, while others seek out any available niche to live and reproduce themselves—even a busy city centre.

Wildlife in the city

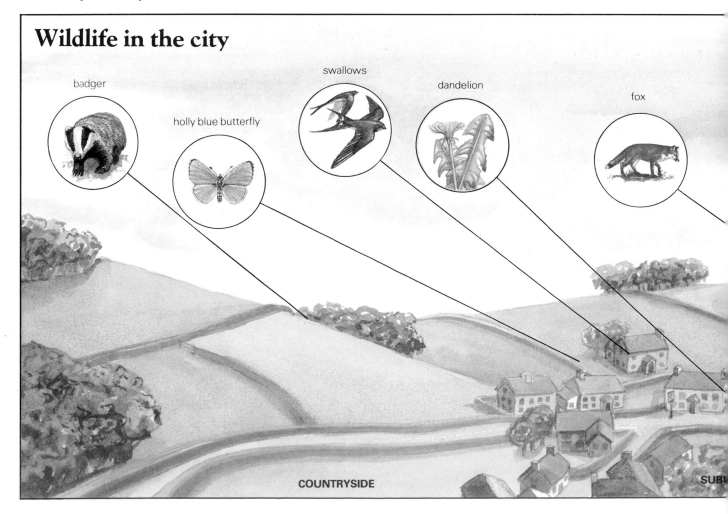

badger

holly blue butterfly

swallows

dandelion

fox

COUNTRYSIDE

SUB

Garden life Gardens present a much more managed facet of urban ecology but nonetheless are extremely rich sources of wildlife. Particularly conspicuous are hoverflies such as the black and yellow, wasp-mimicking *Syrphus ribesii,* or the honey bee-mimicking species of *Eristalis.* Larvae of the former, like ladybirds, are the gardener's friend as they are voracious predators of aphids.

In the large gardens of the mid-1930s private housing developments, a wide range of birds are found. Most numerous are blackbirds, song and mistle thrushes, robins, wrens and blue and great tits, all of which are species that normally nest in bushes or holes in trees. Mature gardens, with enough space for trees and shrubs, provide abundant nest sites. Nestboxes and bird tables also encourage large bird populations. In old inner city areas where houses are smaller and packed together with small gardens, bushes and shrubs and trees are less frequent; here the most common birds are the house sparrow and starling, which nest in or on buildings. Although they are not considered glamorous their sociable nature means they are welcomed in the gardens of many town dwellers.

Tawny owls are sometimes found in areas of privately owned housing nesting high up in holes or in the forks of trees. As they move further into the city their diet changes from mainly small mammals in rural areas to small birds in city centres. Another conspicuous predator of today's cities is the fox, especially in areas of mature gardens. During the ribbon development of the interwar years plots of land were built upon at random, leaving tracts of rural land with isolated fox populations. As these areas were in turn developed, foxes moved into the surrounding suburbs and from there into city centres. Here, in addition to their normal diet, they take food put out for birds and, in affluent areas of some towns, high quality food is left for them. One Bristol resident owns a chain of steak houses, and the local foxes live on steak and cheese.

Above: Sparrows thrive in close proximity to man, and those that live in parks or gardens where they are regularly fed become very tame. They do best in the parts of towns where gardens are very small and there are few trees and shrubs. Like starlings and feral pigeons, they nest in or on buildings, using whatever material is available.

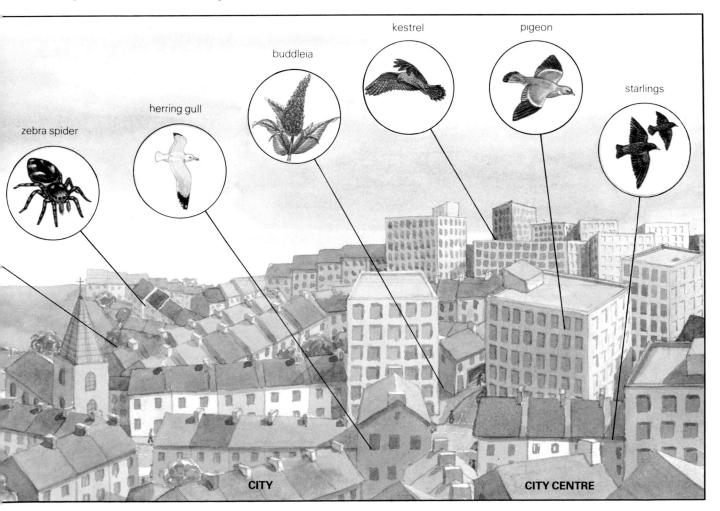

zebra spider

herring gull

buddleia

kestrel

pigeon

starlings

CITY

CITY CENTRE

PAVEMENTS: LIFE ON THE STREET

Among the many artificial habitats we have created in our towns and cities, pavements must seem among the least habitable. Yet, even there, beneath our trampling feet, plants and animals can survive and obtain enough food and water for their needs.

The pavement is a mosaic of different micro-habitats, some very harsh and others more hospitable to life. The harshest of all environments are the paving stones themselves. Only encrusting algae and lichens can survive on these, and even they are often killed by pollution from nearby houses, factories and passing cars, and also from being trampled underfoot. One species of lichen that can survive in such conditions, because it tolerates high levels of sulphur dioxide in the air, is *Lecanora dispersa*; in towns and cities it is black yet in rural areas it is white.

The parts of a pavement most favourable to life are the ribbons of soil between slabs and at the base of walls. Both habitats can build up high levels of nitrogen from the waste products of dogs, in contrast to the paving slabs themselves where these products are quickly washed away by the rain. Furthermore, the bases of walls are rich in calcium which is leached out of the mortar in the brickwork.

Extreme conditions Any plant or animal trying to survive on a pavement has to be able to tolerate extremes of heat. On a summer's day pavements heat up rapidly and, moreover, the buildings surrounding them (especially if tall) reflect the sunlight on to the pavements, increasing the temperature even further. At night they cool off just as swiftly and by dawn can be close to freezing point. Such enormous fluctuations in temperature within a single day can be tolerated by only a few plants, but the sow thistle thrives under these conditions. This species, a robust yellow-flowered member of the daisy family, is most often seen growing at the bases of walls. Here too can be found garden escapes such as snapdragons and wallflowers taking advantage of the nitrogen- and calcium-rich nature of the habitat, as well as the shelter it provides.

The extremes of heat are deadly to many of the animals living on the pavement. Therefore, during the heat of the day creatures such as slugs, earthworms and centipedes hide away under the paving slabs. In the country all these animals live beneath rocks and boulders; to them the paving slabs of the city

Above: Plantains surrounding a drainage hole — here conditions are often damp and therefore much more fertile than the rest of the pavement.

Opposite page: A stray hedgehog can occasionally be found wandering along a city pavement or road.

Right: Some parts of a pavement quickly dry out. Wall screw moss survives this sudden drought by twisting its leaves to help retain water.

Water bears

Living among the thicker colonies of lichens found on pavements are water bears, minute primitive creatures perhaps no more than 0.5mm long. They are able to survive in such a hostile environment as that of a pavement by their ability to shrivel up and remain in this state for many months. As soon as water hits the pavement, they miraculously 'come alive' again.

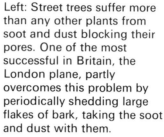

active water bear

shrivelled specimen

Left: Street trees suffer more than any other plants from soot and dust blocking their pores. One of the most successful in Britain, the London plane, partly overcomes this problem by periodically shedding large flakes of bark, taking the soot and dust with them.

Below: Take a close look at a pavement on a hot summer's day and you will probably see dozens of red mites scurrying around. From standing height, however, they are quite invisible.

are simply an extension of this habitat. To appreciate fully the animal life of pavements a nocturnal sortie is needed. The concrete slabs, which were heated up during the day, lose their heat at night and become much colder than the air above. The consequence of this is that moisture from the relatively warm air condenses out on the cold slabs and enables soft-bodied creatures such as slugs and earthworms to emerge from their moist hiding places to feed. The slugs browse on the plants along the cracks and kerbs of pavements, while the earthworms search for dead leaves and other decaying matter to drag down into their burrows, where they will slowly feed on them the following day. The activities of both animals are visible the following morning as silvery trails of dried mucus.

The problem of feet Sow thistle and wallflower are tall fleshy plants that can survive only in a sheltered site such as close to a wall where they will not be trampled under people's feet. Out on the open pavement only low-growing, prostrate or rosette species can survive such rough treatment. Dandelion and knotweed, for example, are both low-

Below: Sow thistle grows well on pavements at the base of a wall, where conditions are often damp and nutrient-rich. This species is one of the largest and most robust in the daisy family, growing to a height of 1.5m (5ft).

growing, robust plants capable of rapidly re-growing from side shoots after being extensively damaged. Mosses such as silvery thread moss keep low enough to be able to survive on open pavements. This moss rarely sets seed. Instead, small portions are accidentally broken off and kicked along by people walking. With luck the piece of moss becomes lodged in a suitable site for colonization.

These tussocks of moss provide a home for herbivorous springtails, which in turn attract their predators, the small rove beetles. As night falls these beetles are joined by their larger relatives, the ground beetles such as *Pterostichus cupreus* and *Harpalus affinis*, both of which are black. They scour the pavements looking for small creatures such as springtails to devour. Their larvae are also carnivorous and feed in the crevices between paving slabs.

The problem of dispersal Many plants that grow in between the stones and concrete face problems of reproduction and dispersal. There may not be another member of the same species close by, so cross-pollination becomes impossible, and there are also likely to be few suitable sites that a plant can colonize and thus perpetuate the species. Most of the more successful pavement plants overcome the first problem by pollinating themselves and the second problem by producing large numbers of wind-borne seeds, which are dispersed over the widest possible area so that the plant gives itself the best opportunity to colonize a new site.

One plant that follows both strategies is mossy pearlwort, a small green-flowered member of the campion family that persists between paving slabs, protected by the slight elevations of the surrounding stones. Mossy pearlwort frequently pollinates itself; later in the year it develops seed capsules borne on stalks. At first the stalks are bent down towards the ground to allow ants to carry away the seeds and thus disperse the species. After a while, however, the plant adopts an alternative strategy to increase the chances of its being dispersed: the stalks straighten up

Street scene

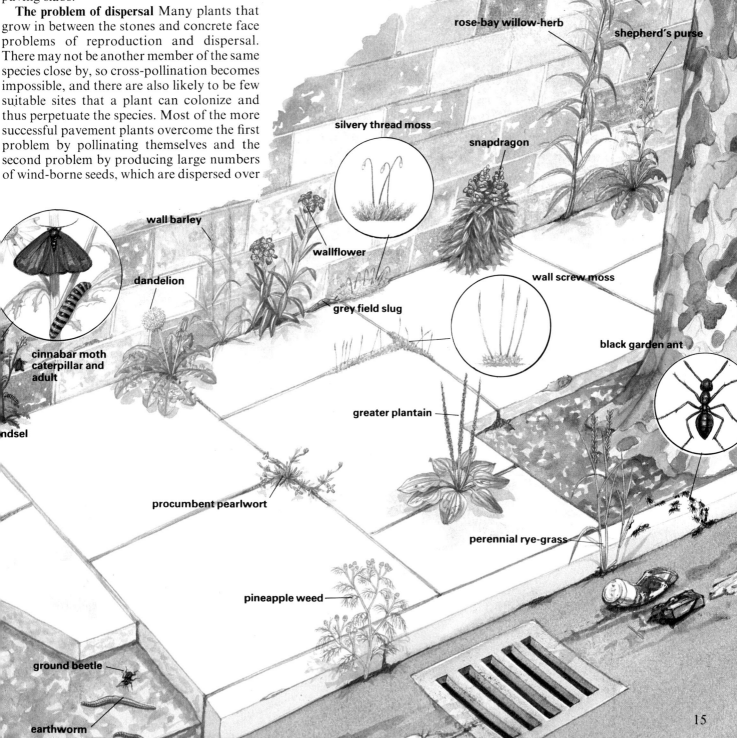

rose-bay willow-herb

shepherd's purse

silvery thread moss

snapdragon

wall barley

wallflower

dandelion

wall screw moss

grey field slug

black garden ant

cinnabar moth caterpillar and adult

greater plantain

ndsel

procumbent pearlwort

perennial rye-grass

pineapple weed

ground beetle

earthworm

and the remaining seeds (which are almost as fine as dust) can be caught by the wind and carried away.

Many other plants have tiny seeds attached to a structure shaped to aid dispersal. That familiar urban shrub, buddleia, has winged seeds while dandelion and rose-bay willow-herb both have their seeds borne on para-chutes.

Perhaps the most successful plant at dis-persing itself is pineapple weed, a species that, since its introduction to Britain during the last century, has spread spectacularly throughout the country. Now common in the larger muddier gaps in pavements, pineapple weed produces tiny seeds that stick to the mud and

Above: Many of the most successful plants of pavements are annuals, which are quicker to move in and colonize a new niche than biennials or perennials. A prime example is pineapple weed, which soon spread through Britain when it was introduced here just over 100 years ago.

Left: Annuals have another advantage over perennials. Pavements can become extremely cold in winter and the safest way for a species to survive this period is as dormant seed, rather than as a plant, a strategy that is much better suited to annuals than perennials. Shown here is the annual grass, wall barley.

Below: Dandelion, one of the most familiar plants of the pavement.

cities is the black garden ant, *Lasius niger*. In its natural habitat it nests under stones and logs, but the modern expansion of paved areas has created an ideal artificial habitat for this ant. Here it finds the optimum conditions of high temperature, moisture and air that its grubs and pupae need if they are to grow quickly.

There is a plentiful supply of food for these pavement ants in the form of honey-dew, the sticky secretions produced by aphids feeding on the leaves of street trees such as lime, plane and flowering cherries.

If a pavement were allowed to go un-checked, without regular cleaning and repairs, a succession of plants would move in and it would slowly disappear under a layer of soil and vegetation. Man's activities prevent this from happening, instead maintaining the pavement at an early stage of succession. The result is an artificial, but unique, mixture of plants and animals, which find the patchy habitats provided by pavements ideal living places.

are transported on people's feet and the wheels of vehicles. The latter have been largely responsible for the species' spread through the country. In one experiment a car with freshly washed tyres was driven around the Midlands for 100km (65 miles) after it had been raining heavily. It was then hosed down and the rinsings collected; when they were examined the rinsings were found to contain 220 seeds of pineapple weed, 387 of annual meadow-grass and 274 of chickweed. All three plants are typical of much-trampled rural areas such as farm gateways and footpaths as well as more urban sites.

Animal dispersal The need to disperse and find new sites to colonize is one reason why ants are the most familiar animals on our pavements. On one or two consecutive evenings around mid-summer the winged males and queens emerge from their sub-terranean nest. They enjoy a brief flight of freedom before mating and returning to their underground world.

The most common species to engage in these 'marriage' flights over our towns and

Urban centres in the British Isles

Glasgow

Edinburgh

Newcastle-upon-Tyne

Belfast

Leeds

Hull

Manchester

Dublin

The Midlands

Birmingham

Cork

South Wales

London

Bristol

Southampton

population density

	0-199 per square mile
	200-899 per square mile
	900+ per square mile

NATURAL LIFE IN OUR TOWN PARKS

Although St James's Park (below) was first laid out in the 17th century, most town parks date back to Victorian times. Parks are essential places of rest in towns, and can at the same time become important habitats for wildlife.

Town parks are usually the first places that come to mind at the mention of urban wildlife. To generalise can be misleading, for town parks range from fauna-rich examples such as Sutton Park near Birmingham and Richmond Park on the edge of London to the type which is little more than a football pitch. Lying between these extremes of biological richness and poverty, the majority of our town parks belong to the tradition of Victorian pleasure gardens.

In the last century, philanthropists and local authorities bought pieces of urban land and laid them out as public gardens. Here the urban working class could find relief from dirt, drudgery and poverty in the presence of

green plants, birds and relatively fresh air—without having to journey out to the open countryside.

These parks mirrored the private gardens and grounds of the Victorian rich. Because they were thought of as gardens they were planted with ornamental trees and shrubs; they had flower borders in which annual bedding plants were the order of the day; they contained ornamental pools, statues and buildings, and the grass was close-mown.

Changes in their management have taken place since the Second World War, brought about partly by the pressure of rising costs, bringing the need to make economies and use less labour. An interesting result of this is that nowadays some parks—Hyde Park and Holland Park in London for example—have areas where the usual park-keeping work is kept to a minimum and natural life is allowed to continue relatively undisturbed.

What may be found in a town park by way of wild plants and animals depends on many factors. Besides the particular style of management under which a park is run, these include the size and structure of the park, and its position in the city; and whether it lies near or far from other places in which there is plenty of wildlife. If you know the pieces of the jig-saw you can build up a picture for your own local park.

Life on the rocks The most basic of all habitats is bare rock. This supports a range of lichens and they in turn provide a home for tiny insects and mites. The more polluted the air and the more acid the rock, the fewer lichens will grow. Since the 'rock' in town parks ranges from concrete kerbs to marble statues, and from brick buildings to paving slabs, there is usually a great variety of sites for the growth of lichens. The further away a park is from sources of air pollution—and this generally means the further it is from the city centre—the greater the variety of lichens you can find.

Soil From rock is derived bare soil, which is often heavily trampled and compressed, with hardly any decaying plant remains. Here little life is found, but quite a number of solitary bees and wasps burrow in the hard packed ground to make their nest chambers. Whether or not you have these fascinating insects in your park depends on the food available to them in the park or nearby.

Bare soil is also found in plenty in the flowerbeds themselves, in between the clumps of cultivated flowers or shrubs. Here the rich earth is untrampled and forms a perfect habitat for weeds. No matter how carefully the park may be tended these colonizing plants inevitably find a foothold. They are by nature pioneer plants, whose specialized ability is to spread seed fast and take advantage of any place where the earth has been opened or disturbed. A characteristic of pioneer plants is that they produce large amounts of seed, which makes them a boon

to all seed-eating birds.

Mown grass, or lawns, form another major ingredient in the park's mixture of habitats. The range of plants which grow in a lawn varies according to the past management of the lawn and the kind of treatment it has received. If it has been regularly mown, fertilised and subjected to weedkillers then it will be poor in terms of the variety of plants and small animals which can live there. It will therefore be unattractive to birds, amphibians, reptiles and mammals. If, at the other extreme, it is cut infrequently, like a hay meadow or a pasture, it can contain a wealth of different plants with butterflies, moths, gaudy beetles, jewel-like spiders, voles, toads and birds in plenty.

Shrubberies If the park is to attract birds, shrubberies are a vital part of the picture. Without shrubs there will be no warblers, such as black-caps, to enrich the park with their song. If ornamental foreign shrubs are mixed with native ones such as hawthorn, pussy willow, holly and ivy then there are riches indeed for wildlife. Native species are more interesting because they support more insects: introduced shrubs are unfamiliar to our native stock of insects, and an insect can live on an alien shrub only if it manages to adapt to it—which some are doing successfully.

Woodland Trees and woodland add another dimension. As with the shrubs, the native

Above: A grey squirrel demonstrates its uninhibited style of scavenging. Such plentiful supplies keep the numbers of grey squirrels higher than in natural woodland.

Nature relieves stress

Over a hundred years ago it was realised that urban man needed open green space. Now the need is felt for a closer link with nature and for parks to be given a role more akin to that of nature reserves. We also know that open spaces with trees, water and grass play an important part in reducing the pollution of the air. They help to absorb dust and smoke, and fumes from cars, so letting light and health back into the city centre. They deaden noise and draw a green curtain in front of sights best left unseen.

Left: A small tortoiseshell butterfly on a honeysuckle shrub (*Lonicera aurea nitida*). The foodplant of its caterpillar is the stinging nettle, no more than a nuisance to gardeners and public alike. If the odd patch of nettles survives, the park will be alive with butterflies and a great many other colourful insects in summer.

Opposite page: The pink horse chestnut (*Aesculus × carnea*) can be seen in parks and gardens throughout Britain, planted as a highly ornamental tree. Its pink flowers appear in May. The tree reaches a height of about 20m (65ft).

Below: The pochard has a resident British population which is enlarged in winter by the arrival of migrants from the north. These colourful birds can be encouraged by sympathetic park management – not least by providing a marshy waterside.

oaks and limes support more wildlife than foreign trees such as sycamore, tulip tree or acacia. However, some exotics add variety and interest; and if you want to see tree-creepers, there is no better place to look than on a Wellingtonia tree with its soft bark so loved by these small birds.

In park woodlands there is a direct conflict of interest between the needs of wildlife and the demand for public safety. From the point of view of the wildlife, dead and dying trees are among the most important parts of a woodland ecosystem. In a park they are almost always cut down and taken away, but sometimes even in town parks small amounts of wood are left lying on the ground. This gives a home for the large and beautifully marked longhorn beetles, whose larvae are a prized delicacy for the great spotted woodpecker and the golden-furred noctule bat. A small supply of rotting wood, even a dead treestump cut almost level with the ground, may be adequate for toadstools, ferns and mosses to grow, or for beetles to burrow in.

Lakes and pools The final piece of the jig saw is open water. At one end of the scale there are large lakes, rivers and streams, and at the other small pools, drinking fountains and temporary puddles. Water is vital to all forms of life. It is irresistibly attractive not only to those species which obviously depend on it – fish, ducks, frogs, newts and various insects such as dragonflies – but also to dry land animals and birds which come to drink. For any piece of land to be really attractive to a wide variety of animals and plants, open water and a marshy fringe is an absolute necessity.

Most parks have some permanent water and many birds make their home on it. Coots and moorhens, and the ubiquitous mallard, are usually on town park lakes and ponds all year round, and Brent and barnacle geese and Bewick's swans may appear in winter. You can also often see tufted duck and pochard, and sometimes the introduced mandarin duck, the males instantly recognisable by their exotic colouring and upstanding orange 'sails' on the wings. All these birds eat bread thrown to them by people in the park. Where concrete has not been too liberally applied, a gentle bank allows ducklings to climb or hedgehogs to escape if they fall in while trying to get a drink. Frogs and newts are able to come and go on the gentle gradient, and the marshy fringe is beneficial to the insect community too.

Take away any of these pieces and the picture is incomplete: the park loses something of great value to wildlife. So far as wildlife in the British Isles is concerned, the most important components are open water and marsh, woodland with a good shrub layer and meadow grassland. The more of these a town park possesses, the closer nature is to the town centre.

FINDING REFUGE IN THE GARDEN

With over 16 million gardens at its disposal it is not surprising that our wildlife takes advantage of this widespread habitat. A mature garden may play host to some 60 bird species, 300 plant species and thousands of different insects – so long as gardeners do not overdo the pesticides and fertilizers.

Of all the habitats around us none is more frequented – and yet more likely to be overlooked as a haven for wildlife – than the garden. Occupying over a thousand square miles of Britain's land area, gardens represent a significant resource not only for the householder but also for the various plants and animals that live there.

Gardens are enormously variable in the sort of opportunities they offer wildlife. Most, however, are suburban, and so can quickly become colonized by the flora and fauna in the countryside nearby. Where two habitats meet, the border zone – in this case between the concrete jungle and the surrounding countryside – often has a specially rich assemblage of wildlife because it provides some of the features of both habitats and draws recruits from each.

Stocking the garden A newly plotted garden will contain little more than the few invertebrates – earthworms and snails, for example – that inhabit any patch of bare soil. A garden put down to lawn offers little more, but if the gardener progressively introduces herbaceous plants, vegetables and shrubs, the habitat quickly increases in complexity and is able to support a surprising diversity of wildlife. Many herbivorous insects and other invertebrates are very specific about what they like to eat. Each invertebrate is, in turn, preyed upon only by certain sorts of other animals, so that even a small mixture of plants can generate quite an elaborate series of food chains.

The sap of the broad bean, for example, is the lifeblood of hosts of aphids which, gorging themselves to excess, secrete the surplus in the form of sugary honeydew. This now attracts ants which exploit the honeydew as food. The broad bean is not entirely at the mercy of the aphids, however, for ladybirds and their larvae are voracious aphid consumers. Tits will also feed on the supply of aphids.

The richest garden habitats are usually ones that have been cultivated long enough to boast mature shrubs and trees in addition to the 'field layer' of plants below. The pooled effect of lots of neighbouring gardens, each with individual ideas and input of effort,

creates a patchwork habitat whose sum is more complex than the parts. Some simple invertebrates such as slugs find all their needs in one strawberry bed while other creatures, like birds, have to range over several gardens to gain their livelihood.

Exceptional resident With so many different habitats blended into one, there are few animals we may call typical of gardens in the sense that they are more common there than anywhere else. One, however, is the blackbird. Over the last 150 years, the blackbird's preferred habitat has shifted to gardens and parks where it lives at much higher density than it does in its traditional woodland haunts.

The garden contains fewer blackbird predators. In the wood, weasels, squirrels, hedgehogs and rats all raid their nests, whereas the cat is the worst threat in the garden. Blackbirds also seem to survive better in gardens during the winter, mainly because householders have become very conscientious about feeding birds. More recently collared doves have also invaded well-vegetated gardens and magpies are infiltrating some

A varied and luxuriant garden such as the one above supports more kinds of plants and insects than a piece of countryside of the same size. The shrubs and trees provide shelter for birds, and the long grass for small mammals such as shrews. The neat and very attractive garden, left, probably will not support as many species as the one above. The colourful flowers will certainly attract nectar-seeking insects in summer, but the lack of shrubs or other shelter makes it difficult for other animals to set up home. Another disadvantage of a tidy garden is that if you do not leave decaying matter about, you have to keep adding nutrients to the soil.

suburban areas, notably in Dublin where householders fear they will scare off the more familiar garden birds.

Once a male blackbird succeeds in annexing a garden territory he may be resident for as many years as he survives. Other birds such as robins and tits may do likewise, but it is very difficult to separate genuine residents from brief visitors. In winter, for instance, the British Isles are invaded by legions of continental blackbirds, starlings, and finches, and the birds we see feeding on the lawn are as likely to be breeding in Poland next summer as in the holly bush at the end of the garden. Similarly, studies show that hundreds of different tits pass through a single garden in the course of a winter, though without individually ringing birds the impression is of seeing the same few tits each day. Gardens thus offer permanent quarters for some animals, a temporary refuge for others.

On the move Many insects, especially pollen and nectar feeders, are the most fleeting of visitors. In a painstaking 5-year study by Denis Owen in a Leicester garden, a remarkable tally of 11,000 individuals of 21 butterfly species was caught, marked and released. Few were recaptured in the same garden proving the great mobility of butterflies and many other winged insects through suburban districts. A notable exception is the honeybee which, having discovered a good herbaceous border, will return to feed there again and again.

While the particular blend of vegetation is largely under the gardener's control, much also depends on where the garden is situated: whether in the north or south of the country, how close to the sea, whether it commands a sunny aspect, and so on. A factor of overriding importance is soil type. Snails, for example, flourish only in areas where a chalky or limestone soil yields the calcium they need for building shells. A widespread survey of gardens in the West Midlands, where much of the soil is sandy, showed that

Right: The goldfinch often nests in gardens, choosing a lofty site such as a tall apple tree. In autumn you may see flocks of these birds feeding on the seeds of various weeds, particularly thistles.

Below: Soldier beetles, here seen mating on the head of an umbellifer, are attracted to the flowers in an herbaceous border, where they also prey on smaller insects.

Left: The startling colours of the tiger moth warn birds of its unpleasant taste. Its hairy caterpillars feed on nettles and docks.

Opposite page: The burnet rose, a native wild flower, is often seen in gardens.

Below: By leaving some bits of decaying plants around the garden, a gardener may help to spare his seedlings from the attention of garden snails, which have broad vegetarian tastes.

the garden snail, which has a particularly thick shell to construct, was virtually absent. Many lime-loving plants, such as vetches and the hoary plantain, likewise have a patchy distribution as weeds in British gardens.

Garden props What also helps to mould the garden's character is the variety of artefacts – walls, outbuildings, paths and fences, for example – that the gardener introduces. These offer a wealth of opportunities: nesting sites for birds, shelter under stones for smaller animals and crevices and dry sheds for hibernation. Walls provide a surface for mosses and ferns to cling to, and the dry stone wall in particular an internal labyrinth for mice, voles and hunting wrens. Often these garden structures resemble some feature that the animal has been accustomed to using in the wild. Great spotted woodpeckers, for example, periodically explore old clothes poles, as they would a tree-trunk, for grubs; the warmth of the compost heap attracts bumblebees to build their nests there and toads to overwinter, while the doorstep provides an occasional anvil stone for thrushes to crack open the snails they find along the foot of the walls. The garden pond is colonized at an astonishing rate by aquatic life, including frogs, toads and newts in search of spawning sites. Birds visit it to drink and bathe while insects swarm over the surface, tempting swallows and wagtails and the occasional dragonfly.

The role of the weed Apart from the plants the gardener contrives to establish on the soil, there will be many interlopers from outside. So strong is the propaganda against weeds that people think of them almost as a separate class of plants, somehow having an inferior pedigree to cultivated varieties. However, it is the weed species' capacity for survival as either fast-growing annuals (eg chickweed and shepherd's purse) or seemingly indestructable perennials (eg dock and dandelion) that has guaranteed their vigorous history of success.

Some, such as clover and bird's-foot-trefoil, enrich the soil, while others are specific food plants for insects and, when they seed, for small mammals and birds. Nettles, for instance, are the staple diet of the caterpillars of several butterflies, notably red admirals, tortoiseshells and peacocks and are also eaten by numerous moth caterpillars, including the exotic garden tiger. The creamy flower heads of umbellifers like cow parsley and hogweed are sought for their nectar by beetles and flies, and in late summer these venues are daily the scene of minor dramas if one cares to watch. Occasionally a wasp may hurtle in to snatch and carry off a hapless hoverfly, devouring it at leisure in a quiet spot. All in all there are sound reasons for controlling weeds, but a compelling case for keeping a wild patch somewhere in the garden. Too much pesticide may kill insects which are vital for the pollination of some flowers.

THE NATURAL HISTORY OF WALLS

A newly-constructed wall offers little opportunity for wildlife, but such is the tenacity of nature in colonizing new habitats that even these barren surfaces are gradually exploited by a whole range of plants, invertebrates and even mammals.

Above: The wall of Wadham College, Oxford has a fine display of 'garden escapes' including spectacular red valerian. The flora of a wall is naturally affected by the surrounding habitats and the reservoir of species they contain. Walls near the seaside often have plants native to cliffs or salt marshes, while plant life on walls in mountain regions often reflects the alpine or arctic plant communities found at high altitudes.

Two surveys of the plant life on walls, one carried out in Durham and the other in Cambridge, have revealed that in each of these cities the walls are host to some 185 species, ranging from the horse mushroom to the fig tree. Where there are plants there are animals, from the microscopic organisms and insects that find food and shelter, to the small mammals and birds that hunt or are hunted in the crevices and among the foliage. Walls, in their great variety of building materials and situations, support a fascinating range of wildlife communities.

Conditions for growth The range of plants that you will find on a particular wall is influenced by a variety of factors. First,

since most walls are vertical stone or brick structures, we can expect to find on them some similarities with the communities of cliffs and rocky places. Thus, about 11% of the plants found on the walls of Durham are typical of rocks, cliffs and scree. Some of these, such as pellitory-of-the-wall, wall lettuce and wall rue, are even better known from walls nowadays than from their once wild haunts, as their names testify.

The nature of the building materials strongly influences the flora the wall attracts. For example, many plants require a plentiful supply of calcium. Plants naturally occurring on chalky or lime soils therefore find limestone walls inviting. Moreover, until recently brick and stone were joined with lime mortar, which crumbles as it ages, providing a mosaic of crevices; here calcium-loving plants, such as stonecrop, shining cranesbill and wall rocket, establish themselves.

The washing action of rainwater (leaching) may even spread the lime content of mortar to the main material of the wall, enriching the otherwise sterile brick and allowing it to support a modest plant growth. Compared with mortar, however, modern cement is a much harder compound, resistant to colonization except where cracks appear and debris accumulates.

Until recently mosses and lichens were conspicuously absent from our cities, where they could not survive pollution from smoke and

Right: In its chosen hole in a wall the spider *Segestria* builds a silk tube with a net of radiating threads at the entrance. This door-mat transmits the slightest vibration made by an alighting insect, and brings the spider rushing out to seize its prey.

sulphur dioxide. With cleaner air, however, they have staged a comeback in places, but the richest encrustations of lichens and the lushest mosses are still to be found on walls in the open countryside.

Some ferns on the other hand, notably the hart's tongue fern, are much less sensitive to certain kinds of atmospheric pollution, establishing themselves and even thriving on chimney stacks. In the days of steam trains, such ferns likewise adorned sooty railway bridges and station platforms.

Old and new walls In general, the older the wall the more life it supports, since weathering and the action of the plants and animals themselves provide nooks and crannies for more and more species to settle. An old, neglected wall is capable of supporting a rich community, often including quite large trees and shrubs such as holly, yew, elder and hawthorn. The ancient sandstone walls of Durham city, for example, are graced by some handsome wych elms.

A new wall on the other hand is an almost

lunar landscape, barren of soil, cover or water, and often highly exposed to the sun's rays. Only the simplest plants are capable of pioneering such extreme conditions: these are the lichens and mosses. Often they hug the wall in cushion-like patches that trap moisture and so help the plants to resist the frequent periods of drought.

Opportunist plants Because they are such changeable, marginal habitats, often subject to extreme conditions, walls favour opportunist plants. We therefore find on them a host of annuals all of which have the ability to grow rapidly, flower and cast hardy seeds within one season. This pattern of growth makes them capable of unexpected feats of survival in any situation where the slightest opportunity exists. Common examples are rue-leaved saxifrage, shepherd's purse, groundsel and common mouse-ear chickweed. Their seeds are light and can easily be dispersed by the wind, so they readily encounter new sites where they can lodge.

Specialisation The pioneering plant species help to accelerate the process of creating a less hostile environment in the wall. Acid produced by plant roots, for example, may help to dissolve mortar. Even so, the more sophisticated plants that follow are again often highly specialised for surviving in temperamental conditions. Stonecrops are, like cacti, so-called 'succulents', having rotund fleshy leaves which can store water. The leaves of navelwort are also fleshy but disc-shaped (hence its other name, wall pennywort), while some wall grasses reduce water loss by having inrolled leaves or leaves with waxy outer layers.

The success of various species of toadflax in colonizing walls is partly due to an ingenious adaptation: the leaf and flower stalks always twist to face the light, but once pollinated the flowers seek the dark, and turn to

Right: Rusty back fern on a stone wall at Malmesbury, Wiltshire. The fern is a specialist, adapted to survive in habitats where occasional long droughts prevent other species from growing. When a drought sets in, it curls up as if it were dead, but with the first rains it unfolds again and flourishes once more.

deposit their seeds in the deepest crevices, where the chances of germination are at their best.

Crevices likewise provide the chief attraction for most of the wall's animal inhabitants, whether serving as likely sources of food, breeding sites, lairs from which to pounce on prey, or else refuges from predation. Old limestone walls are often pockmarked with small recesses, just wide enough to admit spiders and insects.

Invertebrate life in walls The plants on a wall, sparse as they may be, provide food and shelter for a microscopic world of little-known invertebrates – springtails, tardigrades, nematodes and some rotifers. These live modestly inside mosses and lichens, feeding mostly on the plant tissue, as well as on the litter of dead material (detritus) that surrounds the plants. Like their hosts, these animals possess a remarkable resistance to desiccation. Many simply shrivel up in dry conditions, absorbing water and resuming normal activity when it rains.

We normally associate algae with lakes or the seaside, but the green slime that coats damp walls and tree trunks throughout the country is also an alga, the primitive *Pleurococcus*. It is the plankton of the wall, forming an appetising pasture that is grazed by woodlice, millipedes, some molluscs, a few caterpillars, and several relatives of the domestic booklouse. Many of these delicate creatures shun the hot, arid surface of the wall by day, emerging only at night to feed.

Hunters on the wall To the human eye, the invertebrate population hidden within the labyrinthine world of walls may seem sparse, but some vertebrate predators find it a rich hunting ground. Voles, mice and shrews assiduously patrol the maze of tunnels inside

Above: The beautiful St Peter Port daisy on a granite wall in St Peter Port, Guernsey. The species owes its success to the Victorians' love of rock gardens—it was introduced from Mexico around 1860 as a rockery plant, and quickly spread to walls throughout the island.

Right: A wheatear nesting in a very old wall in the south of Ireland. Wall crevices are used for nesting or roosting by many small birds.

Ruby-tailed raider

On summer days solitary mason bees (above left) can be seen endlessly inspecting walls for the ideal chamber in which to lay a small batch of eggs. Each egg is then provisioned with a larder of pollen and nectar to nourish the hatching grub. This done, the bee plays no further role in raising her offspring, leaving them to their fate.
At this stage, the parasitic ruby-tailed wasp (below left) can therefore breach the tiny hive unmolested, and take her toll. The wasp lays her own eggs near the bee grubs; when they hatch they feed on their infant hosts.

old walls, snapping up springtails, spiders, beetles and woodlice, while also savouring some of the more nutritious seeds and plant shoots. Here, they in turn may fall prey to the marauding weasel, whose slender form fits into the narrowest of small mammal runs.

Wrens and dunnocks are also adept insect eaters, often disappearing inside cavities of dry stone walls, to emerge several yards further along. More compact, vertical walls are harder to exploit, but nimble tits, flycatchers and even house sparrows will perch precariously, or hover a few inches from the wall, to pick off prey.

If the wall is clothed in honeysuckle, ivy or some other flowering climber, the gleanings are so much the richer. Ivy, being the last plant to flower profusely in autumn, is a Mecca for flying insects. As many as 31 species of moths and 27 species of flies have been recorded feeding on its honey and nectar in September and October, while if a hive is not far away, honey bees are attracted in hordes to this common plant of our mature walls.

THE WILDLIFE IN OUR HOMES

An Englishman's home may be regarded as his castle, but it is invaded by many forms of wildlife that can be difficult to control. The presence of some of the species may seem surprising in what is for them often a hostile and alien environment.

Above: This interesting, if somewhat alarming, growth by the window of a derelict house is dry rot fungus (*Serpula lacrymans*) and rust spores.

Among the problems that wild creatures have to face when living in a house are drought, restricted daylight and constant disturbance, and the successful interlopers are those that have adapted to withstand such conditions. Carpet beetles, clothes moths and meal moths, for example, can survive quite happily without water, while most house pests are nocturnal and only become active when the household is asleep.

The fact that these intruders are present at all shows that houses do offer them some advantages – warmth, shelter and a plentiful food supply. If damp penetrates, then drought, one of the chief disadvantages, is eliminated and the way is opened for a wider range of plants and animals to take up residence.

Plant life is severely restricted by lack of water and suitable 'soil' in which to grow. The most successful plants to be found in the house are fungi, probably because they are not reliant on daylight for their survival. The notorious dry rot fungi attack and destroy only damp wood (contrary to their name), while moulds grow on damp wallpaper, newly plastered walls and food such as bread and cheese.

Green algae will grow on window surrounds where condensation provides sufficient moisture and also in the water of vases and fish tanks where these receive sufficient daylight.

Insect invaders Moulds provide food for plaster and fungus beetles, while larvae of the death watch beetle and wood boring weevils can only eat wood that has been softened by fungi. The furniture beetle feeds on all kinds of wood in the home but can also survive quite happily out of doors in dead tree stumps and old hedges. Although the house longhorn beetle is probably an immigrant, as it seldom survives out of doors and only occurs in the south, its small population can cause large-scale damage: its larva bores large holes in beams and rafters and has even caused roofs to collapse.

Many small creatures are associated with man's food and have lived with man from the time he first began to store berries, grain and dried meat. Spider beetles, biscuit beetles, meal moths and flour mites feed on a wide range of stored foods of vegetable origin. Most of these are adapted to survive with little or no moisture, although flour mites require damp food. Larder beetles feed on carrion in the wild, but readily eat scraps of meat and cheese and will even attack fur coats.

The warmth-loving cockroach and house cricket are scavengers and will eat food left out overnight. The house cricket was at one time tolerated in houses and the cheerful chirping of the 'cricket on the hearth' was a welcome sign of life on cold winter evenings.

Mice and rats, on the other hand, have always been unwelcome and can cause extensive damage in the larder, gnawing through packages and soiling food with their droppings. Houseflies and bluebottles are similarly unwelcome because they feed on carrion outside and spread disease when they settle on our food. Wasps and ants are particularly attracted to meat and sugary foods in summer, while fruit flies like fermenting fruit and alcoholic drinks.

Carpets and fabrics provide food for the larvae of clothes moths, house-moths and carpet beetles. In the wild these creatures scavenge the nests and burrows of birds and mammals, but have also adapted to life in the home. Silverfish are primitive insects that feed on a wide range of plant and animal matter and are also prolific indoor scavengers. They seldom cause serious damage, but do indicate the presence of damp. The related firebrat prefers hot dry situations and is mostly found in such places as bakeries and large kitchens. Another scavenger is the house dust mite, which feeds on human skin scales shed among bedding and furniture and produces a dust that can affect asthma and hay fever sufferers.

Lofty intruders The attic, one of the least disturbed places in the house, may harbour a varied fauna. A number of birds have forsaken their natural nesting places for the eaves or rafters. Swifts, swallows and, to

some extent, house martins now rely on houses for nesting sites. Starlings, house sparrows and pigeons frequently nest in roof spaces and the moths, beetles, fleas and mites associated with them can also be a considerable nuisance. Other aerial intruders include wasps and bees, which build their papery nests in the attic and in turn provide homes for such creatures as the brown house-moth.

House mice are common inhabitants in attics and at one time the black rat was also found here, although it has been ousted by the brown rat, a less nimble creature that seldom climbs very high. The edible dormouse is also found here. Bats sometimes take up residence

Right: More than a hundred bats roosting under the roof of a house. Bats roost during the day in almost any place that is protected from direct sunlight; but most are found in buildings and hollow trees, while some hibernate in caves.

Below: Silverfish (*Lepisma saccharina*) like damp conditions, but will also raid food cupboards and feed on paper, the glue on cartons, and flour. They are up to 2cm ($\frac{3}{4}$in) long.

Above: Cockroaches enjoy the warmth of a house and make the most of food left out as they scavenge at night. This is an American cockroach (*Periplaneta americana*); this species is about 3cm ($1\frac{1}{4}$in) long. During the day, cockroaches hide in out-of-the-way places such as under floors, behind skirting boards and in ventilation ducts.

Left: First introduced to Hertfordshire at the turn of the century, the edible dormouse (*Sciurus glis*) is particularly fond of raiding apple stores. At one time this attractive little mammal was considered a culinary delicacy by the Romans.

Below: The house mouse is common in both town and country. It is particularly dangerous in houses that have old-fashioned electrical wiring, for it is quite capable of chewing right through cables and so making the wiring unsafe.

residence here, finding its way in via broken sewers and drains. The house mouse is also at home here, particularly in the winter months; in country areas it may be replaced by either the wood mouse or the yellow-necked mouse. In very damp cellars, toads have been known to thrive and, where sufficient light filters in, ferns have become established. A curious inhabitant of the wine cellar is the small yellow V-moth, whose larvae feed on the mouldy corks of wine bottles, sometimes to the detriment of the contents.

The parasites Of all the household pests, those causing the most alarm are the parasites. The human flea is still to be found in Britain, mainly in slum areas of large cities. The most common fleas are cat fleas, which are equally at home on dogs and will also bite humans. Bird fleas migrate from nests in the roof and may also bite humans, although they cannot survive long away from their natural hosts.

While body and crab lice are less common now in Britain thanks to improved hygiene, head lice are increasingly found, particularly among young children. The entire life cycle takes place on the hair so that transmission of the parasites is by direct contact. Bedbugs are fortunately on the decline; these hide by day in crevices and behind loose wallpaper, emerging at night to seek a human host.

Predators in the home are few. The most common are the much maligned house spiders, which prey on insects and other invertebrates. They usually spin their untidy webs in the corners of rooms, under the eaves or in crevices and can survive equally well outside. Those found running across the floor or trapped in the bath are usually casual visitors driven in by the cold or wet.

Changing environment As homes have developed through the ages, so their wildlife has changed. Since at one time most houses were made entirely of wood, it is not surprising that wood-feeding organisms were great home-lovers. With the advent of insecticides and preservatives and the gradual replacement of wood by metal and plastic, however, they are becoming progressively more scarce. Similarly clothes moths are less common since nylon and other synthetic fibres have largely replaced wool. Improved standards of hygiene have played their part, too, and the vacuum cleaner has proved to be a deadly enemy of many indoor creatures, removing the dust and debris in which they breed.

in roof spaces, particularly in the winter when they leave their natural roosts in caves and hollow trees for the warmth and security of man's dwellings.

Lowly residents Cellars are interesting habitats for wildlife since they tend to be damp and are often left undisturbed for long periods. The brown rat frequently takes up

The introduction of central heating has also had a profound effect on the fauna of houses since many species cannot tolerate the resulting low levels of humidity. On the other hand, some of the warmth-loving species thrive under these conditions. The increasing popularity of houseplants, too, gives scope to a whole new range of wildlife in the shape of greenfly, thrips and similar insects.

DOWN IN THE DUMP: COMPOST HEAP LIFE

To many people a compost heap is nothing more than a pile of useless rubbish—a dumping ground for kitchen waste and garden weeds. But inside, the heap teems with life—from the swarming (and beneficial) bacteria, worms, proliferating fungi and insects, to hibernating snakes or toads.

Below: Well-kept compost heaps in a large garden. All the many millions of micro-organisms in such heaps are essential if the material is to be of any use. Drainage is important since the micro-organisms cannot act properly under water-logged conditions—instead of crumbly compost you may end up with a soggy, smelly mess. Usable compost is friable and sweet-smelling, with no recognisable plant remains.

A well-made compost heap can rapidly turn waste vegetable matter—old cabbage stalks, tea leaves, potato peelings, grass cuttings, and so on—into valuable plant food for spreading on the garden and feeding the next generation of flowers and vegetables. The process depends upon the activities of armies of microscopic plants and animals, and some larger organisms as well, which feed upon the refuse and break it down gradually into simple substances which can be absorbed by plant roots. This is, of course, exactly what happens to fallen leaves and other dead vegetation in natural habitats: it is nature's way of recycling her materials.

The compost community If you dig into the centre of a compost heap you will find it remarkably warm: the temperature may reach 60°C (140°F), thanks to the activities of millions of unseen bacteria. Their chemical attack on the softer plant materials releases energy in the form of heat, which effectively cooks the material in the centre of the heap. Most living things, including weed seeds, are killed by the heat. The temperature is obviously lower towards the outside of the heap and weeds are not always killed here.

A powerful microscope is needed to see the bacteria and the many other micro-organisms, such as protozoans and actinomycetes, that inhabit the compost, but some of the fungi are easier to see. Look for their fluffy threads spreading over dead leaves around the edge of the heap. Many of the fungi are simple moulds, and you might see the spore capsules of *Mucor* on rotting fruit or

Below: Quite a find in a compost heap—the egg batch of a slug. These round, transparent eggs can be produced by any slug, since these animals are hermaphrodites.

Left: *Lithobius forficatus*, a centipede commonly seen in compost heaps, where it can find a wide range of small invertebrate animals to feed on.

Below: A grass snake–this species may well be attracted to the heat within a compost heap for hibernation during the winter. If you disturb one, it may react like the one shown here and 'feign death'.

worms' droppings also contain finely divided organic matter mixed with valuable minerals. One of the most conspicuous species in the compost heap, especially where animal dung is incorporated in it, is the brandling (*Eisenia foetida*), which is purplish brown with bold orange bands. *E. rosea* is also very common, and easily recognised when adult by its bright pink body and very swollen orange clitellum.

Related to the earthworms, although much smaller, are the pot worms or enchytraeids. These are small white worms which you will often see in clusters among the decaying leaves on the outside of the compost heap. No more

other food. The capsules are like minute black pin heads on slender stalks, giving the fungus its common name of pin mould. You will sometimes find delicate toadstools, such as *Psathyrella gracilis*, sprouting from the edge of the heap. The fungal threads all help to break down dead leaves and twigs and soften them up for further assault by bacteria and an assortment of small animals.

Huge numbers of animals belong to the compost community. Many are microscopic, but others can be seen with a simple magnifying glass or even with the naked eye. These animals include both vegetarian and predatory species, all bound up in elaborate food webs. Those that actually eat the decaying vegetation do not always digest it fully, but they always break the material up into small particles before passing it out in their droppings. It is then much easier for the bacteria to get to work on the material and finally reduce it to the structureless organic matter that we call humus–matter that is essential to the maintenance of soil fertility. The dead bodies of the animals also contribute to the richness of the compost.

Worms and other legless residents Several species of earthworms invade the outer parts of the compost heap and contribute significantly to the processes of decomposition by dragging plant remains in to where they are more readily attacked by the bacteria. The

Below: A batch of grass snake eggs–also a likely find in a compost heap. These eggs are not guarded or incubated by the female snake–once they are laid she abandons them to their fate. The eggs take about six to ten weeks to hatch, the young usually emerging around late August.

than a centimetre long, they feed on decaying matter. They could be mistaken for fly maggots, but they have no obvious head such as is found in most compost-inhabiting fly larvae.

Examination of some of the less decayed material from the outer part of the heap with a microscope may well reveal numerous silvery 'hairs' waving about. These are roundworms, or nematodes–among the most numerous of all animals. There will be millions in your compost heap. Some are predators of the protozoans, but most are scavengers feeding on the decaying material itself and contributing to its eventual conversion to humus.

The decaying matter of the compost heap attracts large numbers of slugs and snails, belonging to several different species. Largest and certainly the most interesting of the slugs is the great grey slug (*Limax maximus*). Up to 18cm (7in) long, this mottled grey creature may form quite large colonies on the compost heap. Resist the temptation to remove it, for it feeds only on fungi and decaying matter and does no harm in the garden. The pearly white eggs of these slugs are commonly found in the compost heap.

Among the commonest snails is the cellar glass snail, a pale grey animal with a pale brown glassy shell. Its smaller cousin, the

prey in the compost heap and are therefore quite numerous. Most individuals are of the species *Lithobius forficatus*–shining brown and moving very quickly on their 15 pairs of legs. They are about 3cm (1in) long when mature. The flat-backed millipede (*Polydesmus angustus*) is often mistaken for a centipede. It is much the same colour as *Lithobius*, but a close look will reveal two pairs of legs on each segment, not one as in centipedes. Like the other millipedes, *Polydesmus* is a vegetarian and it revels in the decaying vegetation of the compost heap. You might even find one standing guard over its nest–a small chamber fashioned from its own excrement and saliva. Woodlice also revel in the moist conditions of

Opposite left: A common toad catching a beetle larva on the end of its long sticky tongue. Like the grass snake, the toad finds the heat of the compost heap ideal for comfortable hibernation in the winter months. Even during the rest of the year the toad, which is mainly a nocturnal animal, may hide away in the compost heap, only emerging to begin hunting as dusk falls. Compost heaps can therefore be regarded as a useful contribution to toad conservation.

garlic glass snail, may occur with it. The shell of this species is much darker and shinier, and the animal smells strongly of garlic when handled.

Numerous flies breed in compost heaps, and their legless larvae wriggle throughout the moister parts of the heap. The pale-bodied, black-headed larvae of the fungus gnats are especially common. Even the adults crawl about in the compost. They are very delicate, hump-backed flies and are often accompanied by numerous moth-flies or owl-midges. These are very small flies with pointed wings densely clothed with hair. Their tiny larvae are white and pointed at both ends.

Many-legged animals The mites are usually the most conspicuous of the arthropods to be seen when the compost is examined closely. They are very numerous and they move about freely. Many are spiky creatures with relatively long legs, while others look more like mobile sand grains–encased in smooth shells with tiny legs protruding just enough to trundle the animal slowly along. The mites imbibe fluids from living and dead organisms, with fungal threads playing a major role in their nourishment. Springtails are also very common, leaping vigorously about when disturbed but otherwise wandering slowly and chewing the decaying matter. Both groups fall victim to the fascinating false scorpions–miniature versions of the real thing except that they lack the tail and sting. Although the animals are only 2-3mm long, their pink claws look distinctly menacing as they creep slowly through the compost. False scorpions are by no means abundant, but they are well worth looking for; if touched, they pull in their claws and scuttle backwards at a remarkable rate.

Centipedes find a wide range of suitable

the compost heap. Large species such as *Oniscus asellus* are usually very obvious, especially at night, but the most common species–*Trichoniscus pusillus* and *T. pygmaeus* –need to be searched for because they are under 5mm long.

Compost lodgers The abundance of small animals in the compost heap attracts plenty of predatory creatures which may take up temporary residence. These lodgers include numerous beetles, such as the devil's coach-horse and the violet ground beetle–both fond of a good meal of slugs–and also a variety of larger animals such as the hedgehog. The

Above: Many different types of fungi can be found growing in profusion in compost heaps, from simple moulds to such delicate toadstools as this *Psathyrella gracilis*. The fungal threads help to break down vegetable matter–dead leaves, twigs, cabbage stalks, potato peels, apple cores and so on–and so soften them up sufficiently for bacteria to move in and continue the process.

Left: The moist conditions of the compost heap are ideal for woodlice, and several species can often be found there. The one that is easiest to see because it is fairly large is the one shown here–*Oniscus asellus*. This species, and the even commoner but much smaller *Trichoniscus pusillus* and *Trichoniscus pygmaeus*, are most active during the hours of darkness.

warmth of the compost heap is an added attraction for some of these larger animals, and it is not uncommon for hedgehogs, grass snakes and slow-worms to nest there. They may also use the heap for hibernation, together with frogs, toads, and newts. The compost heap can thus be regarded as a useful contribution to their conservation.

Less welcome lodgers are the rats and mice which frequently excavate snug nests for themselves and their young, emerging at night to sniff out our freshly sown peas and beans. The wasp is another generally unwelcome lodger, although there is no denying its value in controlling garden pests. It is likely to nest in your compost heap only if there is a fair amount of uncompacted twiggy material from which it can hang its nest. Bumble bees are more frequent lodgers, often taking over abandoned mouse nests in the heap. It is possible to watch their comings and goings throughout the summer and to see just how much pollen they bring in on their hind legs. Keep your eyes open for the remains of any nests and the bees' waxy cocoons when spreading the mature compost on the garden.

Right: The woodier components of the compost heap often support the attractive pink or orange pustules of the coral-spot fungus, which occurs regularly on old pea sticks.

Below: A compost heap can provide food and shelter for a host of animals.
1 Bumble bee and nest.
2 Ground beetle–preys on small invertebrates.
3 Springtail–feeds on vegetable debris, algae etc.
4 Robin–our best-known insectivorous garden bird.
5 Garlic grass snail–shelters within the heap.
6 Brandling earthworm–a common compost worm.
7 *Mucor* fungus with spore capsules.
8 Hedgehog–hibernates in the warm, dry heap.
9 *Actinomyces* bacteria–vital in the breakdown of organic matter.

Compost heap creatures

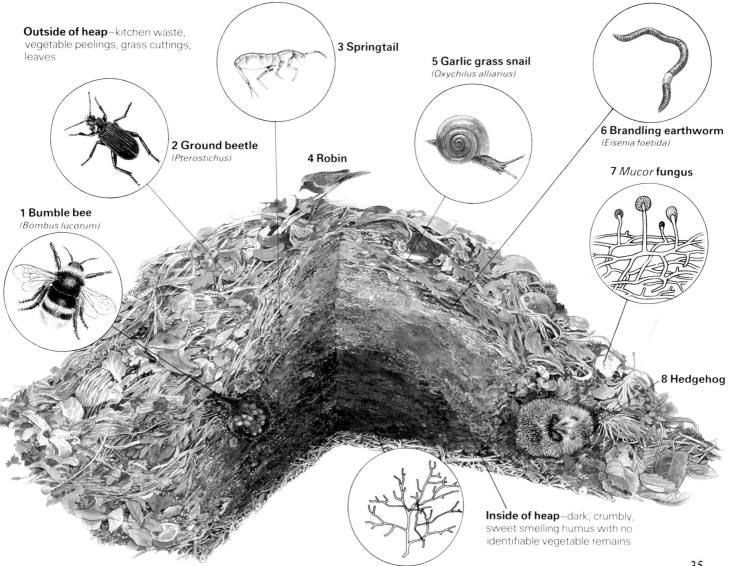

Outside of heap–kitchen waste, vegetable peelings, grass cuttings, leaves

3 Springtail

5 Garlic grass snail
(Oxychilus alliarius)

6 Brandling earthworm
(Eisenia foetida)

2 Ground beetle
(Pterostichus)

4 Robin

7 *Mucor* fungus

1 Bumble bee
(Bombus lucorum)

8 Hedgehog

Inside of heap–dark, crumbly, sweet smelling humus with no identifiable vegetable remains

9 *Actinomyces* bacteria

TIP LIFE: A THROW-AWAY SOCIETY

To many of us, the rubbish tip is just the end of the road for all our unwanted articles: but on the heaps of refuse life begins anew, and wildlife finds a new habitat.

Although rubbish tips may seem to be unlikely havens for wildlife, they support an astonishingly large and varied number of plants and animals, including some species that are seldom seen elsewhere in Britain. Rubbish tips are among the few places where common species can be seen side by side with the more exotic: wild flowers, cultivated blossoms and even sub-tropical vegetables seem at home.

Urban rubbish tips are relatively recent phenomena, originating in the 19th century when the populations of towns increased dramatically. Rubbish is usually transported to areas of wasteland on the outskirts of towns where it is dumped. In the current method of disposal, known as controlled tipping, the rubbish is deposited in shallow layers, each covered by a layer of soil. Sites chosen for tipping are usually those considered unsuitable for building or agricultural development and include such places as heathland and marshes.

Being set apart in this way, the rubbish tip is an ecological island – it has conditions quite different from those of the adjoining land, and therefore has its own characteristic plant and animal communities.

A new life for gulls Until the middle of the 19th century gulls were regarded as seabirds or else birds of the open countryside. Gradually, however, they became adapted to urban conditions and are now among the

Above: A corporation tip, for gulls a providential supply of food. The tip develops as a habitat. First comers are the scavengers; these, many of them invertebrates and microscopic creatures, convert the waste materials into nutrients for plants. As plants grow, plant-eating animals and insects take up residence, some to end up as food for the predators. The warmth of decay often stimulates the growth of plants and animals.

Right: House crickets sometimes breed in huge numbers in the warmth of the tips.

chief scavengers on refuse, taking over niches previously dominated by such birds as crows. Gulls have found well-established rubbish tips, with their deposits of food and abundance of insects, so attractive that they have forsaken the sea for the security of this man-made habitat. The lesser black-backed gull, for example, once only a summer visitor to Britain, is now partly resident, thanks to this reliable food source.

Predators and prey Gulls are drawn to rubbish tips not only to feed on the waste, but also to prey upon some of the small animals found there. The first visitors to rubbish tips are scavengers that feed on the raw refuse before it becomes covered with soil or overgrown. Apart from gulls, the most common scavengers are crows and starlings, brown rats and house mice, and insects and other invertebrates. The largest predator to be found on rubbish tips is probably the fox, an animal that has readily adapted to urban life and not only hunts living prey but also scavenges among refuse.

Other predators include bats, some of which are said to be particularly attracted by the chirping of crickets. In the London area the noctule bat is the one most frequently encountered, while elsewhere such species as pipistrelle and serotine bats are common visitors.

The largest group among the rubbish tip predators is the birds; besides gulls, crows and starlings these range from kestrels and owls to robins and flycatchers.

Breaking down the waste Scavenging among the refuse are armies of invertebrates: among insects most readily associated with rubbish are flies – bluebottles, houseflies, fleshflies and the tiny owl midges. Springtails are found in great numbers, and there is one springtail species whose only British habitats are the industrial rubbish dumps of South Wales and Lancashire. Other invertebrates include woodlice, earthworms and roundworms.

These small organisms consume the waste food and other organic substances such as paper and leather. Their natural cycle, and the growth of bacteria and some fungi, all work together to convert the organic materials of the rubbish tip into fertilizers that nourish the colonizing plants.

Plant succession Conditions for plant life on refuse tips are extremely unstable. Any plant that colonizes this type of habitat has to be fast growing and able to withstand sudden changes in the environment. In the midst of the process of converting waste into fertilisers, periods may occur when nutrients are washed away and plants show distinct signs of chlorosis (yellowing of the leaves) due to shortage of nutrients, such as nitrates. Groundsel, shepherd's purse, petty spurge and fat hen are among the quickest to become established, and mosses, which grow rapidly, provide a degree of shelter for other plants that consequently flourish.

Perennial plants soon become established and the familiar docks, daisies and dandelions appear at an early stage in the development of a dump. These are followed by such plants as thistles, hawkweeds, rosebay willowherb and stinging nettle, the latter in places where the soil is particularly rich in nitrogen. As well as common wild plants, various cultivated garden species may be found. These are garden 'escapes', which find their way to tips in a number of ways, for example by being transported there in seed form by birds or by the wind, or as part of garden refuse. As a result, many sites are adorned by such attractive flowers as evening primrose, hollyhock and Michaelmas daisy.

Butterfly bush One of the garden plants to have established itself in many urban areas is the buddleia shrub, otherwise known as the butterfly bush. Where it grows on rubbish tips, its flowers are visited by many butterflies, particularly the small tortoiseshell and peacock whose caterpillars may feed on nearby nettles, and the large and small whites from brassica plants which include cauliflower, kale and cabbage. Rosebay willowherb is the foodplant of the spectacular elephant hawkmoth caterpillar, while ragworts support the black and orange banded caterpillars of the day-flying cinnabar moth.

Exotic plants Kitchen refuse contributes its share of interesting plant species, beside the better-known vegetables such as potatoes and cabbages. Refuse tips support imported vegetables and fruits such as melons and mung beans which have found their way from the kitchen rubbish bin. They often flourish for a time until they are killed by cold weather.

The bird seed that arrives at the tip via the refuse from the cages of budgerigars and

Above: Plant-eaters such as this vole come to the tip once the plant life is well established. Other herbivores that may be found there are mice and rabbits, and a vast number of insects. Seedheads attract sparrows, chaffinches and goldfinches.

much at home among the ash and rubble of rubbish tips, for its natural home is the ashy volcanic soils of Sicily.

Hothouse conditions The processes of decomposition taking place in the rubbish layers cause a considerable build-up of heat. In fact, rubbish tips behave like giant compost heaps and the increased temperature permits the survival of various species that are otherwise seldom seen in the wild in Britain. The house cricket is a native of North Africa and southern Asia, and is so much at home in the congenial warmth of the rubbish tip that its numbers have grown spectacularly in this habitat. For similar reasons both common and German cockroaches can be seen, and on sites near docks and shipyards other foreign species of cockroach may occur. House mice survive the winter months among the refuse.

Future of the tip It is very likely that these fascinating man-made habitats may not be with us for many more years as more economical methods of waste disposal have been devised due to pressures on land use and to conservation considerations. Modern waste disposal methods include incineration, reclamation of metals by mechanical sorting and composting of organic waste to produce fertiliser. Although these methods may be more acceptable to society today, an interesting question arises as to what will happen to the animals that frequent rubbish tips, particularly species such as gulls that have adapted their feeding and migration habits.

Visitors beware While rubbish tips offer fascinating fields of study, it should be remembered that they are potentially dangerous places, with haphazard deposits of poisonous or inflammable material, broken glass, and piles of rubbish that may collapse at any moment. You should therefore seek permission and advice before visiting a tip.

canaries often produces plants that would not usually be seen in Britain. The most common of these are canary grass and sunflowers. Another item in bird seed is hemp, which also sometimes grows on the tips – in hot climates this plant yields the drug marijuana.

Some of the more unusual plants have seeds that lie dormant and buried for many years but germinate when favourable conditions prevail. The notoriously poisonous thorn apple, a native of America but once widely grown here for medicinal purposes, is a typical example and is found on refuse tips from time to time. Oxford ragwort is very

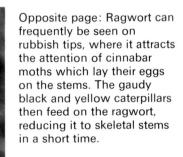

Opposite page: Ragwort can frequently be seen on rubbish tips, where it attracts the attention of cinnabar moths which lay their eggs on the stems. The gaudy black and yellow caterpillars then feed on the ragwort, reducing it to skeletal stems in a short time.

Left: The beautiful peacock butterfly can be found on buddleia or thistle plants — both of which abound on and near rubbish tips. If nettles spring up among the rubbish, the peacock butterfly may lay her eggs on them. The caterpillars then feed on the nettle leaves until it is time for them to pupate.

MOTORWAY VERGES: GRASSY HAVENS

The verges bordering Britain's 1800 miles of motorway provide valuable strips of undisturbed grassland for the insects, mammals and birds that have been ousted from neighbouring land by agricultural or urban developments.

Above: On this stretch of the M20 in Kent, broom flourishes among mixed grasses. The picture was taken before 1975 when the verges were cut regularly. To save money they are no longer cut and the wildlife is left undisturbed.

Since the first motorway was opened in Britain in 1958, some 34,000 acres of land have been used up. But this has not all been lost to tarred carriageways. Over the years 25,000 acres of grassy verges bordering motorways have become a distinct grassland habitat, colonized by many plant species and inhabited by birds, mammals and insects.

This habitat has the particular advantage of being largely out of bounds to man the trampler, picker and collector and is, for the most part, not managed by the motorway authorities. This means that verges can develop thick cover over a period of years.

There are two 'green' parts to the motorway: the central reservation and the verge. Most study has been done on the verges as the central reservation is out of bounds even to the naturalist.

Cover for wildlife By creating these areas of extensive grassland, man has unintentionally extended the preferred habitats of a wide range of animals and plants. In summer the long grasses provide a world of passages for a multitude of small mammals such as mice, shrews and voles; here they can forage in relative security except when they break cover and are spotted by the resourceful kestrel—companion of busy roads, dual carriageways and motorways. On older motorways such as the M1 bramble thickets develop and spread in large, dark masses against the uniform grass verge. These thickets offer ideal nesting sites for birds such as the blackbird and dunnock, and excellent cover for rabbits. Even motorway service stations have become extra sources of food for birds such as the chaffinch, sparrow and pied wagtail which have learned to take advantage of car park titbits.

Trees are often planted to improve the motorway landscape, especially to soften the hard appearance of bridges and service stations and to hide ugly places both on and off the route. The Department of Transport has planted over one million trees and shrubs every year during the last 15 years or so, 63 species in all. These, along with the grasses, help to stabilise the soil against erosion and provide extra food and shelter for wildlife. Shrubs and trees also help to deaden the noise of traffic.

What cannot be seen from the car are the drainage ditches, some of which hold water all year round, and which become overgrown with thistles, teasels and willowherb. These hold surface run-off water, and provide freshwater habitats in which aquatic insects such as dragonflies, damselflies and mayflies thrive.

The strip of land at the bottom of a sloping verge, where the hard shoulder meets vegetation, holds the wind-blown corpses of car-killed insects. These are feasted upon by countless ants. If you walk along this boundary in the summer you may see a large number of killed and injured bumble-bees littering the ground. On the hard shoulder and the road itself you can see reptile, bird and mammal casualties.

Change in vegetation Although motorway verges start life being seeded (by the motorway authorities) with clover and a mixture of grasses – usually red fescue, rye grass,

Above: It is on motorways that most people spot kestrels today. They hover above the verges, hunting out small mammals and beetles, preferring live prey to carrion.

Below: The field vole moves into the verges from adjoining fields, often carrying the seeds of wild flowers and shrubs with it. Its main predator is the kestrel.

meadow grass, crested dog's-tail – they eventually develop their own type of vegetation. This depends on the underlying bedrock, the soil, the adjacent habitat through which the motorway has been cut and, to a lesser extent, what is dumped there by man. The vegetation develops through a series of stages.

The sown grasses quickly form a tightly-knit covering into which other seedlings cannot intrude unless the soil is disturbed in some way. But once this happens – for example when small mammals make scrapings or wear passages through the vegetation, or when there is a fire that leaves a bare patch – seedlings of other grasses, wild flowers and shrubs blown there by the wind or carried on birds' feet can become established. About one quarter of all our 2000 wild flowers and a third of our grasses have been found on motorway verges. Some of the most frequent colonizers are cowslips, dandelions, buttercups, vetches, campions and hogweeds. Garden escapees such as buddleia and Michaelmas daisies are also a familiar sight.

The next stage in the development of the verge occurs when scrub species invade – mainly hawthorn, blackthorn, bramble, gorse, broom and elder. Their seeds are often carried from nearby scrubland or in the surface water from the adjoining land. Sometimes, however, it takes many years before verges become dotted with scrub species – the M4 in Wiltshire, started in 1971, is still largely grass-covered.

The last stage in the natural process of plant succession is the emergence of trees such as oak, ash and sycamore. An oak tree, for example, can grow from an acorn deposited by a squirrel or bird.

Not all plants colonize motorway verges by themselves. Columbine, autumn crocus, Breckland thyme, caraway, greater bell-flower, fritillaries, harebells, Jacob's ladder, salad burnet and yarrow, have been planted on the M1 and M5. On the M1, 326 species of

Above: Ox-eye daisies are one of the first motorway colonizers; once established they spread quickly and attract butterflies and other insects to the verges.

Right: A pair of six-spot burnet moths use a dandelion stalk to mate on.

Below: Gorse has been planted on the right hand verge of this 10-year-old stretch of motorway. Dandelions and daisies grow on the central reservation.

flowering plants (both wild and planted) have been found, and on the M20 in Kent, 306 species have been recorded.

Surviving pollution It is surprising that so many plant and animal species survive along motorways as they are exposed to considerable chemical pollution and noise disturbance. Such toxic chemicals as cadmium, lead, nickel, mercury and zinc have been found in the tissues of grasses, fungi, molluscs, insects and small mammals. The vegetation and soil within 2.5m (8ft) of the hard shoulder are usually heavily contaminated with surface deposits, washed or splashed off the carriageway. These deposits often contain mineral particles but can be mixed with oil, rubber, dust and rust. Bare patches of ground often develop along the hard shoulder in winter where salt spray from road-salting operations (about 100,000 tons are used on motorways and main roads in England and Wales each year) has killed off the vegetation. However, the hard shoulder acts as a buffer zone, leaving the sloping part of the verge relatively undamaged. The central reservation plants, not protected by buffer zones, are particularly vulnerable to salt accumulation. An interesting consequence of salting operations is the appearance of certain coastal grasses, for example reflexed saltmarsh-grass. This and other coastal species, which are accustomed to large quantities of maritime salt spray, have been creeping inland along the Kent motorways and roads.

Surprisingly, it does not seem that the verge animals are harmed by either salt or lead contamination of plants. Butterflies such as the Essex skipper and six-spot burnet are abundant on the M20 in Kent. Bird scavengers, such as magpies, rooks and other crows, brave the roar of traffic to take advantage of the insect and mammal casualties on the hard shoulder. Vibrations from passing vehicles are thought to bring earthworms to the surface where they are eaten by voles or rooks. The voles in turn are devoured by kestrels.

Motorway deaths The number of motorway casualties of larger mammals such as badgers and foxes is quite high, particularly on newly opened motorways. This is because the motorways cut across some well-established paths which the animals still attempt to use, sometimes with fatal consequences. Conservation measures on the M3, M5 and M53 include badger tunnels and culverts that have been adapted for the badgers' use. On the M6 in Cumbria and the M1 in Northamptonshire, measures to protect deer include mirrors to reflect car headlights, warning signs, and netting to prevent the deer leaping on to the roads.

Next time you travel down a motorway give a thought to the wildlife interactions going on in the verges; you are travelling through one of Britain's reservoirs of wildlife.

LIFE ALONG THE RAILWAY TRACKS

From the carriage windows of a train there's always the chance to see some wildlife–whether it is curlews and shelduck on the glistening mud of Poole Harbour, a glimpse of fallow deer in the New Forest, or seals basking on the sandbanks of the Tay.

Above: A single line track with a shrub-covered embankment. The plants do not seem to suffer from the passing of trains and act as hosts for a wide variety of animal life.

It is now perhaps too late for anyone to produce a field guide for train-borne naturalists–a book which would tell them what might be seen from the carriage windows. The post-war years, which have seen the great upsurge of popular interest in Britain's wildlife, have also witnessed the decline and mutilation of its railway system.

Conditions were very different in 1904, when the first edition of Stanford's *Geological Atlas* appeared. This admirable book devoted a chapter to 'descriptions of the geological features observable along the main lines of railway'. It explained the scenery through which the passenger was travelling, named the rock strata so conveniently exposed in the railway cuttings, and drew attention to the brick-yards, quarries, gravel-pits and collieries along the way. It also gave its readers occasional snippets of palaeontology–that here the London, Tilbury and Southern Railway was crossing the terraces of Pleistocene gravel which had yielded the remains of mammoth, hyaena and hippopotamus, and that the magnesian limestone by the North-eastern line, to the south of Durham, was noted for its fossil fishes.

Many of the old lines referred to in Stanford's atlas, let alone their original names, have passed into history, but it is still true to say that no-one with an interest in geology or any other branch of natural history need ever be bored when travelling by train–provided, of course, that the journey is made in daylight and above ground. It is surprising perhaps that the promoters of British Rail, in stressing the advantages of their method of transport over the use of the motor car, have not publicised the fact that from their carriage windows you can spot curlews, oystercatchers, herons and shelduck on the glistening mud of Poole Harbour or the Devon estuaries, and have more than a fleeting glimpse of the fallow deer in the New Forest, the soaring Welsh buzzards, or the seals that bask on the sandbanks of the Tay.

Plant sanctuaries Just as the railways have a good deal to offer observant naturalists, so they have also been of benefit to Britain's wildlife. The relatively inaccessible embankments and cuttings can be sanctuaries for plants which have long since vanished from the neighbouring land through urban expansion, industrial development and changes in farming methods. Sutton Park in the West Midlands now retains the only sizeable examples of heathland to have survived the growth of Birmingham and its Black Country satellite towns, but you can still find heather on some of the suburban railway banks of Solihull and Sutton Coldfield. Primroses and cowslips, which have been brought to the edge of extinction in many parts of the countryside, can also flourish on railway banks, the primroses often making a brave show in the built-up areas, as anyone who has made an April journey from London to Brighton can testify.

Cow parsley, gorse and broom, bluebells, harebells, foxgloves, knapweeds and willowherbs all add their colours to railway lines in the appropriate season, and naturalised garden plants can also make a significant contribution to the railway flora, especially around towns. Lupins are much in evidence

sticky groundsel

sea mouse-ear

strapwort

Danish scurvy-grass

biting stonecrop

Above: Bladder senna, once planted on London's railway banks, now spreads by itself.

Below: Any lake, pond or gravel pit you see from a train is likely to be frequented by swans and other water birds.

around Birmingham, and bladder senna which was first planted deliberately on London's railway banks, is now able to spread there without human assistance. Beside the track there are beds of horse-radish, pink blankets of soapwort, yellow stands of golden rod, lurid splashes of everlasting pea, patches of Michaelmas daisies, thickets of butterfly-attracting buddleia and tall forests of the all-too-successful Japanese knot-weed.

Birds, insects and reptiles Recognising the larger birds from carriage windows is relatively simple, especially when an embankment gives the observer an elevated view of the countryside. The range of vision is more restricted in the cuttings, but even here the odd snatch of bird song may betray the presence of a robin, chaffinch or willow warbler. At one time, too, the railway cuttings were a favourite haunt of the red-backed shrike, now a bird that is very rare in the British Isles.

Some of the more obvious butterflies can be identified from the train. It would be hard to miss a male brimstone or a male orange-tip, and if the train should make an unscheduled stop beside some waste ground, the passenger-naturalist may be compensated for the delay by the sight of a buddleia bush laden with peacocks and small tortoiseshells. In the south of England one trackside insect might even be *heard* from the train: Dr David Ragge, Britain's foremost authority on crick-

Left: Not so easy to see from a train are the plants growing on the track itself – an inhospitable ribbon of stony desert between the rails which can only be colonized by low-growing species able to withstand dry conditions and extremes of temperature. Some are more usually found in maritime habitats. They include biting stonecrop, sticky groundsel, Danish scurvy-grass, sea mouse-ear and strapwort. Danish scurvy-grass is one of the coastal plants which have been brought inland with shingle ballast, and has been recorded at several places between London and the Midlands. Strapwort has only one truly native locality – Slapton Ley in Devon – but it has been found along inland railway lines.

...ts and grasshoppers, has picked up the loud, high-pitched 'song' of the great green bush-cricket from inside the Cornish Riviera Express.

It is not possible to see any reptiles from the window-seat, but their presence has been confirmed by those few naturalists who have been allowed access to railway property. Slow-worms have often been found, and the dry banks and track-ballast make ideal basking places for adders and common lizards.

Mammals The small rodents which form part of the adder's diet can also find a home by the railway. Wood mice and short-tailed voles can even inhabit urban railway banks. The brown rat is also found and must be just as common a railway resident in farming country as in town. It is no wonder that we so often see a cat lurking in the long grass along the tracks.

Rabbits, which may also fall victim to the stalking cat, are more in evidence than most mammals because of their size, abundance and the fact that, although they are more

Above: A profusion of plants has sprung up among the rails in this shunting yard, in a little used area. In the foreground is rosebay willowherb (the tall pink spikes), and spear thistle, and in the background are a few specimens of the most famous train-travelling plant of all – the Oxford ragwort. A botanist has recorded seeing a few of the winged fruits of Oxford ragwort float into a railway carriage near Oxford and drift out again just before Reading station.

Below: Rabbits appear to be quite at home along railway tracks – apparently not regarding the trains that thunder by as a disturbance! They will even come out near the tracks to feed in daylight.

active at night or in the twilight, they will show themselves in daylight if undisturbed. Evidently they do not regard the noise of a passing express as disturbance. Rabbits are largely responsible for the holes seen in the railway banks, but the larger excavations are the work of foxes and badgers which also take advantage of these well-drained sites. They are beyond the reach of most human beings and there is plenty of food available. The foxes have received a lot of publicity, and for many commuters on their way to town, the sight of a vixen sitting with her cubs in the sunshine has made a pleasant start to the working day. The scene has been captured more than once by press photographers.

Migration routes Human beings are not the only living things to have used the railways for getting about. The railway banks are green corridors running into our cities from the surrounding countryside, and there seems little doubt that foxes and rabbits have used them to penetrate the built-up areas. It can explain the occurrence of wild rabbits in the Princes Street Gardens, alongside Edinburgh's most famous thoroughfare, and account for their former presence on waste ground within five minutes' walk of Southampton's main station. Foxes can now make the occasional appearance in Central London, even at such unlikely places as Waterloo, Blackfriars and Trafalgar Square.

Railways have also influenced plant distribution. The tiny spores of ferns and the plumed seeds of many flowering plants may travel many miles in the slipstream of a moving train or suspended in the air within the train itself. Ferns have colonized the damp brickwork of stations, bridges and tunnel entrances, and in the days of steam the conditions were particularly favourable for the

early stages of their development wherever locomotives were frequently halted by signals. Some ferns made their appearance far beyond their natural range in Britain. The brittle bladder fern is essentially a plant of the rugged north and west, especially Scotland, Cumbria and Wales, but the trains took it to the English lowlands of the east and south-east. Another western fern which the railways have helped to spread eastwards is the rusty-back, an attractive plant with rust-red scales on the underside of its fronds.

The plant most celebrated for this method of dispersal, however, is the Oxford ragwort. This species is a native of Sicily and southern Italy, where it grows on volcanic ash. It was first recorded growing wild in Britain in 1794, on the walls of Oxford, to which it had apparently escaped from the Botanic Garden. It seeded itself by the Great Western Railway at Oxford around 1879, and then began its remarkable spread across the country, reaching Reading before 1896 and the fringes of London by the turn of the century. Its appearance in Wales, at Cardiff in 1898, may have been due to a direct introduction from southern Europe via the seaport, but it seems more likely that the seeds were carried inside a railway carriage from Swindon, where it was already well-established.

We can be quite certain that insects, spiders and other invertebrates have also been carried by passenger trains, as stowaways in the luggage van or through being sucked in through the windows, but rail transport is unlikely to have been a major factor affecting their distribution. During World War II, however, it was thought likely that London's

Underground trains were responsible for the limited spread of the culicine mosquitoes found breeding in the water that collected under the platforms and elsewhere. These insects added considerably to the discomforts of the many Londoners who were using the tube stations as air-raid shelters. The only animal passengers now making much use of the Underground, apart from human beings and their dogs, are the street pigeons (feral rock doves) which forage on the platforms on the Inner Circle and are occasionally seen taking a tube train to another station. The noise of the trains passing by does not seem to disturb them at all.

Above: Take a spring railway trip through almost any part of England that is wooded and you may be rewarded by the sight of a mass of bluebells in flower. The land around railway tracks is usually left undisturbed, thus allowing the plants to flourish.

Below: Look out for fallow deer grazing in the open. Although the trains may startle them at first, it seems that the deer soon learn to ignore them.

WILDLIFE AMONG THE TOMBSTONES

Many rural churchyards are ancient and contain a wealth of interesting flowering plants and associated wildlife. As traditional meadows become more scarce churchyards are increasingly valued for their species-rich grassland.

Below: The village of Carrigrohane in Ireland's County Cork has a quiet churchyard with a mature grassland. Its multitude of plant species assures a fine community of meadow-dwelling animals.

Until recently churchyards received little attention from naturalists, but now their value for wildlife is beginning to be recognised. It is clear that in towns churchyards provide 'oases' for birds, insects, small mammals and other wildlife, especially if they are not kept too neat and tidy. In parts of the country where trees and hedges are few and far between they play a similar role. In general, however, the importance of rural churchyards lies in the fact that in many parishes they constitute the last relics of ancient meadow, once one of our richest grassland habitats and now disappearing fast under the pressures of modern farming methods.

The one or two acres of grassland in a country churchyard may have been undisturbed for hundreds of years, apart from the periodic digging of graves for burials. The grass will probably have been cut or grazed annually, but is unlikely ever to have been fertilized, drained, ploughed up or reseeded, in contrast with most of our ancient meadows and pastures which have been 'improved' in this way to increase their productivity. These techniques, while very successful in agricultural terms, have one unfortunate side effect: they transform herb-rich grassland, supporting a high diversity of insects and other invertebrates, into virtual grass monocultures

of little interest to naturalists.

The most productive of the modern hay meadows are those which are ploughed up and reseeded every few years in order to maintain their high yield. These are known as leys. Even if they are left after a while to develop naturally again, they may take hundreds of years to acquire a flora as rich as the original one. This makes the remaining areas of ancient meadow all the more highly valued. There are over 10,000 medieval churches in England alone; taking an average of 1½ acres for the area of a churchyard there could easily be some 15,000 acres of ancient meadow preserved in this fashion.

A rich flora Churchyards contain a wealth of flowering plants. In a recent survey of 80 churchyards in Suffolk, well over 200 different species of herbaceous flowering plants were recorded. Almost half of the 50 species found most often are characteristic of old meadows or pastures. These include cowslip, ox-eye daisy, knapweed, field woodrush and dove's foot cranesbill. Primrose, lesser celandine, cuckoo pint and wood avens are amongst the attractive species fairly frequently recorded. Churchyards also harbour a few rarities— including the man and pyramidal orchids.

One word of warning: not only do some churchyards contain 'garden escapes' such as snowdrops and bluebells; seemingly wild flowers have sometimes been planted deliberately, so a splendid show of daffodils or cowslips may not have quite the significance that it seems to have at first sight.

Bones in the soil The plants you find in a churchyard vary according to the chemistry of the soil, which in turn usually reflects the geology of the area. One noticeable peculiarity of churchyards is that lime-loving species (known as calcicoles) are often more frequent than in the surrounding countryside. These plants include the green-winged orchid, burnet saxifrage, the delicate quaking grass and the gladwin, or stinking iris.

It may be that the calcicoles grow in the parts of the churchyard where bone fragments have enriched the calcium and phosphate content of the soil, and also where material eroded from tombstones or the masonry of the church has added these chemicals to the soil.

Animal habitats Areas of herb-rich grassland, left to grow tall in spring and summer, are inhabited by a multitude of insects and other invertebrates such as slugs and snails. These provide an easy catch for small animals such as hedgehogs, slow worms and the smaller mammals, that move about in the relative safety of the herb layer.

The presence of rabbits, mice and voles is an invitation to larger predators. As well as owls, some of which live on the premises, foxes visit the churchyards, even in towns and the suburbs of larger cities such as Bristol, Glasgow, Birmingham and London.

Under the surface of the earth, moles bur-

Above: Valerian is a likely plant to find on the walls or even roof of an old rural church. Others are the colourful stonecrops and pellitory-of-the-wall.

Left: The noctule bat feeds on insects in flight for about an hour; just before sunset is the time to watch for it.

Encouraging wildlife
Parochial Church Councils are often willing to do what they can to encourage wildlife in the churchyard. The key to management for wildlife lies in choosing the most suitable time for cutting the grass so that while the churchyard does not become overgrown, the right conditions are there for interesting plants to flower and set seed. Instead of weekly mowing, the grass should be cut only twice or three times a year—this can even result in saving the parish some of its hard-earned cash. The first cut should be at the end of June, the second in October.

row their way among the graves. They are said to be harmful to agriculture because of their attacks on earthworms among other things, but whether they do noticeably reduce the worm population is hard to tell. The earthworms burrow to a depth of a metre or two and carry upwards the soil they remove in burrowing. Some species eject it in worm casts on the surface, others leave it directly beneath the grass roots. The result of this is a slow undermining of the grave stones, which may sink gradually or lean over as the years pass. Rabbits and moles have a similar effect.

Trees and shrubs provide birds with shade and shelter, cover and nest sites and, in autumn, yield a harvest of fruits. The yew is a

esting tree for goldcrests and spotted flycatchers, and in winter there is no better
shelter for any bird to roost than its dense
foliage. The red, fleshy outer part of the fruit
is eaten by many birds. The inner seed is
poisonous, but does not harm the birds as
they do not digest it. The foliage of yews, too,
is poisonous for livestock, and this is the clue
to their being found in churchyards–here
they could safely be grown for their wood
without endangering cattle, sheep or pigs.

Other wildlife of the churchyard is there by
reason of the church itself–noctule bats need
some form of enclosed space which they can
enter and leave safely, and where doors or
shutters do not close them in. Belfries are
ideal for this purpose.

Barn owls hunt mainly by hearing, and so
the quieter the environment, the better they
compete with other predators. Their hearing
is highly specialised: the ear is adapted to be
particularly sensitive to high-pitched sounds
such as the squeaks of field mice. Churchyards in their silence are therefore ideal for
this slowly dwindling species.

If any general pattern of the churchyard
wildlife can be detected, it is that where more
types of habitat are represented–grassland,
shrubs, evergreen trees, masonry, eaves and
roof vaults, for example the greater a variety
of wildlife will be present.

Clues to the past There are a number of
plants which can be used as indicators of the
past history of a site. The presence of goldi-
locks (the woodland buttercup), dog's mercury or the wood false brome grass in a
churchyard, for example, suggests that originally the site was adjacent to or even part of a
wood. The small-leaved lime is a good
indicator of ancient woodland and is sometimes found in churchyard boundary hedges.

Above: The gladdon or
stinking iris. The purplish
mauve flowers have
an unpleasant smell which
attracts flies and beetles.
The flowers are succeeded
by plump pods which split
on ripening to reveal rows
of fiery orange berries, fully
exposed in winter.

Right: Slow worms live in
moist places and take to
the shelter of crevices under
flat stones. They are
predators of slugs.

Below: These tombstones
are made of limestone and
the lichens that grow on
them are the bright orange
Caloplaca heppiana and
whitish grey species which
include *Diploicia canescens*
(formerly known as *Buellia
canescens*) and *Caloplaca
teicholyta*.

There are other clues to a churchyard's age
and history: a round churchyard often
indicates a Saxon origin, and a boundary
hedge can be roughly dated by counting the
number of species in a 30-yard length. Many
churchyards have been extended since Victorian times by taking in adjacent pasture or
arable land; the richness of the old churchyard flora is often well demonstrated here,
for the new part usually has far fewer species,
and none of the rarer ones.

It is often noticeable that the older part of
the churchyard is raised several feet above
the level of the surrounding land. In many
cases this can be attributed to the accumulation of material from the centuries of burials.
Other churchyards stand higher because they
were created on raised sites such as ancient
settlements.

Churchyards are usually best visited in
May, when many of the spring-flowering
species are out and the grass has not yet been
cut, but visits at other times of the year will
reveal species missed earlier or not previously
identifiable.

Trees, shrubs and flowers of urban habitats

The plant populations of the urban environment fall mainly into two groups: those deliberately planted for beauty, shelter, food or shade (coming from any part of the temperate world); and those that have invaded naturally, either as remnants of the former countryside hanging on in fragments of semi-natural vegetation, or as colonizers, making use of some aspect of the town's fabric, whether it is the newly-dug soil of a vegetable patch, the bare mortar of a wall or a heap of rubble on a building site. There are also plants that cannot so readily be assigned to either group, in that they may have been deliberately introduced to begin with but have found conditions to their liking and gone wild.

Those trees, shrubs and herbs deliberately planted in cities and gardens are probably the most obvious. These include the ubiquitous and welcome street trees, which may be pines, limes, plane trees, cherries or one of many other species, planted by town councils for public amenity reasons; or the trees, shrubs and herbaceous flowers of every suburban garden, which may be any of thousands of different species or varieties.

Perhaps more interesting, in the way they have coped with the urban environment, are the wild plants that rapidly appear wherever the ground is not intensively maintained or covered with concrete. Every garden has a host of wild flowers, however hard the owner tries to eradicate them – a typical garden has sixty to a hundred wild plant species in it, most of them considered to be weeds by the owner. A cultivated, fertilised garden is a wonderful place for any plant that can grow quickly and seed itself regularly, but many urban niches are much less hospitable. Mortar in walls and buildings, especially if it is the older, softer lime mortar, supports many flowers and ferns despite the apparent absence of food and water. The walls and bricks themselves may be increasingly covered by crusty or powdery growths of tiny lichens and algae as the air becomes less polluted. And waste ground, rubbish tips, building sites and other transient environments provide a surprising range of possibilities for those plants hardy enough to cope with them and mobile enough to find them.

Left: The robust, low-growing dandelion is sure to be found wherever there is a tiny amount of soil for its roots to cling to — between paving slabs, against walls and in any waste place. Its spreading rosette of leaves helps it to resist trampling feet and its light, wind-blown seeds ensure wide dispersal.

CHECKLIST

This checklist is a guide to some of the plants you can find in towns, cities, parks and gardens in Britain. Although you will not see them all in the same place, you should be able to spot many of them throughout the changing seasons. The species listed in **bold** *type are described in detail.*

TREES
Buddleia
Forsythia
Hawthorn
Hornbeam
Horse chestnut
Laburnum
Lilac
Lime
London plane
Norway maple
Ornamental cherry
Rowan
Snowy mespil

FLOWERS
Clover
Comfrey
Common horsetail
Creeping thistle
Couch grass
Daisy
Dandelion
Greater plantain
Ground elder
Groundsel
Hairy bittercress
Hedge bindweed
Hedge parsley
Honesty
Ivy-leaved toadflax
Orange hawkweed
Oxford ragwort
Pineapple weed
Prickly sowthistle
Rosebay willowherb
Scarlet pimpernel
Shepherd's purse
Spear thistle
Stinging nettle
White dead-nettle
Yarrow
Yellow corydalis

Left: Walnut trees are no longer grown in Britain for their nuts and timber, as they once used to be. Today they grace many a park and garden. The walnut can easily be identified by its pale grey, almost white, bark which is smooth when young but becomes deeply fissured with age.

COLOURFUL STREET TREES

Do you know what trees are planted in your street? Today, the range of street trees is greater than ever before, from exotic cherry trees to unusual varieties of our own native species, all selected to meet the special conditions of the roadside.

Above: Most street trees are deciduous to provide a suitably cheering splash of colour each spring as they burst into leaf and then flower. Very rarely are conifers seen planted along streets, but you sometimes see an evergreen broad-leaved tree, the most common examples being the holm oak and the golden privet. The latter, shown here, forms a small compact tree, growing to no more than 4.5m (15ft) high, which makes it an ideal tree for street planting.

The planting of street trees in Britain began in the middle of the 17th century when the famous diarist, John Evelyn, advocated planting trees in London. Under his direction, trees were planted in several areas of London, including the Mall and St James's Park. During the next 200 years the planting of street trees continued on a small scale, in both London and other British cities, but it was not until the latter half of the 19th century, when the suburban areas began to grow, that street trees became common in residential areas.

Early street trees The first trees planted in London were planes, horse chestnuts and limes. All these are fine trees for parks and large squares, but quite inappropriate in a small street.

In early suburban areas, planes were often planted on both sides of narrow streets, and the subsequent pruning and lopping that was required reduced the trees to a hideous shape. Similarly, horse chestnuts are not the right size for suburban areas, and when pruned their soft wood becomes susceptible to diseases. Common limes share the same problem and have the further disadvantage of attracting swarms of aphids, which leave a black sticky mess that drips on to pavements and parked cars. Moreover, in a dry season the leaves turn a rusty brown in July and fall from the trees.

What are the requirements? Town planners slowly realised that only certain trees were suitable for street planting. They had to satisfy some fairly stringent conditions.

The most obvious requirement is size, both above and below ground. The branches must not intrude into the road or interfere with overhead wires, power lines or street lights. Nor should the roots be likely to interfere with underground cables, gas or water pipes or sewers.

It is best if street trees do not bear fruits that are juicy and colourful, otherwise inquisitive children will invariably try to climb them and damage either themselves or a branch. Juicy fruits that fall to the pavement can also be a hazard to pedestrians and attract insects.

Longevity, hardiness to the local weather, compatibility with the local soil and immunity to diseases are also important factors. In connection with the last criterion, it is never wise to plant the same type of tree throughout an area since, in the event of an epidemic of disease, whole streets of trees could die.

One final demand is that the trees should have a long bole, otherwise they could impede the vision of motorists. This is one reason why conifers are rarely planted as street trees—many bear foliage right down to ground level. They also offer the temptation to be taken home for Christmas!

Street cherries Until World War II town planners frequently turned to ornamental cherry trees to provide a splash of spring colour in our streets, and they are still among the most common street trees. Some of the most popular are *Prunus* × *hillieri* 'Spire' which has a suitably narrow growth habit and pink flowers, *Prunus* × *sargentii* 'Rancho', another narrow tree with pink flowers, and *Prunus padus* 'Watereri', which bears long tassels of white flowers.

Many cherry trees planted before the War have suffered badly from subsequent road widening. To accommodate a new road, the trees have often needed to be severely pruned, sometimes becoming lop-sided in the process. The pruning was often carried out at a time when the sap was not rising and so the wounds were susceptible to fungal infections.

Latest trends Most cherry trees are attract

Left: To make way for buses and lorries this tree had to be severely pruned on one side, leaving it lop-sided and ungainly.

Right: Road-widening has left these trees placed perilously in the road, with the result that they have had to be lopped to no more than a trunk and a few short stumps for limbs.

Below: Ornamental cherry trees look their best in early spring when they are in blossom.

ve only for as long as they remain in flower. For the rest of the year they are often fairly dull. They can also be expensive to look after, and so the trend in recent years has been towards planting native or naturalised trees that are cheap to maintain, yet have attractive foliage.

As local authorities have been forced to cut back on services, so cost has become an increasingly important factor. It is now essential that most trees being planted are quick to establish themselves, transplant easily and grow strongly during their first year.

The obvious choice is to plant suitable varieties of our own native trees, since they are usually self-reliant and easier to establish than trees native to other countries. Examples include a variety of hornbeam, *Carpinus betulus* 'Fastigiata,' and the Dawyck beech (*Fagus sylvatica* 'Fastigiata'), which are both upright forms whose leaves turn a beautiful golden colour in the autumn, and two types of hawthorn, *Crataegus monogyna* 'Stricta' and *Crataegus oxycantha* 'Coccinea Plena', the latter being a lovely domed tree often called Paul's Double Scarlet. Two beautiful flowering trees are Voss's laburnum (*Laburnum* × *watereri*) and the snowy mespil (*Amelanchier ovalis*).

Many of our most popular native street trees come from just two genera, *Acer* and *Sorbus*. Among the former, a variety of sycamore, *Acer pseudoplatanus* 'Brilliantis-

simum', with leaves that are first shrimp-pink and then turn pale bronze and finally green, and *Acer platanoides* 'Crimson King', with its purple-crimson leaves, are notable. The genus *Sorbus* includes some beautiful whitebeams, such as *Sorbus aria* 'Lutescens', and the rowan (*Sorbus aucuparia*).

It is good to see that our native trees are finally being given the recognition they so richly deserve. So often in the past, some brightly flowering foreign tree has been acclaimed without considering the beauty and practical advantages of our own species.

1 *Carpinus betulus* 'Fastigiata', an upright form of hornbeam.
2 *Sorbus aria* 'Lutescens', a variety of whitebeam.
3 *Fagus sylvatica* 'Fastigiata', Dawyck's beech.
4 *Acer platanoides* 'Crimson King', a variety of Norway maple with crimson leaves.
5 *Amelanchier ovalis*, the snowy mespil, an American tree now naturalised here.

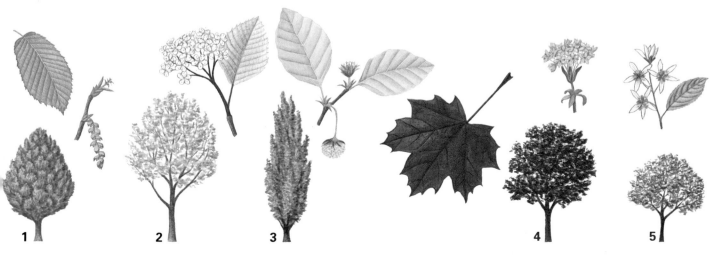

1   2   3   4   5

PRIDE OF LONDON: LONDON PLANES

The London plane, the most characteristic tree of London's streets and parks, also thrives in other towns and cities. You can recognise it immediately for the mottled bark that it sheds in great slabs, so ridding itself of pollution and dirt.

Left: A typical view of a London plane, growing here in Fitzroy Square in central London. London planes thrive in cities not only because they can withstand pollution, but also because they are tolerant of the periodic rigorous pruning which is necessary to prevent the branches obstructing overhead wires and high vehicles like buses.

Below: **London plane** (*Platanus x hispanica*). Deciduous, introduced, grows up to 35m (115ft), lives up to 200 years. Common especially in London but also planted in other towns and cities in the southern half of England. Flowers May, fruits late summer-early autumn.

One tree above all dominates the London landscape–the London plane. Planes make up over 60% of London's planted trees, lining streets and avenues, and gracing parks, squares and gardens. It is an unmistakable species, with distinctive peeling bark, shining green summer foliage, and dangling seed-balls in winter.

Opinions differ about the origins of the London plane. One idea is that it grew from a cross between the oriental plane (*Platanus orientalis*) which grows wild in Turkey and Greece, and the western plane or buttonwood (*P. occidentalis*), a native of North America where it is the tallest deciduous tree. Other theories, and indeed the current one, favours that it is merely a variety of the western plane. This hybrid theory suggests that it was crossed in Spain or the south of France in 1650, and first planted in England in Ely and Barnes, Surrey in about 1680.

The London plane grows vigorously and is resistant to air pollution. This has made it increasingly popular as an ornamental tree in towns and cities. Most of London's planes were planted at the beginning of the 20th century but some, such as the giants around Berkeley Square, are about 200 years old.

Outside London the plane has been widely planted in parks and along roads in southern England and the Midlands. Further afield, it has been cultivated in many European cities, notably in Paris.

New bark for old The London plane is a handsome tree, reaching a height of 35m (115ft) or more. The tallest on record–48m (145ft)–grows at Blandford in Dorset. Numerous side branches sprout from the contorted and arching main limbs, dividing to form intricate layers of drooping twigs. The trunk is tall, massive and smooth apart from occasional bumps and wrinkles.

The bark, the tree's most striking feature, flakes off in sheets, leaving the trunk dappled with various shades of brown, grey and yellow. As the tree grows, it breaks out of its old 'skin', shedding the older grey or brown bark to reveal the new yellowish bark beneath.

It is thought that this bark-peeling habit has helped the London plane to tolerate city life. All trees 'breathe' through pores in their bark, and in an urban environment these soon get clogged by dust and soot. But as the London plane constantly replaces old bark with new, its trunk does not become so coated with the grime that harms other trees. In effect the plane regularly renews its air filter.

Glossy leaves, green catkins Rain water washes off accumulated dirt from the smooth glossy surfaces of the leaves. These large leaves, which cast a pleasantly cool shade in summer, are alternately placed along the twigs and unfurl from cone-shaped buds which are almost completely encircled by a

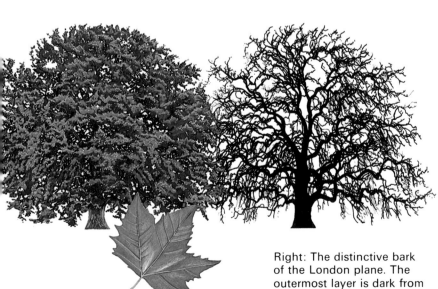

Right: The distinctive bark of the London plane. The outermost layer is dark from continued exposure to dirt and pollution. It flakes off to reveal large, pale and as-yet unpolluted patches of bark.

scar left by the previous year's leaf-stalk. They appear in mid-May and are at first covered with a woolly brown down that is later shed as they unfold and expand. The leaves display great variation from tree to tree but generally they are made up of five broad lobes, each with a deeply cut margin.

The base of the leaf-stalk is hollow where it joins the twig, and encloses the developing bud that lies dormant through winter before sprouting the following spring. The upper surface of the leaves is a rich shining green, while the underside is less bright and more yellowish in colour.

The London plane is a wind-pollinated tree that flowers in May and June. The round flower heads are made up of tightly packed green flowers which are either all female or all male, although both sexes are carried on the same tree. The flower heads hang on the tree throughout winter and start to disintegrate the following year, releasing hundreds of seeds.

Tough timber Although the London plane is planted purely for ornament it yields a timber that is highly regarded by craftsmen. The pinkish-brown wood is tough and hard and has been widely used by manufacturers of keyboard instruments, and cabinet makers. London plane timber is sometimes called lace-wood because of the intricate patterns made by the grain, and is cut into thin sheets of veneer for use on high quality furniture.

Male and female flower heads

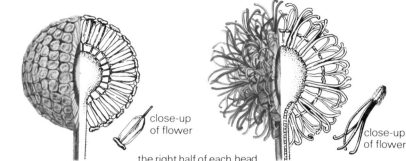

close-up of flower

close-up of flower

male flower head

the right half of each head is cut away to show the individual flowers.

female flower head

Right: The leaves and ripening fruits of the London plane. The fruits usually dangle singly or in pairs on stalks up to 10cm (4in) long throughout the winter. The seeds are not reliably fertile and London planes are generally raised from cuttings.

Below: In autumn the leaves turn various shades of yellow before falling to the ground, and for a few weeks London's parks become a mass of golden colour.

CHERRIES FROM THE ORIENT

For hundreds of years, cherry trees have been cultivated in the Far East for their ornamental blossom. These same trees are now being planted in Britain, where they bring a welcome splash of colour to our towns and cities in spring.

'Tai-Haku'

large single white flowers

'Amanogawa'

pink semi-double flowers

Above: Most ornamental cherry trees in Britain are varieties of the Japanese cherry; two common ones are 'Tai-Haku' and 'Amanogawa'.

Next page: A Sargent's cherry in full blossom. This species is one of the earlier cherries to flower.

Below: 'Kanzan' is the most widely planted of all the Japanese cherries.

Among the most attractive of all the trees in Britain are the ornamental cherries, so called because they are planted for their appearance rather than for their fruits, which are usually inedible. Ornamental cherries are becoming increasingly popular in towns and cities since many are small compact trees, ideal for growing in the confined space of a street or a small garden.

There is now a wide range of varieties to choose from, with differing flower colours and branching patterns. Even outside their flowering period, some ornamental cherries have distinct and beautiful barks and on many the leaves are brightly coloured, both in spring when they emerge and in autumn before they fall.

Oriental cherries Britain's native cherries, the gean or wild cherry and the bird cherry, have been valued for their ornamental qualities for hundreds of years, but almost all the ornamental cherries being planted nowadays originate in the Far East, especially in China and Japan. Both these countries have a profusion of cherry species growing wild which have long been cultivated for their ornamental value rather than for their fruits. In Japan, especially, flowering cherries are venerated. Temples, shrines and other holy places are planted with them; they are frequent subjects for Japanese art; and there is a host of legends and traditional stories surrounding them. Japan is famous for its massed plantations of cherries, which attract hundreds of thousands of visitors at blossom time each year.

The oriental cherries were introduced to Europe during the 19th century, when trade routes to the Far East were opened up. But many of the varieties that had been cultivated in the East for so long arrived in Britain only during this century. Their introduction and subsequent popularisation was due to one man – Captain Collingwood Ingram.

Japanese cherry The first oriental cherry to be introduced to Britain was the Japanese cherry (*Prunus serrulata*), also known as the oriental cherry. It arrived in Britain in 1822 from Canton in China, though it is more commonly grown in Japan, where varieties of this species are greatly treasured and known as Sato Zakura (Japanese for 'village cherries'). Despite its popularity in Japan, this species is actually native to China but was introduced to Japan many hundreds of years ago.

The Japanese cherry is the most widely planted ornamental cherry in Britain. Of the hundreds of varieties that have been developed around the world, at least 60 are grown here. They differ mainly in the colour and arrangement of the flowers and in the flowering period. They all have purple-brown barks with rows of protruding lenticels. The leaves, which are oval with a long tapering point and toothed margins, turn a handsome pink, red or golden-yellow in the autumn. Japanese cherries can grow as tall as 15m (50ft), but most are much shorter than this.

Common varieties The most popular variety of Japanese cherry grown in Britain is 'Kanzan', which bears masses of deep pink, double flowers in April. So many flowers are

Above: The variety 'Cheal's Weeping' has pink or white flowers, which appear at the same time as its leaves, usually in late April. This variety often has a lop-sided shape.

Right: The Yoshino cherry, a popular hybrid flowering in March or April.

Seasonal colours

leaf opens reddish purple

spring

becomes dark green when mature

summer

turns orange or crimson in September

autumn

produced that the branches, which for most of the year are fairly upright, hang down under the weight.

Another commonly grown variety is 'Shim-idsu', which has pendulous branching clusters of flowers. Each cluster consists of three to six large, white, double flowers. They open just after 'Kanzan' in late April or early May. Two other common varieties with very different habits are 'Amanogawa' and 'Cheal's Weeping'. The former has a narrow upright shape and resembles a Lombardy poplar; its flowers are pink and semi-double. The latter variety has very pendulous branches that may almost touch the ground; its flowers can be either pink or white. Both these varieties flower earlier than 'Kanzan'.

The variety 'Tai-Haku' has a most unusual history. In 1923, Captain Collingwood Ingram noticed an unusual cherry tree growing in a garden in Sussex. At first he could not identify it; but, during a visit to Japan, he discovered that it used to grow there but became extinct during the 18th century. The Japanese called it 'Tai-Haku'. Ingram later reintroduced it into its native country, but no one yet knows how it came to be growing in a Sussex garden. The flowers of 'Tai-Haku' are white and spectacularly large – up to 8cm (3in) across, which is larger than those of any other variety.

Sargent's cherry Another popular ornamental species is Sargent's cherry (*Prunus sargentii*). This is named after Charles Sar-

gent, of the Arnold Arboretum in Boston, USA, who on a visit to Japan in 1890 discovered it growing on the slopes of Mount Fujiyama. Sargent's cherry sometimes grows as tall as 20m (65ft), which is a notable height for a cherry. The bark resembles that of the Japanese cherry, except that it is smoother and glossy. The flowers open in the middle of April and are borne in clusters of two to five densely massed along the branches. The flowers themselves are pink and single.

The leaves on a Sargent's cherry are also attractive. Appearing slightly after the flowers have opened, they are reddish-purple at first and, with the pink flowers, make a striking combination of colours. As the leaves mature they turn dark green, but in autumn become a spectacular bright orange or crimson. Sargent's cherry is one of the first trees to change colour in the autumn, often as early as the beginning of September. In shape, its leaves resemble the leaves of a Japanese cherry.

Rose-bud cherry This is another species of ornamental cherry native to Japan. The rose-bud cherry (*Prunus subhirtella*)–also known as the spring cherry–was introduced to Britain in 1895. There are many varieties of this species, including those with double flowers and others with a weeping habit. But one variety in particular, 'Autumnalis', is especially popular since it flowers throughout the winter. Not surprisingly, it is also known as the winter-flowering cherry. The majority of its pale pink flowers appear in November or April, but in between these months a small number of flowers regularly appears on its otherwise bare branches.

In the wild, the rose-bud cherry can grow to a height of 20m (65ft), though cultivated trees are usually much smaller.

Tibetan cherry Not all ornamental cherries are grown for their flowers. The Tibetan cherry (*Prunus serrula*) is planted primarily for its unusual and attractive bark. In autumn the outer bark peels away in narrow bands from the trunk and branches to reveal new bark of a rich mahogany-brown colour with rings of paler lenticels. Unfortunately, the flowers are relatively insignificant for an ornamental cherry, being small and white. Since they emerge at the same time as the leaves, they tend to be obscured.

The Tibetan cherry is native to western China and was introduced to Britain in 1908. In cultivation it grows to a height of about 8m (25ft).

A profusion of hybrids These four species and their varieties cover most of the ornamental cherries grown in Britain. But there

are also many hybrids that have been developed from these and other species. One particularly common hybrid is the Yoshino cherry (*Prunus × yedoensis*), which is a cross between the rose-bud cherry and the Oshino cherry. The Yoshino is one of the earliest cherries to flower, appearing in March. The single flowers are pink or white. Many other hybrids and varieties are still being developed.

Above: The Tibetan cherry is unusual among ornamental cherries in being planted for its brightly coloured bark rather than its flowers. Its bark is at its best in the autumn, when the outer layer peels away in bands to reveal rich mahogany-coloured new bark.

Shapes of trees

Most varieties of Japanese cherry are small trees, usually around 3-4m (10-12ft) high, with an open, spreading crown (**1**), but a few have radically different habits. The variety 'Cheal's Weeping' (**2**) has a weeping or pendulous habit in which its branches reach almost down to the ground. Another variety goes to the opposite extreme. This is 'Amanogawa', which has an upright, columnar habit (**3**) and is said to be fastigiate. All its branches are short and swept strongly upwards from a central stem, so that the tree resembles a small Lombardy poplar.

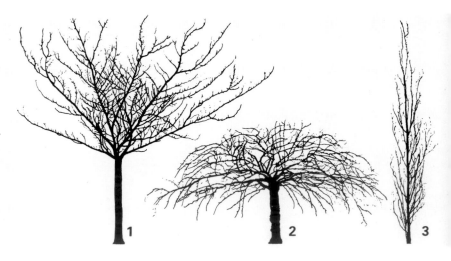

GOLDEN CHAINS OF LABURNUM

The spectacular springtime show of yellow flowers gives laburnum its common name of 'golden chains' or 'golden rain'. But the laburnum also has its dark side, for it is one of the most poisonous trees growing in the British Isles.

Common laburnum
(Laburnum anagyroides)

short densely-flowered racemes

Scotch laburnum
(Laburnum alpinum)

long sparsely-flowered racemes

Voss's laburnum
(Laburnum × watereri)

long densely-flowered racemes

The three major laburnums (above) differ most noticeably in their flowers. Voss's laburnum (below) is now more widely planted than the other two.

Like so many of the more colourful trees that grow in Britain, the lovely laburnum is not native to this country. It comes from the mountainous areas of central and southern Europe and was familiar to the ancient Romans. Their great naturalist, Pliny the Elder, described it as a 'tree from the Alps, with hard white wood and long yellow flowers which bees will not touch'. He was right that honey bees are not attracted to this tree, because its flowers do not produce nectar. But the wood is not white; the sapwood is butter-yellow and the heartwood is a dark chocolate-brown. Nevertheless, the name laburnum is derived from the Latin for white sapwood.

Species of laburnum From its native countries, laburnum was gradually introduced to the rest of Europe and reached Britain in the latter half of the 16th century. The first laburnum to be introduced to this country was the common laburnum (*Laburnum anagyroides*). This was followed about 30 years later by another species, *Laburnum alpinum*, which was found to grow much better than the common laburnum in the harsher conditions of Scotland. This laburnum is now known as the Scotch laburnum.

A third laburnum, now more widely planted than either of the other two, is Voss's laburnum (*Laburnum × watereri*). This is a hybrid between the common and the Scotch laburnum and is in many ways superior to them, particularly in its flowers. It also has a narrower crown, which makes it popular in small gardens.

All laburnum species flourish in the British Isles; indeed, they have become adapted to the British climate better than any other introduced tree. Not surprisingly, both the common and the Scotch laburnums became naturalised soon after they were introduced, helped also by the fact that both species set seed abundantly. The best place to see a naturalised laburnum is in wild hilly country.

Similarities and differences Apart from some minor differences, laburnums resemble each other closely. They are small trees, growing no more than 9m (30ft) high – which is why they have long been popular as street

trees and for planting in small town gardens. The bark is smooth and olive-green, sometimes turning brown with age. The trunk is slender, seldom exceeding 30cm (1ft) in diameter.

The leaves are unusual in that each consists of three short-stalked leaflets – laburnum is the only tree commonly grown in the British Isles to have this leaf arrangement. The leaflets are up to 8cm (3in) long; their upper surfaces are pale green and smooth, the lower surfaces light-grey and hairy (hairless on the Scotch laburnum).

Laburnum is a member of the pea family and this is shown in the shape of its flowers. These consist of five bright yellow petals arranged in typical pea fashion – one large 'standard' petal, two 'wings' and two more connected to form a 'keel'. The flowers are borne on long pendulous racemes that vary in length from 15cm (6in) to 30cm (1ft). On the Scotch laburnum the racemes are longer than on the common, but they are also narrower and the flowers are more widely spaced. The Scotch laburnum blooms later – around the end of June, which is about three weeks

Above: Like all members of the pea family, the laburnum bears its seeds in pods. The pods, which are borne in clusters, are pale green and hairy when young.

Right: The pods turn brown and lose their hairs as they mature. When ripe they split open, twisting as they do so to force out the seeds. These are brown on the Scotch laburnum, darker brown on Voss's and black on the common laburnum.

Opposite page: The inverted triangle shape of the laburnum is most distinctive when the tree is in flower.

Below: The flowers on Voss's laburnum are as densely clustered as they are on the common laburnum but they hang in much longer racemes.

In case of poisoning

All parts of the laburnum, especially the seeds, are highly poisonous. Symptoms appear an hour after ingestion. The victim suffers from a burning sensation in the mouth, nausea, severe thirst, abdominal pains, sweating and headache; in severe cases, death follows. Fortunately, it is rare for a child to eat a lethal quantity of seeds (15 to 20). Nevertheless, immediate treatment by a doctor is advisable, even if only one or two have been eaten. Wherever possible, remove any laburnum seeds growing within reach of children.

after the common laburnum.

The flowers of Voss's laburnum combine the best features of the other two: its racemes are as long as those of the Scotch laburnum but the flowers are larger and more densely borne, like those of the common laburnum.

Peas in a pod All plants in the pea family have their fruits borne in pods. In the case of the laburnum, these pods are slender, hairy and light green when immature. They turn brown and lose their hairs as they ripen in July and August.

When the pods are ripe they twist and split along their margins, forcing out the small hard seeds – these are black on the common laburnum and brown on the Scotch laburnum. (One or two seeds at the stalk-end of the pod are often left behind if the twisting action was not strong enough to force them out.) If the tree is growing in the wild this has the advantage of spreading out the interval at which the seeds are distributed, and so increasing the chances of a seed finding conditions favourable for germination.

Deadly poisonous Although the laburnum is widely planted for its beauty it is, nevertheless, an extremely poisonous tree in all its parts – roots, leaves, flowers and seeds. The seeds are particularly poisonous and every year there are cases of young children falling ill after eating them. There are also a few cases of cattle being poisoned after browsing on the pods, though rabbits and hares seem to be unaffected.

The poisonous nature of laburnums is another reason for the popularity of the hybrid Voss's laburnum. As well as having prettier flowers than either of the other two it produces far fewer seed pods and so attracts children less. The seeds themselves and other parts of the tree, are just as poisonous as on other laburnums, however.

Two-tone timber Over the centuries laburnum wood has been greatly prized by cabinet makers for its hardness and its contrasting colours. The difference in colour between the sapwood and the heartwood has given rise to what is known in the furniture trade as 'oyster work'. These are small discs or roundels of wood formed by cutting across a laburnum branch to expose concentric rings of growth. The inner rings are chocolate brown heartwood and the three or four outer rings are butter-yellow sapwood. Laburnum branches can also be cut at an angle to give oval slices. Both sorts of cut are used for decorative inlay work and veneers. Furniture carrying oyster work was particularly popular during the reign of William and Mary; today it fetches a high price at auctions.

Laburnum wood is also ideal for turning work – fruit bowls, egg-cups and so on – since it is hard, close-grained and takes a high polish. Pulleys and blocks made from laburnum last almost for ever, and the chanters of Scottish bagpipes are frequently made from this wood because it can be bored accurately

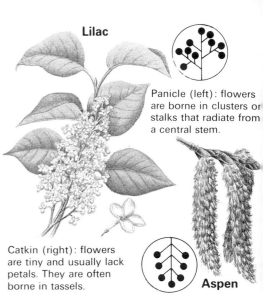

Lilac

Panicle (left): flowers are borne in clusters or stalks that radiate from a central stem.

Catkin (right): flowers are tiny and usually lack petals. They are often borne in tassels.

Aspen

LILACS IN THE SPRING

Since first being introduced to Britain more than 300 years ago, lilac has become one of the most popular of our garden shrubs. The emergence of its sweet-smelling blossom in May is a sure sign that summer is just round the corner.

Above: A lilac bush in flower. Many of the lilacs being grown today are specially bred varieties that offer a range of flower colours from white, through pink or blue, to deep violet. The original lilacs introduced to Britain had pale pinkish-violet flowers, the colour now called lilac.

Lilac belongs to that small group of plants that are so familiar in Britain that people mistakenly assume they are native. In fact, most lilac species are native to Asia, with just a few species being found in eastern Europe. All lilac species are members of the same genus, *Syringa*, which is itself a member of the olive family (known to botanists as the Oleaceae).

Like other members of this large family, such as privet, ash and forsythia, lilac grows

extremely well in the British Isles. One great advantage is that it is tolerant of both acid and alkaline soils. Indeed, on a small scale lilac has become naturalised in this country.

First to arrive The earliest species of lilac to be introduced to Britain, and still the one most commonly grown here, is the common lilac (*Syringa vulgaris*). This species is native to eastern Europe and Asia Minor (the word 'lilac' comes from the Persian word for bluish: 'lilak' or 'nilak'). It first appeared in western Europe in the 16th century and was introduced to Britain in 1621 by the naturalist John Tradescant, who later became King Charles I's gardener.

In appearance, the common lilac is typical in many ways of most *Syringa* species. It is a shrub or occasionally a small tree, growing no higher than 8m (25ft). Usually, it has several stems growing from the base although there may be just a single slim trunk. The bark is smooth and grey.

The leaves are mid-green, smooth-surfaced and have a characteristic heart-shape. They are folded along the central vein so that, when seen in cross-section, they are shaped like a 'V'. The leaves can grow to a length of 15cm (6in).

The flowers emerge in May on pyramidal panicles about 15-20cm (6-8in) long. On common lilac, the flowers are, not surprisingly, lilac-coloured, but on other species of lilac they can vary from white to pink, mauve, blue or deep purple. The panicles may also be much longer on other species, sometimes reaching a length of 45cm (18in). The flowers are followed by the fruits. These consist of flattened capsules that split, each releasing two winged seeds; they ripen in October.

Lilacs from Asia Soon after the common lilac reached Britain, the first of many lilacs native solely to Asia was discovered. This was the Persian lilac (*Syringa laciniata*), named after the country in which western botanists first discovered it growing. In fact, it had been cultivated in both Persia and India for centuries. The Persian lilac is much smaller than the common lilac, rarely reaching more

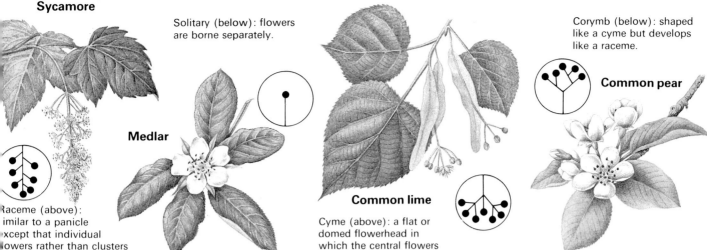

Sycamore

Solitary (below): flowers are borne separately.

Medlar

Common lime

Cyme (above): a flat or domed flowerhead in which the central flowers open first.

Raceme (above): similar to a panicle except that individual flowers rather than clusters are attached to a stem.

Corymb (below): shaped like a cyme but develops like a raceme.

Common pear

than 2m (6ft) in height. It is unusual among lilacs in having leaves that are lobed rather like those of an oak. It produces violet-purple flowers in May.

The Persian and common lilacs were crossed several times in attempts to produce a superior lilac. The most notable success came in 1795, when one Monsieur Varin, the Director of the Botanic Garden at Rouen in France, produced a hybrid that was named the Rouen lilac (*Syringa × chinensis*). This is a handsome shrub, still popular among gardeners. It grows to a height of 4.5m (15ft) and bears large compound panicles (ie several joined together) of lilac-coloured flowers in May. At this time of the year, the whole bush may be covered with flowers.

Other lilacs follow During the 19th century, many more lilac species were discovered and brought back to Britain as botanists began to explore the Far East. The famous plant hunter, Robert Fortune, discovered *Syringa oblata* growing in a Shanghai garden in 1856. Unfortunately, it does not flower well in this country because its blossom appears early in the year. Often, a spell of warm weather in early spring induces the flower buds to grow, only for them to be killed soon after by a sudden cold snap.

Despite its frequent failure to flower well, *S. oblata* soon proved itself to be a useful source from which to breed hybrids and varieties. Many of the beautifully coloured lilacs grown today are crosses between the common lilac and *S. oblata*. Much of this work was done by the French horticulturists Victor Lemoine and his son Emile in Nancy during the 1870s.

Several of the far-eastern species of lilac resemble small trees rather than shrubs. For example, *Syringa pekinensis* grows to a height of 6m (20ft) and always has a single trunk. In June its spreading branches are covered with a profusion of cream-coloured flowers borne on small panicles 7-12cm (3-5in) long. This species was discovered in northern China at the end of the last century.

Hungarian lilac During the 19th century one further species of European lilac was found to place alongside the common lilac. It was discovered in 1830 growing in Transylvania and the Carpathian Mountains of Eastern Europe by the Baroness of Josika. It is now known as the Hungarian lilac (*Syringa josikaea*).

This lilac is not one of the most attractive but, like *Syringa oblata*, it has proved to be a useful source for hybrids and varieties. Many of the finest modern lilacs were raised from this species by Dr Isabella Preston, who worked in Ottawa, Canada, during the 1920s. One of the most popular of her hybrids is 'Bellicent', a large, arching shrub with clear pink flower trusses about 25cm (10in) long, which appear in May.

Lilac for medicine Traditionally, lilac used to play an important role in folk medicine, the flowers and bark being used to reduce fevers. Lilac must have made an unpleasant medicine since it has an extremely bitter taste.

The wood from a lilac shrub has few commercial uses nowadays, though in Victorian times it was used for decorative inlay work.

Above: Each flowerhead of lilac consists of small individual flowers arranged together in what is called a panicle. This arrangement is shared by some other trees and shrubs, although other arrangements are possible. The main alternatives are catkins, racemes, cymes and corymbs. Flowers may also be borne singly.

Lilac (*Syringa* spp). A genus of introduced deciduous shrubs or small trees that flower in May or June. Their maximum height is 8m (25ft), though they are usually much shorter.

Below: One of the many modern varieties of common lilac. Notice the heart-shaped, partly folded leaves.

EARLY FLOWERING FORSYTHIAS

Introduced to Britain from the Far East, forsythias have never become naturalised here, but they are among our most popular shrubs in parks and gardens due to the blaze of colour they provide early in the year as their yellow flowers open out.

Since they were first introduced to Britain during the last century, a number of forsythia species have been successfully grown here a ornamental shrubs. All but one species o forsythia – and all the species that are so popular in British gardens – come from th Far East. The odd one out is the aptly-named *Forsythia europaea*, which comes from south eastern Europe. This shrub is the leas attractive of all forsythias and so is rarel planted in Britain.

The genus *Forsythia* is named in memory o William Forsyth who was superintendent o the Royal Gardens at Kensington during th latter half of the 18th century. Forsythias ar grouped together in the Oleaceae family

which also includes several other familiar plants, such as ash, privet and lilac.

Ornamental arrivals The first species of forsythia arrived in Britain in 1845. It was introduced here from its native China by the famous plant collector Robert Fortune. Named *Forsythia viridissima*, it is the last species of forsythia to flower each year, in April producing solitary bright yellow flowers along its upright branches.

The arrival of *F. viridissima* was followed about five years later by another forsythia species, *F. suspensa*. At least one variety of this species, which is native to China, was cultivated in Japan hundreds of years ago. *F. suspensa* forms long arching shoots that reach as high as 9m (30ft) if grown against a wall, as it often is. Grown in the open, this species reaches a more modest 2.5-3m (8-10ft) high. Its flowers are borne in pairs or clusters towards the end of March or the beginning of April.

Two other oriental species, less commonly grown in Britain, are *F. giraldiana* and *F. ovata*. The former is native to China, and is the earliest forsythia to come into flower each year, usually around the end of February or the beginning of March. It grows to a height of 4.5m (15ft), which makes it one of the tallest forsythias. *F. ovata* blooms soon after. It is native to Korea and differs in several respects from the other species. In particular, it is by far the smallest and most compact of all forsythias, reaching no more than 1.5m (5ft) in height. Several dwarf cultivars (cultivated varieties) have been derived from this species. The flowers of *F. ovata* appear in pairs in early March.

Cultivars and hybrids Most forsythias growing in gardens are not true species but are cultivars bred from a hybrid, *F. × intermedia*. This hybrid was developed in Germany in 1884 from a cross between *F. suspensa* and *F. viridissima*. The cultivars, of which 'Spectabilis' and 'Beatrix Farrand' are the most popular, vary considerably, but they are all free-flowering shrubs around 2-2.5m (6-8ft) high.

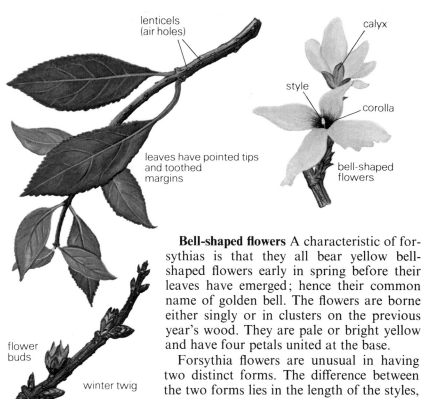

leaves have pointed tips and toothed margins

flower buds

winter twig

lenticels (air holes)

calyx

style

corolla

bell-shaped flowers

Opposite and above: The hybrid *Forsythia x intermedia*. Several of the most popular cultivar forsythias have been developed from this particular hybrid.

Forsythia (*Forsythia* spp.). A genus of deciduous shrubs, all but one being native to the Far East. All bear yellow flowers, either in clusters or singly, appearing Feb-May. The leaves are usually lance-shaped and toothed. The maximum height of the shrub is, exceptionally, 9m (30ft).

Below: One way in which forsythia spreads is by sending out branches that bend down to the ground, where they take root.

Bell-shaped flowers A characteristic of forsythias is that they all bear yellow bell-shaped flowers early in spring before their leaves have emerged; hence their common name of golden bell. The flowers are borne either singly or in clusters on the previous year's wood. They are pale or bright yellow and have four petals united at the base.

Forsythia flowers are unusual in having two distinct forms. The difference between the two forms lies in the length of the styles, which are either long or short – there are no intermediate forms. The reason for having two sorts of style is to ensure that only cross-pollination takes place. On each bush the flowers are wholly of one type or another, but seeds set only when flowers are fertilised by pollen coming from the opposite type of flower. So it is impossible for a forsythia bush to fertilise itself.

A strange consequence of this is that forsythias very rarely set seeds in Britain, since many of the plants grown here have the same type of style. This is because they are derived by vegetative propagation from the few specimens originally brought over here (forsythias propagate vegetatively by sending out suckers or by their branches bending down and taking root where they touch the ground). The original stock of *F. viridissima*, for example, bore long-styled flowers and for many years all the cultivated specimens of this species in Britain had long styles as well. Not surprisingly, long styles were thought to be a characteristic of the species until fresh investigations in China revealed the existence of short-styled flowers of *F. viridissima*.

Lance-shaped leaves The flowers bloom for between two and four weeks. Only when they fade do the leaves emerge. They are usually lance-shaped, though sometimes oval, and vary in length from 5-15cm (2-6in), depending on the species. The leaves turn yellow in autumn but do not fall until the first frosts arrive. A plant in a sheltered position in southern England may retain its leaves well into winter, whereas an exposed plant is likely to drop its leaves much earlier.

Once the leaves have fallen the stems can be seen clearly. They are thin, light brown and covered with pale dots called lenticels, through which the plant breathes. The stems are hollow inside, apart from some pith where they meet each other.

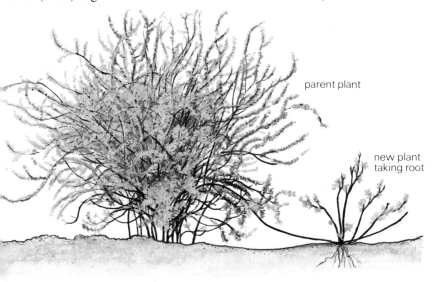

parent plant

new plant taking root

BUDDLEIA: BUTTERFLY BUSH

Less than a century ago no British naturalist had heard of buddleia. Yet today it grows all over Britain, in both gardens and the wild.

Throughout the world there are more than a hundred species of buddleia. They are native to North and South America, southern and eastern Africa and parts of southern Asia, but none is native to Europe. Even so, a number of species have been introduced into British gardens and one has become naturalised here. This is *Buddleia davidii*, the butterfly bush, known in its native China as 'summer lilac'.

The Latin name is derived from the names of two men: Adam Buddle, a 17th century English naturalist, and Père David, a French missionary who discovered the bush in the hills of central China in 1869. (Père David also gave his name to other Chinese wildlife, such as Père David's deer and Père David's maple.)

Butterfly bushes—or buddleias as they are often called—first appeared in Britain in 1890 but they were poor specimens, imported via Russia. By 1898, however, better stock had been received. In the early 1900s, many more bushes were imported into Britain from central China, and most of our naturalised and cultivated buddleias are descended from this stock.

Buddleia structure The butterfly bush is a deciduous or semi-deciduous shrub which may grow to a height of 5m (16ft), though it can bear flowers when it is less than 1m (3ft) tall. Its long, narrow leaves are grey-green, with numerous downy hairs on their undersides that make them look almost white. These hairs, which surround the leaf pores, help to prevent the wind from drying out the leaves. They are an adaptation to conditions in high, exposed areas such as the hills of the plant's native China.

Buddleia flowers are extremely small—no more than a few millimetres across—but they are clustered together in huge numbers on spikes up to 40cm (16in) long. In their naturalised state, buddleias have pale blue flowers, but on garden varieties the flowers can vary from white to lilac, reddish or dark purple.

The clustering of the flowers on the spikes serves to heighten their colour, making them more obvious to insects such as butterflies. The spikes also concentrate the powerful scent of the flowers. This combination of colour and scent attracts many different species of butterfly to feed upon the nectar. The nectar of a buddleia flower is not remarkably different from that of other flowers, yet it attracts butterflies and other insects in greater numbers than almost any other bush.

Garden escape Although it is a recent introduction to the British Isles, buddleia has already found a permanent place in our towns

Above: A naturalised buddleia in flower. The spikes of flowers may appear any time from June to October. After the flowers die, the spikes may stay on the bush for much of the winter.

Below: Small tortoiseshell butterfly on buddleia.

nd countryside. It has been planted in gardens all over Britain and Ireland, from where has spread into the wild via its winged seeds. Buddleia seeds resemble tiny propellers. Once the flowers have died the ripening seeds grow pointing upwards (an unusual phenomenon known as negative geotropism). The seed-cases split at maturity and the wind blows the seeds away from the parent plant.

If these seeds fall among grass or herbaceous plants they seldom germinate. Instead, they seem to prefer to fall on stony ground, for instance among dry rubble, in walls or along railway embankments.

Population explosion Naturalists began to notice buddleias growing wild in the countryside only 30 years after their introduction to this country. Limestone quarries, crumbling walls and areas of bare chalk – all exposed areas with high levels of calcium – were soon recognised as places to see 'escaped' buddleias.

Following World War II the buddleia underwent a population explosion. Every bomb site and building site represented an ideal situation in which the buddleia could flourish and, in just three or four years, some derelict sites became covered over with a dense tangle of these bushes. (One of the early explorers of China noted that buddleia thickets provided 'famous harbourage for leopards'.) Today, in London and other towns and cities any demolition site not immediately built upon becomes a nursery for buddleias.

Introduced plants that spread quickly often displace native plants and therefore disturb the balance between plants and animals in the countryside. But this is not the case with buddleia. It seems to have occupied an ecological niche that was vacant.

Buddleia for food Since buddleias are not native to Britain – nor indeed to any part of Europe – our own native fauna might well have found them unpalatable. The reason for this is that plants evolve in association with the insects of their native land; in a new environment with different insects an introduced plant might take a long time to develop an associated fauna. Buddleias, however, seem to be an exception to this rule.

Several different parts of the buddleia are eaten by British insects. The nectar attracts both common and less familiar butterflies, from the cabbage whites to the silver-washed fritillary, as well as hoverflies. The caterpillars of more than ten species of moth have been recorded on buddleia, most being leaf-chewers.

Most of these feeders eat a variety of different plants, but a few feed on only one other family of plants – the Scrophulariaceae, which includes figworts and mulleins. (Buddleias are classified as a separate family, the Buddleiaceae.) This suggests some sort of chemical similarity between buddleias and members of the Scrophulariaceae, which may help to explain how so many British insects have been able to switch to buddleias as a food source.

In the wake of these feeders have come the predators, such as spiders and ladybirds. So it seems that a complicated food chain is forming – only 90 years after buddleia was first introduced into Britain.

Garden buddleias

The parent species, *Buddleia davidii*, has given rise to several garden varieties with different colour flowers. These varieties are all sterile and cannot, therefore, escape to the wild; they are only seen in gardens. Some of the most popular are: 'Black Knight', which bears heads of deep violet-purple flowers; 'White Cloud' and 'White Profusion', which are white-flowered varieties; and 'Harlequin' and 'Royal Red', both with red flowers, the former having leaves variegated with white.

Feeders on buddleia

Some of the many insects that feed on buddleia at different times of the year. Butterflies feeding on nectar include: (**1**) peacock (*Inachis io*), (**2**) small tortoiseshell (*Aglais urticae*), (**3**) red admiral (*Vanessa atalanta*) and (**4**) large white (*Pieris brassicae*). Among the leaf-feeders are caterpillars of such moths as: (**5**) vapourer moth (*Orgyia antiqua*), (**6**) dot moth (*Melanchra persicariae*), (**7**) mullein moth (*Cucullia verbasci*) and (**8**) scalloped hazel (*Odontopera bidentata*); (**9**) the meadow spittle bug (*Philaenus spumarius*) and (**10**) the weevil *Conius hortulanus*.

LICHENS IN THE CITY

After centuries of decline lichens are now beginning to make a comeback in our towns and cities–a sure sign that our air is becoming cleaner.

It has been realised for more than a century that lichens are much rarer in towns and cities than in the countryside. The first proper study was carried out in Paris, and it was declared that the small number of lichens was due to the production of dark smoke and gaseous emissions, which made the air unsuitable for their growth. This view is still generally accepted today, though the dryness of town air is now thought to be another important factor.

Lichen zones In the 1920s a botanist, Johan

Above: The best place to look for lichens in a town is old churchyards, where you can sometimes find relict lichens growing on the headstones. Shown here is the relict lichen, *Caloplaca heppiana*.

Left: Dark patches of lichen discolouring a street monument in Kettering, Northamptonshire.

Sernander, introduced the concept of lichen zones. He recognised that there are three zones of lichen development in towns. In the centre, and around gasworks, railway stations (with steam trains in those days) and large industrial plants, there was a lichen desert. In the outer part of the desert the barks of trees began to be covered with green algae–only on stones were a few solitary lichens to be found. The next zone was a 'struggle zone' where the tree trunks were beginning to be colonized by lichens, though they were not abundant.

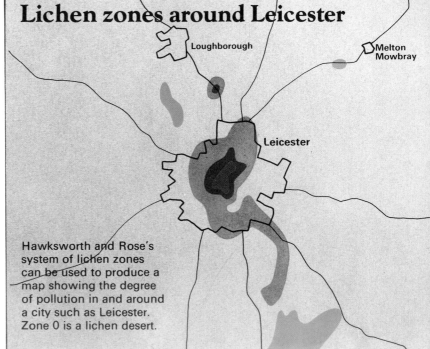

Lichen zones around Leicester

Loughborough

Melton Mowbray

Leicester

Hawksworth and Rose's system of lichen zones can be used to produce a map showing the degree of pollution in and around a city such as Leicester. Zone 0 is a lichen desert.

Rocky outcrops had a denser lichen cover. In the third zone the lichens were abundant on both trees and rocks.

Sernander's work led to the idea of using lichens and zones of lichen species as indicators of air pollution. The chief scale used today was devised by David Hawksworth and Francis Rose in 1970. Based on epiphytic lichens (ones growing on trees) their system recognises 11 zones ranging from zone 0, in which there is a complete absence of epiphytes, to zone 10, which contains species requiring very clean air. Maps of several towns and cities have now been produced showing the pattern of the zones.

Where to look The types of urban lichen that have been most studied are the ones growing on barks, because of their importance as indicators of air pollution. Yet lichens on other substrates are much better represented in urban areas. Calcareous stone, such as limestone, is the most important, with two-thirds of urban lichens occurring on it. The richness of the lichen vegetation on this substrate is due to the alkalinity of the stone, which indirectly reduces the toxic effects of sulphur dioxide–a major consituent of polluted air.

Asbestos-cement roofs have a particularly rich lichen flora–again because of their alkalinty, and also because of their ability to absorb water and their fibrous texture. These roofs have become particularly widespread on factories and garages built since World War II, but they are now in decline following the recent concern over the dangers of asbestos. (For this reason, any lichen studies you may carry out on asbestos-cement must be done with great caution.)

The best places to find lichens in towns are usually old churchyards, especially those with limestone headstones manured by birds.

Here you can often find 18th century headstones with relict lichens on them. These lichens would have colonized the stone a long time ago but, because of the modern level of air pollution, are unable to spread to new surfaces. One such relict is *Caloplaca heppiana*, which forms orange rosettes with lobes at the edge and fruiting bodies in the centre; it is confined to stone buildings and monuments built before the present century.

The most impoverished habitat for lichens in towns and cities is trees and woods. In many towns, fewer than ten lichen species occur on tree bark. Grassland is also poor in lichens, probably because of the combined effects of trampling and mowing, as well as the effects of

Below: The major cause of lichen deserts in cities is the presence in the air of sulphur dioxide, which is produced by the burning of coal and as a waste product in many industrial processes. Conditions are not necessarily as bad as they seem, though; in this picture, taken in north London, the chimneys on the left are emitting poisonous sulphur dioxide while the pair of large cooling towers on the right are producing only harmless steam.

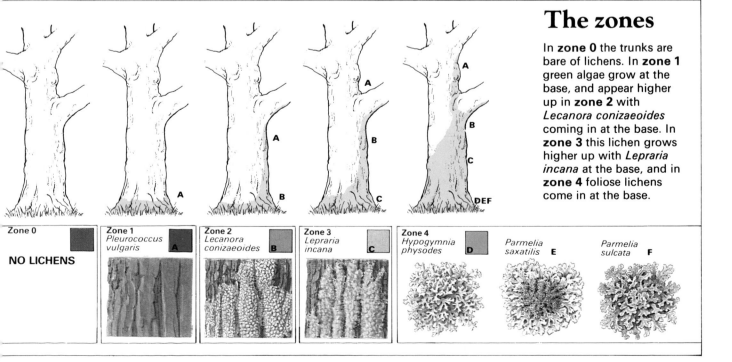

The zones

In **zone 0** the trunks are bare of lichens. In **zone 1** green algae grow at the base, and appear higher up in **zone 2** with *Lecanora conizaeoides* coming in at the base. In **zone 3** this lichen grows higher up with *Lepraria incana* at the base, and in **zone 4** foliose lichens come in at the base.

Zone 0	Zone 1 *Pleurococcus vulgaris*	Zone 2 *Lecanora conizaeoides*	Zone 3 *Lepraria incana*	Zone 4 *Hypogymnia physodes*	*Parmelia saxatilis*	*Parmelia sulcata*
NO LICHENS	A	B	C	D	E	F

air pollution.

Lichens to look for Despite the general poverty of urban lichens, several species are now more common in towns than in the countryside. These are small fast-growing lichens, which tend to be crowded out in rural areas by larger species. Included among them are *Lecanora conizaeoides, Lecanora dispersa, Candelariella aurella, Lecanora muralis* and *Stereocaulon pileatum*. All these species are of particular interest–to consider them one by one: *Lecanora conizaeoides,* also known as the pollution lichen, was unknown in Britain before 1860 yet ten years later it was becoming widespread. It increased rapidly with the general rise in levels of air pollution around this time and is now common in both urban and rural areas of England, Belgium, the Netherlands and northern Germany. It can be seen on the bark of trees, the wood of fences and the clay tiles of roofs. It forms a powdery grey-green coating and looks rather like a green alga, though the latter is a brighter green.

Lecanora dispersa is very variable and unusually forms a white or greyish-white crust, though in city centres a black form occurs, disfiguring white limestone and cement. *Candelariella aurella* is another dark lichen that disfigures buildings. The two can be distinguished by their fruiting bodies. On the *Lecanora* species they are whitish and on the *Candelariella* species they are yellow.

Above: *Lecanora muralis*, one of several lichens now beginning to colonize urban habitats. This species is found on concrete paving stones and on asbestos-cement roofs.

Below: Grey-green patches of *Lecanora conizaeoides* alongside a green alga.

Lecanora muralis is a greyish-green to greenish-brown lichen widespread on rocky outcrops and now abundant in towns, forming circular patches on asbestos-cement roofs and concrete paving stones. Its colonization of pavements in recent years has caused some concern. One local London paper reported that residents feared the lichen might be dangerous to health and destroy property. It is, of course, quite harmless.

Another recent colonizer of towns is *Stereocaulon pileatum*. Before 1950 this lichen was confined to acid rock outcrops on mountains and was quite scarce, yet today it is colonizing walls in towns and cities at a surprising rate–it particularly favours garden walls built of slag.

Encouraging signs The passing of the Clean Air Act and the establishment of Smoke Control Areas in which coal burning was banned have, in recent decades, led to a dramatic fall in the amount of smoke in the air.

The chief form of pollution affecting lichens, however, is sulphur dioxide, and this too has declined, though less spectacularly than smoke. Nevertheless, the level of this gas in London's air fell by nearly 90 per cent between 1964 and 1988, and lichens are enjoying the benefit of this reduction. Small plants of *Hypogymnia physodes* are now colonizing willow trees on Hampstead Heath in north London, where they have been absent for more than a century. South of the Thames a specimen of beard-moss (*Usnea*)–actually a lichen–has been found growing on a willow in Richmond Park. This lichen has not been seen in London since the 18th century.

As yet there are no festoons of lichens hanging from the trees of Hyde Park–for this to be possible much more vigorous efforts are necessary to reduce the levels of sulphur dioxide in the air. Yet, even without these measures, the slow return of lichens to our towns and cities seems assured.

ROADSIDES: PLANT HAVENS

The thousands of miles of roadsides throughout the British Isles represent a large total area and a wide range of habitats. They play an important role in conservation, providing our plant species with room to grow in relatively stable conditions.

Above: Some roadside plants grow best in light shade, or in places where they are shaded for part of the day. Red campion is one such species, growing on shady banks and along hedgerows. It is seen growing here with ramsons (*Allium ursinum*) which smells strongly of garlic or onions, and meadow buttercup, a damp-loving species. Although these species can be found elsewhere—often at the edges of woods—they are very typical roadside flowers.

Roadsides and motorway verges are not simply green fringes to the tarmac; they are made up of a series of different habitats which lie close together, parallel to the road. There is usually a grassy verge or bank, a ditch, and a hedge, although not all these habitats are necessarily present at the same place. Hedges, for example, are common along many roads but in areas such as the Peak District and the Yorkshire Dales they are replaced by dry stone walls, and on certain moorland roads they are absent altogether.

Local geology and geography are important factors, affecting which plants are found along any particular stretch of road. Different soils support different floras, and an open, sunny aspect favours some species more than others. While certain species will grow on almost any type of roadside, others are more restricted and can be used as habitat indicators.

Dry, grassy verges Open, grassy roadsides are often dominated by umbellifers (members of the carrot family). Three common species provide a continuous display of lacy, white flower heads throughout the spring and summer. Cow parsley appears first, flowering from April until June, when it gives way to rough chervil. In July the third species, upright hedge parsley, appears and continues to bloom until September.

Members of the daisy family are typical of sunny banks and verges. Burdocks, thistles, tansy and yarrow are all common here, and the large white flowers of the ox-eye daisy make an attractive show. Both daisies and dandelions grow well in the full sun. However, they are abundant only where the grass is kept short by regular mowing. Their low-growing rosettes escape the cutting blades, but they are rapidly shaded out if grass and taller flowers are allowed to grow.

Acid and alkaline soils Where the underlying soil changes in composition, the same sunny banks and verges support new species. Harebells and ling may appear on acid soils, while in chalky areas, purple-flowered knapweed is common. In the north and west, a typical plant of alkaline soils is the meadow crane's-bill. It is locally common and can be abundant on long stretches of road, where it is said to 'haunt the verges like an encampment of gypsies'.

Two rather rare species are good indicators of the chalky nature of a roadside. Chicory is a tall plant with flowers resembling those of the dandelion, but an unmistakable pale blue in colour. Dark mullein is another tall plant with a rosette of large, felted leaves and a long spike of yellow flowers with hairy, purple stamens. Both species are restricted to chalky areas, although chicory does occasionally grow on sandy soils.

Damp and shady banks Many roadside plants dislike dry conditions, but will tolerate sunny positions where there is an adequate supply of water. Comfrey, for example, grows on open banks and verges where the underlying soil is damp. Meadow buttercup has similar requirements, preferring wetter conditions than the other common roadside buttercups.

Most damp-loving species are found in shady places along the road. Adequate shade can be provided by a hedge, a wall and even a steep bank or, of course, a wood if the road happens to pass through it.

Deeper shade favours woodland species and where conditions permit, they are common roadside inhabitants, especially along old hedgerows. Ground ivy, dog's mercury and wood anemones carpet damp, shaded banks and the glossy, arrow-shaped leaves and greenish hoods of lords and ladies (wild arum) are a familiar sight. In spring, many well-shaded roadsides are brightened by bluebells.

Ditches and hedges Probably the least well-known of roadside habitats are ditches, simply because we are seldom able to see them from the road. The main ditch runs parallel to the road, sometimes connecting with secondary ditches or storm drains cut into the verge at right angles. As the plants grow higher during the summer, all but the widest ditches are gradually overgrown. Very shallow ditches dry out quickly and the plants in them differ little from those of the neighbouring verge, but deeper ditches can support species more usually found by streams and rivers, such as great willowherb and purple loosestrife.

Many of our roads are bounded on either side by hedges. These are commonly of hawthorn which can prove an impenetrable barrier, but some shrubs such as blackthorn, dog-rose and elder flourish there. As well as providing shade and protection from wind, a hedge also provides support for climbing plants. Small climbers such as vetches and bindweed will scramble among the grasses and herbs of the verge, but more robust species such as hops and hedge bindweed are vigorous climbers.

Growing conditions Roadside plants face two major hazards – mowing and pollution –

Above: The attractive mauve, white or pink flowers of comfrey (*Symphytum officinale*) appear from May to September on roadsides where the underlying soil is damp.

Left: Yarrow (*Achillea millefolium*) is a common species on sunny, grassy verges. It grows well on mown strips for although the flowerheads are tall enough to be cut off, this does not greatly damage the plant and it soon recovers to flower again.

both resulting directly from the proximity of the highway. In order to provide motorists with a clear view the grass verges are usually mown twice a year, particularly at junctions and on corners and bends.

Most plants growing on verges flower after the spring mowing, and have dispersed their ripe seeds before the late summer or autumn mowing. Where more regular cutting occurs, the only species that flourish are those which can avoid damage, such as daisies and dandelions, or those which grow again rapidly, such as yarrow.

Pollution Roadside pollution is only likely to be a problem on the busier roads, but it is causing increasing concern. There are a

Above: Common fleabane (*Pulicaria dysenterica*) is frequently found on marshy ground throughout Britain. It is also found in roadside ditches, where it flowers from August to September. Fleabane was once highly valued as an insecticide; the vapour given off when the leaves were burned was supposed to drive away fleas – hence the plant's common name.

Right: Motorway verges are planted initially with grass, which is cared for until it is well-established. After this, the verges are left alone. Pedestrians have no access to motorway verges and so plants growing there have an advantage over those growing on ordinary roadsides, for the flowers are unmolested once mowing has ceased. This is particularly important for the rarer species, and those such as primroses which suffer from overpicking elsewhere.

Below: Ditches that are overgrown or shaded by trees and hedges are cool and damp. They enable species usually associated with stream-sides and water margins — like the tall spikes of purple loosestrife seen here — to grow and spread along otherwise dry roadsides. The hedge not only provides shelter, but acts as a convenient support for such climbing species as brambles and hedge bindweed.

variety of different pollutants, one of which — dust — is common but frequently overlooked. Layers of dust stirred up by passing cars can clog leaves, interfering with photosynthesis and gas-exchange.

The exhausts of petrol-driven cars emit a variety of polluting gases and chemicals, including oxides of nitrogen, some of which are poisonous to plants causing leaf lesions and discoloration. The effects of such polluting gases may spread many miles from the original source.

Engine oil is toxic, and spreads as droplets on vegetation. Oil and chemical spillages can also affect roadside ditches when they are washed into them from the road.

Motorway flora The problems for plants growing beside a motorway are exacerbated by the construction of the road and the volume of traffic which it carries. However, the hard shoulder acts as a buffer zone against some of the pollution, and the effects on the plants may be no worse than on those species that grow beside busy urban or trunk roads.

One additional hazard faced by motorway species is the salt used to keep the carriageways clear of ice in winter. High salt levels are injurious to most species, and there is often a bare strip along the hard shoulder caused by salt-burn. Salt-marsh species such as sea-aster, which can tolerate high salt levels, are now beginning to appear along this strip on some motorways.

SUCCESSFUL INVADERS OF URBAN AREAS

Many familiar plants were first introduced to gardens from abroad hundreds of years ago. Some particularly successful garden escapes now thrive in urban areas, where there is often little competition from native species, and where conditions may be like those of their original habitats.

From earliest times visitors, immigrants, invaders and our own explorers have brought a huge variety of foreign plants to the British Isles. Some were imported accidentally as weeds, like poppies which probably came with the Romans. Other plants were introduced deliberately for food, for herbal medicines, as attractive garden plants or for their supposed supernatural properties. Often such plants escaped from gardens and became established on nearby wasteland. Some of these escapes are now completely naturalised in the British Isles, like the rhododendrons which today cover miles of sandy and peaty soil, or the colonies of bright orange montbretia found in Devon and Cornwall.

Left: **Honesty** (*Lunaria annua*) is a common garden escape that flowers April-June on walls and in waste places. Ht 100cm (40in).

Bees land on the lower lip of the ivy-leaved toadflax and probe deep into the flower for nectar.

Many escapes are still found fairly near human habitation in the disturbed soil of wasteland and road verges where there is less competition from vigorous native flora. The brightest and showiest plants growing wild in towns and suburbs are therefore not always native, but often species that have managed to escape from nearby gardens. These sometimes persist long after the original gardens have vanished under crazy paving and office blocks.

Fertility – or rather the lack of it – is often a problem for introduced plants. Sexual reproduction and seed formation is not so important for the greater periwinkle, for example, because this particular species reproduces vegetatively. For those species that rely on dissemination by seeds the complete loss of or even a slight reduction in fertility can result in their failure to become established in this country, and their eventual disappearance.

There are many factors any of which can influence the success of an introduced species. Climate is obviously crucial: our winters may be too cold or too wet, or the flowers may blossom before our frosts are over. Day length and the intensity of sunlight, temperature, moisture and pollution levels are important. Soil type, altitude and the surrounding native vegetation can make all the difference as well.

Even if all the above conditions are right,

Shepherd's-purse (*Capsella bursa-pastoris*) flowers throughout the year in gardens, waysides and waste places. Ht 40cm (16in).

Below: Ivy-leaved toadflax (*Cymbalaria muralis*) flowers on walls in England, Scotland and Wales from May-September. Length 80cm (31in).

Wallflower (*Cheiranthus cheiri*) flowers April-June in gardens and on walls in lowland areas. Ht 60cm (24in).

White dead-nettle (*Lamium album*) flowers May-Dec beside roads and in waste places. Ht 60cm (24in).

Right and below: **Greater periwinkle** (*Vinca major*) flowers April-June in hedgerows and woodlands. Length 100cm (40in).

unless the species' pollinating mechanism works as well here as in its native country, it has little chance of survival. In practice this often means the plant must come into contact with the right pollinating insects at the right time. So it is no coincidence that those plants that have spent thousands or millions of years evolving to suit their homeland usually find it difficult to get established outside their normal range.

Honesty is a common escape from gardens that often persists for several years nearby. It grows wild in southern and central Europe and was brought here in the 16th century. It is highly valued by flower arrangers for its papery white 'moons'–the remains of its seed pods which have given it the Latin generic name *Lunaria*, from *luna*, meaning moon.

The greater periwinkle was introduced for its medicinal properties. Although it rarely produces fully developed seeds in this country, it produces new plants by creeping along the ground and rooting at the shoot tips. As it spreads over the ground it gradually forms large colonies derived from the single plant. In time the colonies break up, and independent new plants are formed.

Ivy-leaved toadflax, which was introduced in the 1600s, now covers walls all over the British Isles. Its fleshy leaves can withstand drought, and its seed pods grow on stalks that bend away from the light.

The Cruciferae

Most of the urban flowers illustrated here have obvious similarities. The flowers of honesty, wallflower and shepherd's-purse are, like the cuckooflower, each composed of four petals in the shape of a fat cross, hence the family name Cruciferae. Each flower has six stamens–four long and two short–and characteristic seed pods.

The Cruciferae (pronounced croo–sif–er–ee) is a large family. It includes garden aubretia and alyssum, and commercially grown mustard and rape, which provide those amazingly bright yellow fields in June; sweetly scented summer flowering stocks, and vegetables such as cabbages and radishes.

The flowers of this family all have the same basic structure (see below). They are grouped in spikes at the top of the stem and the flowers at the lower end of the spike bloom first. As the flowers mature and are fertilised, the spike grows, spacing out the swelling seed capsules and giving the younger flowers at the tip room for development.

Fruits The seed pod, like all fruits, develops after fertilisation of the ovules which lie in the centre of the flower. As the pod swells, the seeds ripen until they are ready to be shed. The pod usually splits into two from the base upwards, leaving the seeds attached to a

Cuckooflower (a crucifer)

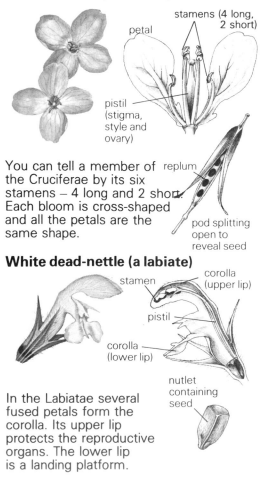

petal

stamens (4 long, 2 short)

pistil (stigma, style and ovary)

You can tell a member of the Cruciferae by its six stamens – 4 long and 2 short. Each bloom is cross-shaped and all the petals are the same shape.

replum

pod splitting open to reveal seed

White dead-nettle (a labiate)

stamen

corolla (upper lip)

pistil

corolla (lower lip)

nutlet containing seed

In the Labiatae several fused petals form the corolla. Its upper lip protects the reproductive organs. The lower lip is a landing platform.

papery white membrane, the replum.

The 'moons' of honesty are particularly resplendent examples. Cuckooflower capsules split open violently, coiling as they do so, and the seeds are immediately shaken free of the replum and flung some distance. In other crucifers, like the wild radish, the pod does not split at all but breaks into segments, each containing a single seed.

Crucifer seed pods come in many shapes and sizes. In wild radishes they are elongated and indented between the seeds, showing where they will eventually break when ripe. Stocks and wallflowers have long narrow pods, in honesty they are flattened circles, and in shepherd's-purse they are heart-shaped.

If you look at the white dead-nettle, a labiate, it is obviously not a crucifer. Notice its differently shaped flowers: instead of the four separate petals of a crucifer, a labiate has five petals, two are fused together to form the upper lip, and three form the lower lip. (Sometimes all five petals are fused to form the lower lip and the upper lip is missing–for example in the wood sage.)

All labiates have five stamens, square stems, leaves in opposite pairs, and they are often aromatic, for example mint, thyme and majoram. When you try to identify which family a plant belongs to, look at as many parts as possible, and especially the seed and flower arrangement.

Cuckooflower or lady's smock (*Cardamine pratensis*) flowers April-June in damp areas. Ht 60cm (24in).

PERSISTENT URBAN FLOWERS

As summer draws to a close, you can find many flowering species – both native and introduced – that thrive in urban areas, spreading as colourful weeds.

The daisy family provides some of the most outstanding examples of the way native and introduced species have adapted to even the most apparently unpromising situations. The willowherb, plantain and poppy families are also well adapted to seemingly inhospitable habitats. Many species flourish in summer and well into autumn and they produce vast quantities of seeds, which is one reason for their wide distribution. They grow in good garden soil, on dry waste ground, in cracks on walls and even out of pavements. They thrive in the concrete jungle of urban areas, often supporting many different kinds of wildlife.

Orange hawkweed is a native species of Europe which is often planted in cottage gardens. A member of the daisy family, it produces numerous seeds; it also sends out stolons which straggle across the ground, forming a new rosette of leaves at their tips. These stolons can grow as much as 30cm (12in) in a season, and the plants soon spread themselves far beyond their original habitat. The orange hawkweed's generic latin name *Pilosella* means 'the hairy one', which is appropriate for all its parts are covered in bristly hairs. The small orange-red flowers eventually form deep crimson ribbed fruits which contrast with the pale pappus hairs.

Thistles The creeping thistle and spear thistle validate the saying that 'there is more to thistles than prickles'. Both have been

Above: **Orange hawkweed** (*Pilosella aurantiaca*) flowers June-Sept in gardens and waste ground. Ht 50cm (20in).

found in Palaeolithic deposits. The creeping thistle has a tap root with lateral roots growing horizontally from it. Once established, this species is extremely difficult to eradicate. The tap root can be as much as 2.5m (8ft) deep and, if even a few inches of the root are left in the soil, a new plant will soon develop.

The creeping thistle also grows easily from seed. The rose-purple flower heads, each with about 100 separate florets, have an abundant nectar supply and the sticky pollen is avidly gathered by bees, which are the main pollinators. The brown shining fruit is topped by a long conspicuous feathery pappus. Of the seeds produced in summer, some may germinate in late autumn of the same year, and others the following spring. By being so versatile this most persistent perennial weed may take over abandoned fields and waste ground, making it difficult for other species to colonize the area.

The spear thistle is less of a problem to eradicate as it is a biennial. Its bright purple

Insect eye's view

Many flowers have honey-guides on their petals to attract insects to the nectar source. Good examples are the pansy and horse chestnut. Yet not all honey-guides are visible to us. Some are visible only in the ultra-violet light to which bees and many other insects are sensitive. When a plant is photographed in ultra-violet light a wide range of different patterns are revealed to us. The basic colours a bee can see are yellow, blue and violet. To a human the evening primrose is yellow, but to a bee it appears to be coloured purple. Bees seem to like vivid colour contrasts.

daylight

ultra-violet light

Spear thistle

Creeping thistle

Garden marigold

Smooth hawksbeard

flower heads mature quickly and the numer
ous seeds are dispersed on the wind. The
germinate in autumn and over-winter as
rosette of spiny leaves. By spring the specie
is much more obvious. The grooved stem
covered in large prickles, and the leaves
which have woolly undersides, terminate i
a long spine reminiscent of a spear. Th
shiny fruits are yellow-brown with gre
streaks.

Both these thistle species are hospitable t
wildlife. The fruits of the spear thistle ar
eaten by beetle larvae, and the spiny blac
larvae of painted lady butterflies live and fee
on the woolly leaves of the creeping thistle
In autumn you also see roundish galls on th
creeping thistle; these are caused by fruit flie

The garden marigold, which was introduce
to the British Isles from southern Europ
in the 16th century, now often grows as
garden escape on nearby waste ground. Wit
its nectar-filled central florets, this old
fashioned single garden marigold attract
insects, particularly bees. (The modern cultiv
ated double orange varieties lack the centra
florets and do not reproduce so freely.)

The greater plantain is another species tha
has been found in Palaeolithic deposits. It
a common perennial weed that varies
size, depending on its environment. In pave
ment cracks it is no more than a few cent
metres high; in fertile soil it may be 30c
(12in) across, and 60cm (24in) high. The ov
leaves are ascending, with prominent rib
The inconspicuous brownish flowers hav
purplish anthers and are usually win
pollinated, although bees and other insec
sometimes visit them for pollen. The capsu
contains many seeds, which are attractive t
birds, particularly pigeons.

Yellow corydalis is an erect or spreadin
tuberous perennial from Europe which ha
much divided, delicate, pale green leaves an
yellow spurred flowers. Its glossy black see
are too heavy to be wind-borne, yet su
prisingly many plants are found on walls
few metres up. The possible answer lies
the fact that the seeds have a fleshy, oil
edible part attractive to ants, which car
them off to their nests above or below groun
level. Birds may also distribute the seeds
their droppings.

The large-flowered evening primrose
found naturalised as a garden escape;
probably originated in the British Isles in t
mid-19th century and may have come fro
North America. Its hairy buds open into
four-petalled golden flower which becom
reddish as it matures. The flowers of th
biennial open at dusk, their strong fragran
attracting night-flying insects. Bees also vis
them to collect pollen, especially in the ear
morning. The pollen grains are bonded t
yellow threads that may become attached
the bees' legs. The stems and the leaf mi
ribs are usually red; but it is a variab
species, and you often see mutations.

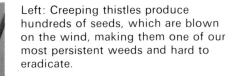

Left: Creeping thistles produce hundreds of seeds, which are blown on the wind, making them one of our most persistent weeds and hard to eradicate.

Large-flowered evening primrose

Yellow corydalis

Greater plantain

Spear thistle (*Cirsium vulgare*) flowers July-Sept in grassland and waste ground especially in chalky areas. Ht 1m (39in).

Creeping thistle (*Cirsium arvense*) flowers July-Sept in fields, waysides and waste places. Very common. Ht 90cm (35in).

Garden marigold (*Calendula officinalis*) flowers June-Oct in gardens and waste ground. Ht 45cm (18in).

Smooth hawk's-beard (*Crepis capillaris*) flowers June-Sept in grassland, heaths, waste places. Very common. Ht 50cm (20in).

Greater plantain (*Plantago major*) flowers May-Oct in short grass, by roads, in farm lanes and cultivated ground. Ht 15cm (6in).

Yellow corydalis (*Corydalis lutea*) flowers May-Sept in gardens and as a garden escape on walls, in pavements. Ht 20cm (8in).

Large-flowered evening primrose (*Oenothera erythrosepala*) flowers June-Oct in gardens, waste ground, sand dunes, railway banks. Becoming more widespread. Ht 80cm (30in).

81

WEEDS IN THE GARDEN

Garden weeds need not be completely eradicated. Some are useful indicators of soil type while others may form an attractive wild patch or even rectify mineral deficiency.

The word weed is a corruption of the Anglo-Saxon word 'woed' meaning a herb or small plant, so its present-day meaning can be defined simply as a wild herb growing where it is not wanted. Not only are the most familiar garden weeds, such as groundsel and bitter-cress, included in this definition, but also anything that springs up in a garden border and is considered undesirable–even orchids may fall into this category.

Most tidy gardeners consider garden weeds as uninvited guests and, if left to complete their life-cycles, many have the potential to smother the plants that have been grown for their beauty or food value. It should be remembered, however, that an aggressive weed in one environment may be a charming wild flower in another. Some weeds can be a valuable addition to the garden, with such virtues as attracting wildlife and adding to both the chemical and physical properties of the soil.

Crossing the garden fence For weeds to be successful they must have effective methods of dispersal; as any gardener realises, many of them have. The seeds of brambles are transported in bird droppings, while thistle seeds are carried into the garden on wind currents. More cunning methods are adopted by such weeds as goosegrass, the hooked fruits of which readily cling to fur and clothing. (Ironically, the spread of the plant is encouraged by the very people who spend hours

Above: Ground elder (*Aegopodium podagraria*), one of our most persistent garden weeds, is capable of spreading through shrub borders unabated by the savagery of a garden hoe or even some of the stronger weed-killers.

Above right: The daisy (*Bellis perennis*) is one of the most common weeds in the garden. It springs up on lawns, smothering the grass with its leaf rosette.

Right: Lady's smock (*Cardamine pratensis*) or cuckoo flower as it is otherwise named, is a weed of poorly-drained soil.

Left: Scarlet pimpernel (*Anagallis arvensis*) is an indicator of alkaline soils.

radicating it from their gardens.)

Some weeds are notoriously persistent. For [ex]ample, the seeds of shepherd's purse can [re]main in the soil for up to 16 years, only [ge]rminating when conditions are just right. [O]ther weeds, such as hairy bittercress, are [ca]pable of producing several generations in a [si]ngle growing season.

Lawn weeds The weeds occurring on lawns [h]ave special adaptations to avoid serious [mu]tilation from the lawn mower. Rosette-[fo]rming species such as ribwort and cat's ear, [fo]r instance, keep their growing tips close to [th]e ground. Irritatingly for the gardener, such [w]eeds depend on the surrounding grass being [c]ut regularly, because this minimises com-[pe]tition for light; if the grass is allowed to [gr]ow longer then these weeds would event-

Stages of colonization

Gardeners know only too well how rapidly bare soil is invaded by weeds. Weed colonization follows a pattern, although it depends on the soil type and nearby vegetation. Here we examine what happens if a previously well-worked plot with soil which is not too acidic or alkaline is left fallow for three years.

Stage 1 In the first year, during the latter part of March, the soil warms up and initiates seed germination. Annuals are the first to appear.

Stage 2 Towards the end of the first year many of the perennial weeds are prominent. Unlike annuals they have long, tough taproots penetrating deep into the soil. Carpet-forming weeds also appear and gradually encroach on to the bare soil.

Stage 3 During the second season a pattern emerges with the stronger perennials choking the weaker annuals. Other weeds encroach on to the plot from surrounding areas. If left uncultivated for a third year there would be a dominance of woody and herbaceous perennials.

An invasion of weeds

Stage 1

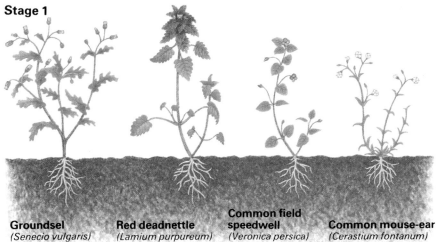

Groundsel
(*Senecio vulgaris*)

Red deadnettle
(*Lamium purpureum*)

Common field speedwell
(*Veronica persica*)

Common mouse-ear
(*Cerastium fontanum*)

Stage 2

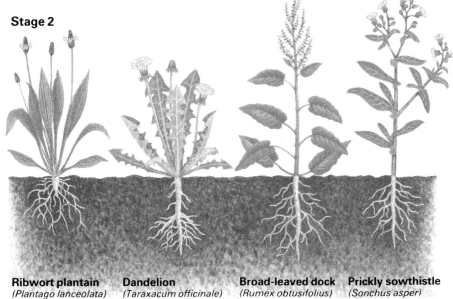

Ribwort plantain
(*Plantago lanceolata*)

Dandelion
(*Taraxacum officinale*)

Broad-leaved dock
(*Rumex obtusifolius*)

Prickly sowthistle
(*Sonchus asper*)

Stage 3

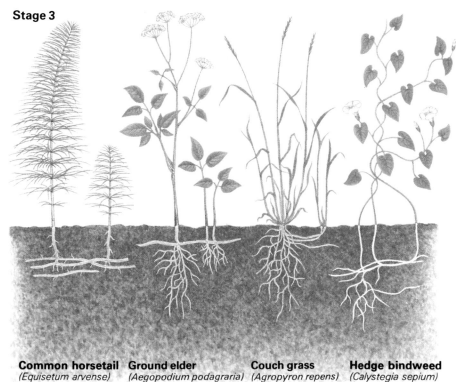

Common horsetail
(*Equisetum arvense*)

Ground elder
(*Aegopodium podagraria*)

Couch grass
(*Agropyron repens*)

Hedge bindweed
(*Calystegia sepium*)

Weeds as indicators

Garden weeds can be useful indicators of soil type. Use this chart to find out the soil conditions in your garden. If marsh pennywort is thriving in the flowerbeds this indicates that you have poor drainage and the soil is too acidic.

1 Marsh pennywort (*Hydrocotyle vulgaris*).
2 Ivy-leaved speedwell (*Veronica hederifolia*).
3 Sheep's sorrel (*Rumex acetosella*).
4 Couch grass (*Agropyron repens*).
5 Coltsfoot (*Tussilago farfara*).
6 Field poppy (*Papaver rhoeas*).
7 Corn sowthistle (*Sonchus arvensis*).
8 Bindweed (*Convolvulus arvensis*).
9 Henbit (*Lamium amplexicaule*).
10 Bird's-foot trefoil (*Lotus corniculatus*).

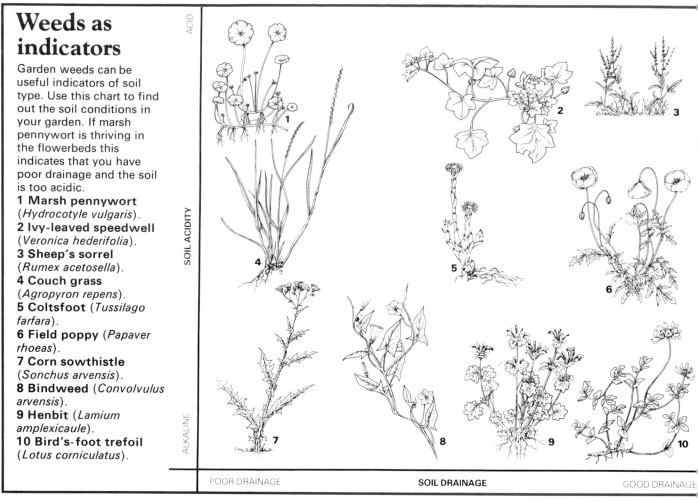

ACID

SOIL ACIDITY

ALKALINE

| POOR DRAINAGE | SOIL DRAINAGE | GOOD DRAINAGE |

ually die out. Other weeds which flourish unabated in lawns are those like clover and pearlwort that form tight creeping mats.

Down the garden path Pearlwort is also an effective colonizer of gravel paths, along with stag's-horn plantain. Both these weeds are particularly resistant to trampling and commonly occur down the centre of a path. The taller weeds which are less resistant to the human foot–groundsel and mayweed–occur on the path's outer limits.

It is hard to believe that any plant could penetrate surfaces like tarmac, but as soon as the slightest crack occurs then dandelion, in particular, is pushing its way up. Thale cress, annual meadow grass and bittercress are also typical weeds of the joints between paving slabs, and thrive well despite the lack of soil.

Flowerbed weeds Although weeds in general are viewed with contempt, it is perhaps the pernicious invaders of flowerbeds for which the gardener saves his most aggressive language. Perennials such as ground elder, rosebay willowherb, creeping thistle and couch grass are among the most persistent intruders, even capable of spreading through shrub borders. It is only hard work with a garden fork that prevents such weeds from over-staying their welcome. Worst of all are bindweed and the horsetails, whose roots penetrate many feet into the soil. Bindweed is particularly effective in smothering other plants and, therefore, of denying them vital sunlight.

Plants as indicators So far it would appear that weeds are a nuisance to the gardener. But there are a number of species which have their uses. Noting the different species of weeds and where they grow, can be of immense help in ascertaining the type of soil there might be in your garden: not only can some weeds indicate the type of drainage in the soil but also which particular minerals are lacking. A sudden crop of daisies may well mean that the soil is deficient in lime. Daisies are rich in calcium and as they die and decompose they naturally enrich the soil with the calcium they have absorbed, thus correcting the deficiency. Docks and dandelions are also good in-

Below: Hairy bittercress (*Cardamine hirsuta*) thrives in sites where there is little soil, for instance, stone wall and the joints between paving slabs. This weed has a very effective means of dispersal and can spread at an alarming rate. One plant capable of producing several generations in one growing season and, under suitable growing conditions, the seed germinates and reaches maturity within 15-20 days, each plant producing more than 100 seeds.

icators of mineral deficiency; their long
taproots are capable of extracting minerals
from deep down in the subsoil.

The presence of the notorious horsetail in a
garden is a clear sign of bad drainage, and
once the fault has been remedied, this plant
disappears as quickly as it appeared.
Although such weeds as coltsfoot and sowthistle also indicate a heavy, badly drained
soil, it could be argued that they are beneficial,
because their penetrating rootstocks are
excellent at breaking up the subsoil. If
groundsel, one of our more common garden
weeds, flowers when only about 5cm (2in)
high, then it is an indication of a soil lacking in
fertility. In a fertile soil a well-grown ground-

Above: A perennial weed
found in gardens is corn
sowthistle (*Sonchus
arvensis*). Another species
which thrives on poorly
drained soils, this plant may
be regarded as beneficial, for
its rootstock penetrates deep
into the ground and breaks
up the subsoil.

Left: Sheep's sorrel (*Rumex
acetosella*) is closely related
to the docks, a group of
plants renowned among
gardeners for their long,
tough taproots which venture
deep into the soil, making
them particularly difficult to
eradicate.

Below: At its best, germander
speedwell (*Veronica
chamaedrys*) can form a
carpet of sky blue. So why
not leave aside a wild patch
in the garden where some of
the more attractive weeds
can grow wild? Both this
species and round-leaved
speedwell (*Veronica
filiformis*) grow in short
grass.

sel plant will reach a height of 60cm (2ft) or
more.

Strong vigorous growth of any of the
leguminous weeds indicates a shortage of
nitrogen in the soil. The bacteria living in the
roots of these plants, which include clovers
and vetches, absorb nitrogen from the air and
store it in the nodules, from where it eventually passes into the rest of the plant. By
cutting off the top of one of these plants and
leaving the roots to decay in the ground, the
soil greatly benefits from a free dressing of
nitrogen.

Patch of wild flowers It can be said that
certain weeds, especially the more colourful
species, have a place in the garden. This does
not mean to say that cultivated borders and
vegetable plots have to be an unruly mass of
ubiquitous weeds. Instead, a small patch can
be set aside and carefully managed. This can
be particularly effective if an area of lawn is
allowed to grow rough, just mowing it once or
twice a year, preferably in the late summer
when the least amount of damage could occur.

Weeds can be naturalised in an area of
established lawn, or better still, the seed of
selected weeds may be sown in with the grass
seed on a freshly prepared piece of ground.
You can use different types of grass, in-
corporating both the taller grasses and the
smaller, finer species. This would then broad-
en the variety of weeds that could be utilised.
(Some weeds prefer to grow in short grass,
others in tall grass.) Once the area has become
established, and harmony between the weeds
and the grasses has been achieved, then the
definition of weed would no longer apply.

Nettles as a plant food Of all the weeds in the
garden that are of some benefit to man, it is
perhaps stinging nettles that head the list. The
average gardener must spend hours trying to
rid his garden of this weed; if only he knew of
the many uses he could put it to. For instance,
if nettles are soaked in rain water for two to
three weeks, the resulting liquid can be used as
a very effective plant food, especially for
tomatoes.

Insects and spiders of urban habitats

Insects have never been the most popular of animals, and the great majority of species are either disliked, ignored or simply unknown to most people. Only in recent years have we started to appreciate and understand the lives of insects and the complex interactions between them, and we are really only just beginning to realise fully how many species there are, and where they occur. Suburbia might at first sight seem an unlikely habitat for insects when compared with, say, ancient deciduous woodland or flowery chalk downland, but some recent studies have shown just how many insects there are in gardens and parks and the other parts of towns and cities.

In one small suburban garden in the Midlands, painstaking work over a number of years has revealed some remarkable statistics. Over a ten-year period some 30,000 individual hoverflies of 91 different species were recorded; well over 500 different species of ichneumon wasp were noted in just three years (over a quarter of the total British species; and 11,000 individuals of 21 species of butterfly were caught and marked during a five-year period. If you think of all the individuals that escaped notice in this garden, and then consider the number that must be present in the hundreds of thousands of parks, gardens and wastelands throughout Britain, you can see how important towns and cities are for insects.

Many insects have just followed their natural foodplants, or their prey species, into the urban setting. Some occur in lower numbers than in the countryside because their foodplant is in short supply or does not grow in the right conditions, but others thrive in the conditions provided by towns, either because their foodplant does well, or their prey is abundant, or they live on some by-product of the human society of the city. The latter group, which includes crickets, cockroaches and houseflies, may be almost confined to conurbations by their dependence on man. The stored food and warmth to be found in our houses, offices and warehouses provide all they need to survive and multiply.

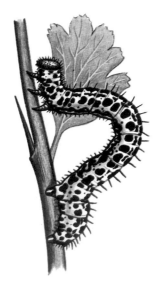

Left: Anyone growing currants or gooseberries in their garden may well come across this caterpillar — the larva of the magpie moth — which feeds on the leaves of these fruit bushes. The caterpillars feed in the spring and the adult moths are on the wing in July and August.

CHECKLIST

*This checklist is a guide to some of the insects and spiders you can find in towns, cities, parks, houses and gardens in Britain. Although you will not see them all in the same place, you should be able to spot many of them throughout the changing seasons. The species listed in **bold** type are described in detail.*

BEETLES
Carpet beetle
Click beetles
Death-watch beetle
Cockchafer
Furniture beetle
Ladybirds
Stag beetle
Violet ground beetle

BUTTERFLIES
Brimstone
Comma
Holly blue
Large white
Painted lady
Peacock
Red admiral
Small tortoiseshell
Small white

MOTHS
Cinnabar moth
Clothes moths
Herald moth
Hawkmoths
Magpie moth
Peppered moth
Tiger moths
Vapourer moth

OTHERS
Aphids
Black garden ant
Bumble bees
Cockroaches
Common wasp
Craneflies
Earwigs
Fleas
Honey bee
Houseflies
Hoverflies
Lice
Silverfish

Spiders

Left: The comma butterfly is one of the more attractive insects to be found in parks and gardens in summer. It is often seen in towns and sometimes drinks the juices of ripe blackberries.

INSECTS AND MAN

The relationship between man
and insects is one of wariness
–a strange situation for
there are as many benefits
to be gained from insects as
there are discomforts.

It is conventional to classify insects as helpful
or harmful when discussing their relationships
with man, but it is often forgotten that the
majority of insects have no obvious connection with man at all. This is not to say that
there is no link of any kind. In ecological
terms nothing lives alone, and if you follow
insect food chains you find some interesting, if
tenuous, connections with our own activities.
Take dragonflies hawking up and down a
stream; they keep well out of our way, but
serve us well by keeping down the mosquito
population. On the other hand, the dragonfly
is one of the hosts of a parasitic flatworm
affecting chickens and their egg-production.

This is a case where one insect species is
both good and bad, but there are many other
insects which all have much stronger and
more tangible human connections.

Bees and other allies The honey bee is at or
near the top of every list of useful insects,
qualifying on several counts. The honey we
take from it in the UK, amounting to some
five and a half million pounds a year, is
obviously very important–and so is the
beeswax we use for making polishes–but these
materials are really far less vital than the bee's
role in pollinating our flowers and crops. In
their relentless search for nectar and pollen,
the bees ensure that flowers are pollinated and
have a chance of setting seed.

Bee stings can be dangerous–a few people
are especially sensitive to them and react
badly, although fatalities are rare–but there is
also evidence that the venom is useful in
treating rheumatic conditions.

Green lacewings (along with ladybirds) are
another group of man's allies because of the
war they wage against greenfly and other
aphids. You can use them for small-scale
biological control in the garden by collecting
the adults and larvae and putting them on
aphid-infested plants, but large-scale rearing
of lacewings for this purpose does not seem
feasible.

Nature's dustmen An entire army of scavengers is employed in clearing up the dead
bodies and the excrement of other animals,
making the countryside more attractive as
well as releasing nutrients for re-use by the

Left: Modern hygiene has
fortunately reduced the
chances of coming across a
bed bug in the house.

Right: A bumble bee's most
important function is the
pollinating of
flowers–Darwin was able to
prove that the amount of
clover seed produced in a
field depends on the strength
of the bumble bee
population. Unlike honey
bees, their small annual
colonies do not make
collection of their honey an
economic proposition for us.

Left: A 7-spot ladybird feeding on aphids. Ladybirds are allies of man because they prey on such pests. Their appetites can be immense, a single large ladybird larva eating as many as 100 aphids in a day. Not surprisingly, in some parts of the world they are used for the biological control of pests. In North America, for instance, the Australian ladybird *Rodolia cardinalia* was introduced to control a pest scale insect.

plant community. They are not driven by an innate desire to tidy up the land, of course; the corpses and excrement are food for these insects and their young.

The burying or sexton beetles are well-known for their disposal of small corpses. Working in pairs, they bury the corpse by digging soil from underneath it. The female lays her eggs on or near the corpse so that the young have a food supply of flesh and maggots.

Crop pests Both on the farm and in the garden crop pests are among the most familiar of the harmful insects. The damage done by the caterpillars of the large white butterfly is all too familiar to the gardener, and anyone who raises brassicas from seed will also know the infamous flea beetles, which chew small neat holes in the seedling leaves. Leather-jackets do equally serious damage below ground.

Aphids, generally known as blackfly and greenfly, are sap-sucking bugs that play havoc with many crops. The mechanical damage caused by thousands of tiny needle-like proboscies projecting into the plants and withdrawing sap causes much distortion of growth, but even more serious are the numerous virus diseases (sugar beet yellow and potato mosaic, for instance) carried by the aphids.

Insect larvae occur in many fruit crops, notably raspberries and apples. Several attack apples, but the most familiar is the grub of the codlin moth, a small pink caterpillar.

Trouble in the store Our problems with insects do not stop when the crops have been harvested. Many pests continue to eat the produce in the store, and they are joined by a large number of specialists—the stored prod-uct pests. On a global scale it has been estimated that about one quarter of the world's food supplies are destroyed at, or after, harvest by pests. Most damage occurs in tropical areas, but many of the tropical insects have found conditions in our granaries and flour mills to their liking and established themselves here long ago.

The grain weevil is one of the most serious grain destroyers. Both adults and larvae feed on grain, and with each female laying up to 200 eggs it is easy to see why infestations build up so easily. The Mediterranean flour moth is another serious pest, causing losses in flour mills.

Forest pests All parts of trees are attacked by various kinds of insects. One of the worst

The good...

Insects can be a great help to man: scarab beetles (**1**) carry out the essential task of burying dung, bumble bees (**2**) pollinate flowers, ladybirds (**3**) control aphids, and honey bees (**4**) make honey . . .

3 Seven-spot ladybird
(*Coccinella 7-punctata*)
feeds on aphids

2 Bumble bee
(*Bombus lucorum*)
pollinates flowers

aphids

larva

4 Honey bee
(*Apis mellifera*) **makes honey**

1 Scarab beetle
(*Copris lunaris*)

rolls dung into ball after burying it

...and the bad

. . . but insects intrude into our lives and we dislike them for it. Moth larvae (**5**) nibble clothes, aphids (**6**) feed on our vegetables, caterpillars (**7**) defoliate trees, and some—mosquitoes (**8**)—imbibe human blood.

defoliate pine trees

7 Bordered white moths
(*Bupalus piniari*)

5 Clothes moth caterpillars
(*Tineola bisselliella*)
feed on cloth

6 Black bean aphids
(*Aphis fabae*)
feed on runner beans

nymphs

8 Mosquito
(*Theobaldia annulata*)

adult

bites into human skin and sucks blood

offenders in Britain is the bordered white moth whose larvae, known as pine loopers, strip the needles from large areas of plantation pine trees. The insect that has caused the most dramatic impact on our countryside in recent years, however, is the elm bark beetle – carrier of the Dutch elm disease.

Pests in the house The most serious household pests are the timber feeders that attack the very fabric of the house. Several species of beetles are involved here, with common woodworm being the most abundant. The woodworm is, of course, the larva which tunnels unseen through rafters, floorboards and furniture. The adult, a small brown bullet-shaped beetle, is commonly known as the furniture beetle. It has been estimated that some 75% of buildings harbour this pest which, when present in large numbers, can reduce sound timber to dust within a few years.

Carpets, clothes and other fabrics suffer from the attentions of numerous pests, including carpet beetles, fur beetles and clothes moths. As far as clothes moths are concerned, it is the larvae that do the damage. They are among the few lepidopterous larvae that feed on animal material – hair, wool and feathers. (Their natural homes are the nests of birds and rodents, where they find plenty of natural fibres.)

Biters of man The insects that attack our own bodies are the most unpleasant of all the pests, and most abundant are the various kinds of flies. Mosquitoes are well-known

Above: Honey bees produce about 5½ million jars of honey a year in the UK.

Right: The housefly is unpopular since it deposits dangerous germs on food.

Opposite page: The cockchafer and its larvae do great damage to plants.

Below: Burying beetles do good by dispersing carrion.

blood-suckers, the females generally needing a meal of blood before they can lay their eggs. Anti-coagulants are injected into the wound while the insect feeds, and these can cause symptoms ranging from mild irritation to severe blistering. Mosquitoes capable of carrying disease still exist here and could cause problems if malaria ever returned to Britain.

Potentially less serious, but even more of a nuisance, are the millions of tiny midges that tickle and bite us, especially in upland areas. Other biters – more correctly described as piercers and suckers – are the horseflies and insidious clegs. The latter fly silently and land on us unnoticed – until the sharp beak goes in for a meal.

Even in the house man is not free from the biters, although modern hygiene has greatly reduced the numbers of fleas, lice and bed bugs. The human flea is now rare, but cat and dog fleas can still be a problem in houses with pets. Typhus fever, dog tapeworms and myxomatosis are all carried by fleas.

Our effect on insects Clearly insects have had a great effect on man, but what of man's effect on insects? Leaving aside the direct effect of the pesticides which we spray on them by the ton, the most important effect has been through changes to the insect's environment, particularly the loss of habitats.

♂

♀

The brimstone (*Gonepteryx rhamni*) is the butter-yellow herald of spring and its colour is thought to have given us the word 'butter' fly. Its wingspan is 5cm (2in); the food plant is buckthorn. Its life cycle is: eggs May-July; caterpillar June-early August; chrysalis July-August; adult July onwards.

BUTTERFLY WINTER SLEEPERS

The cold weather of winter poses a major problem to many creatures. The peacock, small tortoiseshell and brimstone are three butterflies which opt for hibernation in the adult form until spring.

The beautiful peacock and small tortoiseshell butterflies that feed on Michelmas daisies in autumn gardens are the same butterflies that will be out and about searching for flowers on the first sunny, warm day of the new year. The peacock and small tortoiseshell are usually up and about in March, while the brimstone, which favours the flowers of the woodland rides, can often be seen much earlier particularly in the south of England—even in January if the weather is suitable.

These butterflies live for about nine months in their adult stage, much of this time spent in hibernating sleep. Other butterflies have different methods of coping with winter: a few migrate to warmer climates where nectar is available, while others survive the winter in the inactive egg or chrysalis stage or hibernate in the caterpillar stage.

Butterflies need the sweet energy-rich nectar from flowers to give them strength to fly and help them survive their hibernation through the long winter months. During this inactive state their energy consumption is minimal, so they can survive without further food. As a protection against the cold, some sugar in their blood is converted to glycerol which works rather like anti-freeze in car radiators.

Hibernating time In late autumn the peacocks, small tortoiseshells and brimstones search for a safe, dry, dark place where they will be protected from winter frosts. Usually peacocks find a hollow tree, although they will sometimes tuck themselves in a wood pile or a corner of a garden shed. Small tortoiseshells choose similar places, but are also quite likely to come indoors. A hideaway behind a picture in a little-used room is safer than a hollow tree: there are no birds to eat them while they sleep. Brimstones seek dense, evergreen cover in their woodland surroundings —and particularly thick growths of ivy or holly which offer protection.

The butterflies often bury themselves among dead leaves. At rest, the bright wing colours are hidden; only the underside, looking like a dried-up leaf, is visible. This gives

The small tortoiseshell (*Aglais urticae*) after the nectar in an ice plant (above). This butterfly is widespread and common in gardens and other habitats, although less so in northern areas and in Ireland. Its wingspan is 5 cm (2in); the food plant is the stinging nettle. The autumn brood may hibernate in, for example, a shed roof (right). The underside of its wings gives the appearance of dead leaves, wood or bark.

The peacock (*Inachis io*) is very widespread and common in England and Wales, less so in Scotland and Ireland. It is very much a garden butterfly, but you will also find it in open fields, on downland and in woodland. It has a wingspan of 6cm (2½in); the caterpillar's sole food plant is the stinging nettle. When resting the peacock folds its wings, the undersides of which resemble dried leaves and give it excellent camouflage. The female lays her eggs on the underside of the nettle leaf near the growing shoot.

adult butterfly

caterpillar

adult butterfly

chrysalis

All peacock caterpillars of the same brood turn into chrysalids within a few days of each other.

the butterflies particularly good camouflage.

The peacock has a spectacular defence mechanism which it uses if it is disturbed from rest. Opening its wings, it creates an alarming hissing noise as the front and hind wings rub across each other, revealing huge 'eye-spots'. A small bird, startled by the hiss and then confronted by large owl-like eyes, will usually fly off, leaving the butterfly to go back to sleep.

With the first spring sunshine in late March the peacocks and tortoiseshells awake from hibernation; individual peacocks can be seen much earlier in fine weather, when they come out for a short flight. Although the brimstones may be tempted to stir as early as January, they return to hibernate until later. Sometimes tortoiseshells hibernating indoors also wake too early, perhaps because the heating is switched on in a spare bedroom. If you see a tortoiseshell fluttering at a window in midwinter, put it in a cool shed or garage where it can go back to sleep until spring really arrives. There are small migrations of tortoiseshells from abroad which augment our own butterflies.

The new brood of adult brimstones emerges in July and August and spends most of the day feeding. It shows a distinct preference for purple flowers, particularly those of the thistle, knapweed, scabious, bramble and clover. The new brood of adult tortoiseshells, which emerges in late June or July, lays eggs to

The brimstone caterpillar eats the leaves of the food plant—buckthorn.

The small tortoiseshell caterpillar feeds on the same plant as the peacock.

produce a second brood in August and September; this feeds on most garden flowers, especially ice plant and buddleia, and is the overwintering brood. The peacocks emerge later—in August—and are numerous in gardens where they feed on buddleia and in fields where they feed on lucerne, thistle, knapweed, marjoram and clover.

Remember that you need more than flowers to attract butterflies to your garden. An undisturbed corner of a shed will give the butterflies somewhere safe to hibernate and a patch of nettles in a sunny corner of the garden will feed the caterpillars which will turn into chrysalids and eventually become the next generation of butterflies.

Life cycle of peacocks and small tortoiseshells

Butterflies go through four stages: the egg, the rapidly feeding and growing caterpillar, the chrysalis and the adult butterfly. A peacock takes one year to complete a cycle but the small tortoiseshell caterpillar has less growing to do and there is time for two broods each year. The summer brood lives only a few weeks as butterflies.

Egg After feeding for a few days from spring flowers, peacocks and tortoiseshells mate and then the females search for stinging nettles on which to lay eggs.

Caterpillar When the eggs hatch, the crowd of young caterpillars spin a single silk tent in which they all live as they feed and grow.

Chrysalis The fully grown caterpillars crawl away to find a fence or branch from which they can hang down while they turn into chrysalids.

Butterfly Within a few weeks the glistening adult emerges fully grown. The butterflies die several weeks after mating and laying their eggs.

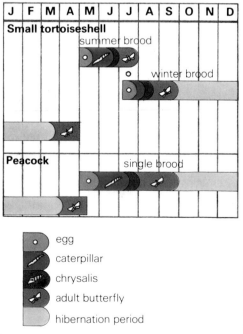

MONTHS JANUARY-DECEMBER

J	F	M	A	M	J	J	A	S	O	N	D

Small tortoiseshell
summer brood
winter brood

Peacock
single brood

○ egg

caterpillar

chrysalis

adult butterfly

hibernation period

CABBAGE PATCH VILLAINS

The most familiar of our butterflies are the whites, whose caterpillars are the scourge of every vegetable gardener and the delight of every child with a jam jar.

In Britain we have six resident species of white butterfly and four occasional migrants, all of which fall within the family Pieridae. The three resident species described here are the large white, the small white and the green-veined white.

Although all three are similar-looking on the wing, the small and large whites are distinguished from the green-veined by being known as the 'cabbage whites', because their caterpillars are voracious eaters of cabbage plants. Indeed, due to the economic interest in pest species, these two white butterflies are probably the most intensely studied of all our butterflies.

Eating habits In addition to eating brassica crops, the caterpillars of the large white eat other garden plants that contain mustard oils, including both nasturtium and mignonette. The small white can also occasionally be found on garden crucifers such as mignonette and arabis. In contrast, the green-veined white does not lay its eggs on cabbage, preferring wild crucifers such as hedge garlic, charlock and cuckoo flower. Researchers assume that before the countryside was sprinkled with juicy hybrid cabbages, the small and large whites must also have fed on various wild crucifers, including our native wild cabbage, hedge mustard and watercress.

Country-wide distribution Large and small whites are common in towns, gardens and agricultural areas, while the green-veined

Above: Mating pair of large white butterflies; the male is the upper individual. Males have fewer markings than females, but this is difficult to see when the butterflies are on the wing.

Below: Large white butterfly emerging from its pupa.

white is their country cousin, frequenting water meadows and uncultivated areas.

The difference between the preferred habitats of the small and large whites and the green-veined is best seen in Scotland. There the green-veined white is extensively distributed over the whole country, with cuckoo flower the main foodplant of its caterpillars. The small and large whites are found in towns and small garden plots, this distribution becoming more obvious the further north one goes in Scotland.

Each year our native British population are reinforced by waves of migrating butterflies from the Continent. All three species described here are common migrants and each year new influxes arrive to swell the numbers.

A double-brooded life cycle As adults, the small and large whites are essentially similar in colour and pattern, the difference lying, not surprisingly, in their relative sizes. The green-veined white is distinct from the other two species in that the veins on the undersides of its wings are sprinkled with fine black scale on a yellow background. In all three species the males have consistently fewer wing mark

Above: **Green-veined white** (*Pieris napi*) and caterpillar. Wingspan 36-50mm (1½-2in).

Above: Small white butterfly uncurling its proboscis to feed. Like most butterflies, it takes nectar from flowers, never eating solid food. Note here the large eyes, furry body and clubbed antennae. When seen close-up, the 'white' wings appear to be faintly speckled.

Left: A communal roost of small white butterflies. Migrants crossing the Channel must rest before they disperse throughout the country. The only way you can tell the difference between this species and the large white is if you have them side by side: then you can see that the small white is, indeed, smaller than the large.

ings than the females.

In an average year, all three species are double-brooded, the first butterflies emerging from March onwards after spending the winter months as chrysalids. These early spring butterflies mate and lay eggs, which give rise to a second brood of butterflies in July. The small and large whites may have a partial third generation in warm years when higher temperatures enable the second brood to develop more quickly than normal and produce a third batch of butterflies in late summer. Many of these will not breed since early frosts would kill off any caterpillars. At high altitudes and in northern Scotland, the green-veined white may have only one brood a year, with the adult butterflies flying in June.

Adult butterflies from spring and summer broods can easily be distinguished on the basis of their wing markings, the spring broods of all three species tending to have much paler markings on their upper sides.

To the casual observer, the sexes are

Predators and parasites: enemies all around

Despite the apparent abundance of cabbage butterflies, they have a difficult time between egg and adult, being assailed on all sides by predators, parasites and disease.

The most obvious killer is the small braconid wasp *Apanteles glomeratus*, which destroys the caterpillar as it is about to change into a chrysalis. Instead of a shiny chrysalis, one finds a mass of bright yellow cocoons (top right) on the dead body of the caterpillar. The female wasp lays her eggs in or on the caterpillar; when they hatch they feed on the caterpillar from inside, only attacking the vital organs when they themselves are ready to emerge and pupate. This type of parasite can account for up to 90% of all caterpillar deaths in some years.

Other important enemies are the tachinid fly *Phryxe vulgaris* and the tiny chalcid wasp *Pteromalus puparum*. The tachinid fly lays its eggs singly on the foodplant or on the outside of the caterpillars of any of the three white butterflies. The fly grub bores into the caterpillar and slowly eats it away from the inside out. The host grows normally and even pupates; but instead of a butterfly emerging, the fly grub bores its way out and falls to the ground to form its own pupa. *Pteromalus*, on the other hand, attacks only the chrysalis stage of the butterfly (below right). A female wasp waits beside a caterpillar changing into a chrysalis, then lays up to a 100 eggs inside it while it is still soft. The eggs hatch into grubs which chew their way out of the chrysalis, emptying it in the process.

White butterfly caterpillars are also attacked by harvestmen, bugs, beetles, birds, spiders, viral diseases and bacterial infections.

Below: **Large white** (*Pieris brassica*) and caterpillar. Wingspan 57-66mm (2¼-2½in).

Above: **Small white** (*Pieris rapae*). Wingspan 46-55mm (1¾-2¼in).

Left: Green-veined white butterfly feeding on the nectar from a flower. The 'green-veined' appearance is, in fact, an optical illusion: a mixture of fine black scales on a yellow background creates the greenish tinge to which this species owes its name.

Below: Caterpillars of the large white butterfly, with the evidence of their villainous eating habits plain to see. Many gardeners may be horrified to learn that they have little hope of clearing their gardens of such pests. Each year the native British populations are reinforced by migrants from the Continent.

deft flick by the chrysalis while it attaches a series of hooks on its 'tail' to the silken mat.

The chrysalis now becomes immobile allowing its cuticle to harden and form the mould in which the adult butterfly will develop. This period of immobility may last two weeks or six months, depending on the time of year. Day length is the trigger which determines whether the butterfly will emerge after two weeks or whether the chrysalis will overwinter.

A secretive feeder The small white is a secretive pest of cabbages and is only obvious when holes appear in the leaves. Its eggs are laid singly or in very small groups on the undersides of cabbage leaves, and hatch into small green caterpillars. These feed individually and eventually develop a velvety texture which helps them to hide on the cabbage leaves, their colour and appearance closely mimicking that of the leaves.

When fully grown, the caterpillars crawl away from the plants and seek out a site for the chrysalis in the same manner as the large white. The overwintering chrysalids are usually greyish-brown and well-camouflaged on palings and garden sheds. The summer chrysalids, which are green, are sited on plant stems or even on the cabbages themselves.

The innocent party The green-veined white never lays eggs on any brassica, preferring the wild crucifers already mentioned. Its conical creamy coloured eggs are laid singly on the underside of leaves and the young caterpillar often conceal themselves along the leaf margin they are eating. The full grown caterpillar similar to that of the small white and matches the leaves of the foodplant. The chrysalis formed in the vegetation, often on the stem of the plant on which the caterpillar reaches maturity.

indistinguishable when the butterflies are flying; and even the trained worker has difficulty in telling which species is flying past.

The pestiferous large white The large white is the obvious villain of the cabbage patch, the females laying batches of 100 or more eggs on either side of dozens of cabbage leaves. The caterpillars that hatch feed gregariously until almost full-grown, then split into smaller and smaller groups until each one is feeding alone. This clustering of caterpillars almost invariably denudes entire cabbage plants and draws the attention of the gardener to the conspicuous, evil-smelling yellow and black caterpillars.

When fully grown, the caterpillar wanders off to find a firm base on which to spin a silken mat in preparation for the change into a chrysalis. Once satisfied with a site, it spins a firm base of silk and then winds a single strand of silk around its 'waist' and becomes motionless. After 24 hours or so its skin begins to split down the centre and the glistening chrysalis wriggles into the world. The old caterpillar skin is eventually discarded with a

COCKROACH SCAVENGERS

The cockroaches you find living in buildings as household pests are invaders from warmer lands, but there are three small native British species living secluded in the wild.

Cockroaches, belonging to the order Dictyoptera, can usually be recognised by their flattened bodies and the big 'shield' (pronotum) beneath which the head is tucked. The antennae are long and slender and perpetually quivering, and the insects run very swiftly on their long spiky legs. The wings of many species are no more than little flaps just behind the pronotum, but some species are fully equipped with leathery front wings and broad, membraneous hind wings. Some of the winged species can fly, but they rarely do so and their wings remain folded neatly on top of the body.

Essentially warmth-loving insects, most of the 4000 or so known species of cockroach live in tropical regions. They are often very numerous on the forest floor, where they feed on a wide range of plant and animal matter, including fallen fruit and leaves and assorted dead insects and other animals.

With these scavenging habits, it is not surprising that cockroaches have moved in with man and become household pests, for our homes and other buildings provide them with abundant food of all kinds. Our buildings also provide them with warmth, and several tropical species have been able to spread all over the world by adopting an indoor life. These are the so-called domestic cockroaches, although they do not live just in houses. In fact, with modern hygiene and insecticides, they are not at all common in houses now, but they still cause problems in

Above: A common cockroach *(Blatta orientalis)* sitting on mouldy bread cleaning its antenna. With their biting jaws, cockroaches can tackle all kinds of solid food and they will chew their way through endless layers of packing material to get at the goods. Stored food must therefore be very well protected where there is any risk of cockroach infestation. Even a small population can do immense damage to food—not by eating it all but by contaminating it with oily secretions and a very unpleasant smell. The best way to avoid infestation is to ensure that there is nothing for the cockroaches to eat—no scraps of food left lying about at night.

warehouses and other heated buildings. They can be especially troublesome in the kitchens of large institutions such as schools and restaurants which are unoccupied at night, for cockroaches are active at night and less likely to be noticed in such places by day until their populations are quite large. By day, the insects retire to heating ducts and other warm refuges where they are difficult to find. Their flat bodies enable them to squeeze through minute cracks in walls and floors.

Egg purses Mating in cockroaches takes place after a simple form of courtship, the female attracting the male by emitting a strong scent. The female produces her eggs soon after mating, enclosing them in a horny, purse-shaped case called an ootheca. Most species drop the ootheca soon after it is formed, but the German cockroach carries it around until the eggs are about to hatch. The oothecae are very easily transported in produce of various kinds, and this is how many new cockroach infestations are started.

The commonest domestic species is the poorly-named German cockroach which is probably a native of North Africa. It is a pale brown insect with two dark stripes on the head-shield. Although both sexes are fully winged, they are reluctant to fly. This cockroach probably arrived in Britain on board ship during the 17th century. Although confined to the ports at first, it spread fairly rapidly through the country. Nowadays it is

the most frequent cockroach in dwelling houses, and it is also common in bakeries, restaurants and hot-houses. In hot summers it often moves outside and establishes itself in rubbish dumps.

During courtship, a pair of German cockroaches stroke each other with their antennae and the male raises his wings so that the female can get at the secretions on his back. He then slides backwards underneath her to mate. The ootheca is 7-8mm long and 3mm wide and the female carries it around, protruding from her hind end, for about five weeks (or rather less in hot conditions). It contains 35 to 40 eggs, and the female usually produces about six oothecae during her life.

Above: The American cockroach *(Periplaneta americana)*, 3-4cm (1-1½in) long, is the commonest shipboard cockroach and, indeed, is sometimes called the ship cockroach. Cannibalism is quite frequent in this species, and in its tropical home it regularly eats small insects.

Below: A female dusky cockroach *(Ectobius lapponicus)* among leaves and grass in Dorset. This species is native to southern England.

Left: **German cockroach** *(Blatella germanica)*, also known as the shiner or steam fly. Ranges from 10-15mm ($\frac{1}{3}$-$\frac{1}{2}$in) in length.

shiny pronotum

long antenna

leathery forewings

Right: **Lesser cockroach** *(Ectobius panzeri)*. Native to southern Britain, under 11mm ($\frac{1}{3}$in) long, and rarely found far from the coast.

Left: **Tawny cockroach** *(Ectobius pallidus)*. Native to southern Britain, much the same size as the lesser cockroach.

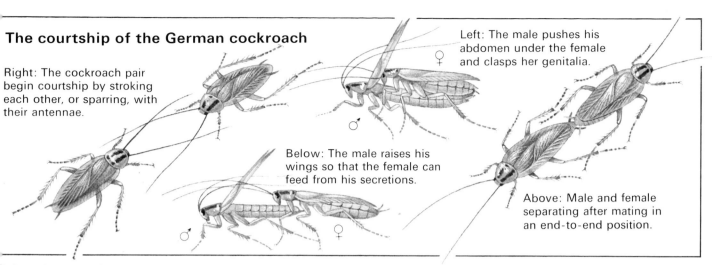

The courtship of the German cockroach

Right: The cockroach pair begin courtship by stroking each other, or sparring, with their antennae.

♀ Left: The male pushes his abdomen under the female and clasps her genitalia.

♂

Below: The male raises his wings so that the female can feed from his secretions.

♂   ♀

Above: Male and female separating after mating in an end-to-end position.

Below: Nymphs of the American cockroach. The young insect is worm-like when it first wriggles out of the egg purse, but it rapidly breaks out of its first skin to reveal the typical cockroach shape. The nymph usually undergoes between six and twelve moults and becomes adult without any pupal stage. The wings can be seen as small buds on the backs of the older nymphs. Maturity may be reached in only six weeks in warm conditions, but the life cycle normally takes longer.

The eggs hatch soon after the female drops them and the young cockroaches mature in about three months at normal room temperature.

The common cockroach, also known as the oriental cockroach and the black beetle, averages 22mm ($\frac{4}{5}$in) in length. The male is deep reddish-brown, while the female is blackish-brown. She has a rather pear-shaped outline, much broader in the abdomen than the male, and her wings are reduced to tiny flaps. The male's wings reach nearly to the end of his abdomen, but he still cannot fly. Probably a native of North Africa or southern Asia, this species arrived in Britain in the 16th century. It was widely distributed by the end of the 18th century and can now be found in houses and other buildings all over the country. It is not uncommon in sewers and on large rubbish dumps, where it may even survive the winter.

The courtship of the common cockroach resembles that of the German cockroach, with the male raising his wings and the female nibbling his back, although he does not actually seem to produce any secretions for her. The ootheca, about 10mm ($\frac{1}{3}$in) long and 5mm ($\frac{1}{5}$in) wide, is carried for a day or two then dropped. It contains about 14 eggs, which hatch in two to three months under normal conditions, but which may remain dormant throughout the winter if not in heated surroundings.

The American cockroach is chestnut brown and fully winged in both sexes, although it rarely flies in Britain. Despite its name, it is a native of Africa and arrived in America via the slave trade. It rarely occurs in houses in Britain, but is common in bakeries, restaurants and sewers.

A courting male American cockroach waves his antennae excitedly and raises all four wings when he picks up a female's scent, but he shows little finesse and quickly thrusts his abdomen beneath her. There is no food for her and she makes no attempt to nibble his back. The oothecae contain up to 24 eggs and are often cemented to the substrate or buried in debris. The eggs hatch in six to twelve weeks under normal conditions and the nymphs take over a year to mature unless they are living in very hot places. In cool buildings they may take as much as three years.

Cockroaches in the wild Our three native cockroaches are all under 11mm ($\frac{1}{3}$in) long and are rarely seen. Although they can be shaken from trees and hedgerows, they are mainly ground-living and can be found in leaf litter and among the turf of rough grass-lands. They also inhabit heathlands and sand dunes. All feed mainly on dead plant material. The three species are the dusky cockroach, the tawny and the lesser. All are confined to southern England, and the lesser cockroach is rarely found far from the coast.

HOUSEFLIES: THE SWARMING HORDES

Many households are troubled in autumn by swarms of flies that come inside to hibernate. Thousands of these insects congregate in roof spaces and other crannies and, on a warm winter's day, may wake up and start buzzing around the room.

Bluebottle fly *(Calliphora vomitoria)* on a flowerhead. Although blowflies of this, and other species, cause meat to become 'fly-blown', they are useful to man because they dispose of carrion.

Many flies enter houses, but only one is the true housefly, *Musca domestica*. This fly is about 6mm (¼in) long, mouse grey in colour and with a 'definite' flight from one place to another. It can be found everywhere in the world, always living in close association with man.

Houseflies belong to the large insect group the Diptera or 'two wings', all of which have only one pair of flying wings. The hind pair are reduced to knob-like organs called halteres, or balancers, which help to maintain steady accurate flight. The Diptera also include midges, gnats and craneflies.

Breeding cycle Houseflies breed in a variety of moist and putrefying substances. Fresh horse dung is preferred but other dung, especially pig or exposed human faeces, are also chosen. Nowadays such dung is inaccessible in cities; here flies breed in municipal refuse tips or other large accumulations of decaying organic material.

The female housefly lays eggs in batches of 100 to 150, in crevices in the dung. In a life of about one month she can lay four or five such batches. The eggs hatch within a day or two and the larvae, which do not have a proper head and are called maggots, burrow into the warm mass, choosing a zone with a temperature of 45-50°C (113-122°F) if possible. Here they feed for about a week, moulting three times. At lower temperatures they take longer to mature.

When full-grown the maggots burrow into

loose soil to become pupae, enclosed in pupal cases formed from their hardened, barrel-shaped last larval skin. After a further one to three weeks, according to temperature, the adult fly emerges by splitting off a circular cap at the front end of the pupal case, using a special inflatable part of its head called a ptilinum. The fly also uses the ptilinum to work its way out of the soil. At this stage the fly's wings are crumpled, but once it emerges from the soil they are pumped up by blood pressure.

The housefly does not seem to have a well-established hibernation stage, but breeds throughout the warmer summer months, its numbers reaching a peak in autumn. After

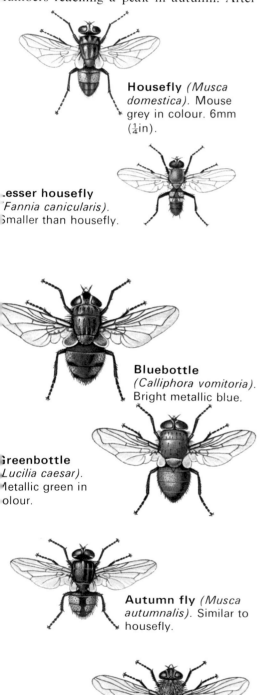

Housefly *(Musca domestica)*. Mouse grey in colour. 6mm ($\frac{1}{4}$in).

Lesser housefly *(Fannia canicularis)*. Smaller than housefly.

Bluebottle *(Calliphora vomitoria)*. Bright metallic blue.

Greenbottle *(Lucilia caesar)*. Metallic green in colour.

Autumn fly *(Musca autumnalis)*. Similar to housefly.

Cluster fly *(Pollenia rudis)*. Holds wings flat on its back.

October most flies die and active adults are seen only in heated buildings. The species is maintained through the winter by slow breeding in fermenting rubbish dumps or in farm livestock sheds.

Food contamination Houseflies generally stay within a mile or two of their breeding site, seeking out human habitations for food and new breeding sites. This is where the danger of food contamination lies, because they fly directly from food to breeding place and back again. They vomit on to the food to soften or liquefy it and, at the same time, defecate on it, causing considerable contamination. Oddly enough, it seems that the fly's faeces are the main source of danger to man, not the huge number of bacteria on the fly's body which appear to dry up readily.

Diseases which houseflies can transmit include infantile summer diarrhoea, typhoid fever and many other intestinal infections and, in warm countries, eye infections. In addition, flies can pass on the eggs of parasitic worms that they have picked up while feeding on faeces. It is therefore very important to take every precaution to prevent houseflies from settling on food

The lesser housefly *(Fannia canicularis)* is probably one of the commonest flies in houses in the British Isles. It looks like a smaller edition of the true housefly, but you can tell the two apart—at close quarters—by the veins in the wings. The vein near the

Walking on walls
People often wonder how houseflies can walk up highly polished surfaces. Between the claws on a fly's foot there are sticky pads that enable it to hold on to almost any surface—glossy painted walls, wallpaper or a plastered ceiling—even when it is vertical or upside down. Landing on the ceiling is another intriguing manoeuvre that presents no problem to the housefly. It performs this by stretching out its legs and doing a half-roll turn. The sticky pads on the feet then hold it firmly in place, and it can walk about upside down without falling off.

Below: Greenbottle fly *(Lucilia caesar)*. Note the brilliant green, shining body and the black hairs on the abdomen.
The larvae of greenbottles are sometimes present in the soil around houses and can be forced up out of the soil in alarming numbers after a heavy rain storm.

Right: Greenbottle and bluebottle flies on a dead chick. They lay their eggs on carrion such as this.
There is a common fallacy that the smaller flies grow into larger ones. This is not true: winged insects are adult and will not grow any bigger. Smaller flies are simply different species.

Left: The flies shown here are only the more obvious and common species of those that enter houses. There are many other species.

middle of the wing in *Musca domestica* bends sharply forwards, while that of *Fannia* is straight. The flight of *Fannia* is 'indefinite'; these flies often circle around light fittings.

Fannia lays its eggs in moist decaying organic matter and can be troublesome near poultry houses where it breeds in the large accumulations of chicken droppings. Its habits differ from the housefly, the females spending more time near their breeding places. The flies indoors are largely males. The maggots have a number of tail-like processes on each segment. As these flies are not attracted to man or his food, they are much less dangerous than the housefly.

Blowflies You can tell when warm weather has arrived by the blowflies–bluebottles (*Calliphora*) and greenbottles (*Lucilia*)–that start buzzing noisily in and out of the house. They are looking for meat and fish on which to lay their eggs.

Bluebottles, shining blue in colour, are about 11mm ($\frac{1}{3}$in) long, while greenbottles are greenish and slightly smaller. They lay five or six batches of up to 200 eggs each in crevices in meat or carcases, and the resulting maggots (fishermen's 'gentles') liquefy the flesh with their saliva so that they can feed on it. They take about one week to become full grown, and then pupate in the soil or in some suitable crack. Another week or two sees the adult flies emerge.

Blowflies are heavily contaminated with bacteria picked up from carrion and garbage, but since they are mainly interested in raw meat, any bacteria they transmit are usually killed by cooking. They do, however, spoil meat, which becomes 'fly-blown'–full of maggots. In urban districts they are particular-

Above: Male and female autumn flies (*Musca autumnalis*). This species is very similar to the true housefly, but does not associate with man, being found in fields with horses and cattle, in the dung of which the larvae feed.

Right: Blowfly pupal cases are characterised by their hard covering and barrel-like shape. The adult flies hatch in one to three weeks, according to the temperature.

ly common near slaughter-houses and around butchers' shops.

Greenbottles have developed a particularl unpleasant habit of laying eggs in the soile and matted wool at the hind end of sheep The maggots eventually infest the fles of the sheep, eating it away. This attract other blowflies and may result in the deat of the sheep, causing much loss to farmers.

Autumn swarms Four or five principa species enter houses in swarms in autumn but the best known are the autumn fl (*Musca autumnalis*) and the cluster fly (*Po lenia rudis*). The autumn fly looks very simila to the housefly, but in the summer frequent fields, not houses. Its larvae feed on the dun of livestock such as horses and cattle. Th cluster fly is slightly larger than the autumn fly, and holds its wings flat on its back; i larvae are parasitic on earthworms.

It can be extremely alarming to enter room in the autumn and find the walls an furniture covered with thousands of flie When the light is switched on they tend t fly about, which is even more frightenin The only thing to do is to spray with insect cide and sweep up the bodies.

In the autumn these flies tend to colle on the outside of buildings, on the sunn side, and as the nights get cooler they mak their way into roof spaces, under tiles an into bedrooms, forming clusters of man thousands of individuals.

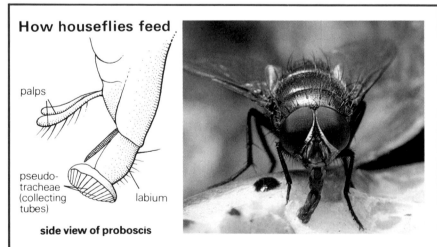

How houseflies feed

palps

pseudo-tracheae (collecting tubes)

labium

side view of proboscis

Flies feed on anything sweet and moist, especially milk, meat, excrement and garbage. (Protein rich food is needed by the females for egg production.) They have the habit of vomiting on their food to soften or liquefy it. This is repeated several times, both on human food and dung and refuse. At the same time they defecate, perhaps every few minutes,

leaving dark spots (see the greenbottle fly, *Lucilia caesar*, above right) so that the total contamination of food can be considerable.
Houseflies, like all Dipterans, feed by sucking up the food they have liquefied with a specially adapted fleshy proboscis (above left). This has many little tubes, called pseudo-tracheae, at the tip.

SPIDERS THAT HAUNT OUR HOUSES

About six or seven spiders habitually live inside houses, notably the large species that runs across the floor at night, and the one you find in the bathtub in the morning.

People who live in the temperate and colder parts of the world spend most of their lives in an artificial climate – that of the houses in which they dwell. Conditions are warmer and much drier indoors than outside, and also more uniform throughout the year. About half a dozen species of spider live in houses in Britain and Ireland. The majority of these do not normally live out of doors in this country, but are natives of warm, dry climates such as that of the Mediterranean. Probably carried across the world in the holds of cargo ships, these spiders have colonized human dwellings far to the north of their native homes.

Most of the spiders you find are females, which are the dominant sex. The males are usually smaller and most of them approach their prospective partners with extreme caution. If the female is not in a receptive state of mind she is quite likely to treat an approaching male as a meal rather than as a suitor. House spiders, like all spiders, feed by injecting digestive fluid into the body of the prey and sucking back the resulting solution. The pair of jaws through which the poison is injected when the spider bites are called chelicerae.

Above: House spider of the genus *Tegenaria,* with its sheet web. These spiders make the cobwebs which festoon ceilings that are not swept regularly. The sheet webs, although very different in appearance from the beautiful orb webs of the garden spider, have the same purpose – to entangle and capture flies.

Top view of a spider

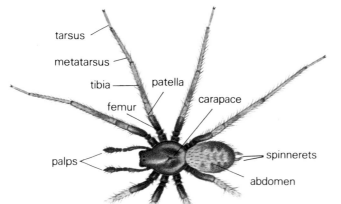

tarsus
metatarsus
tibia
patella
femur
carapace
palps
spinnerets
abdomen

A spider's body is divided into two parts: a combined head and thorax – the cephalothorax – and an abdomen. The cephalothorax is covered by a chitinous 'plate' – the carapace. It has four pairs of legs and a pair of jaws

(the chelicerae), as well as palps, or feelers, which are swollen in males and used to transfer sperm to the females. Some large house spiders can bite humans, but cause no more than a temporary irritation.

Sheet-cobweb spiders The largest and most familiar of the house spiders belong to the genus *Tegenaria.* Those you often see sprinting across the floor at night in the autumn are males looking for females.

Tegenaria domestica is the smallest and lightest in colour of the three house-haunting species. It lives in houses in most parts of the world, but is occasionally found out of doors in Britain in sheltered places such as caves. This spider usually hangs the white silk cocoons that contain its eggs from a ledge near its thick, rather opaque web.

Tegenaria gigantea is larger than *T. domestica,* and with more distinct dark body bars on the abdomen. Also the female's web is flimsier and the egg cocoons are fastened flat against a wall beside the web. In southern Britain *T. gigantea* is common in houses, but becomes less so further north. This is the least house-bound of the three species, and is fairly common on banks and walls out of doors, especially in the south-west. Many of these outdoor individuals make their way into houses in the autumn.

The third species, *Tegenaria parietina,* is about the same size as *T. gigantea* but has longer, hairier legs, and there is often a reddish-brown band along the centre of the abdomen. It is restricted to houses in southern England. The female hides her white egg cocoon inside her web. This species is sometimes called the 'cardinal' spider, from the

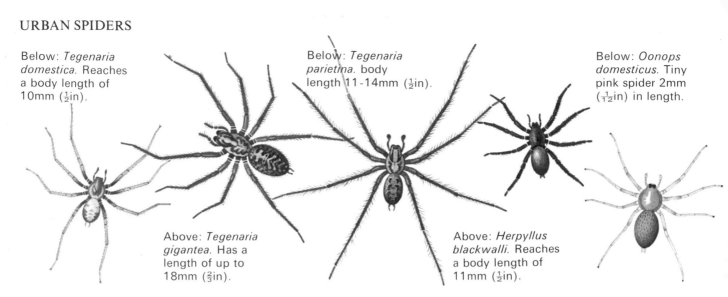

Below: *Tegenaria domestica.* Reaches a body length of 10mm ($\frac{1}{2}$in).

Below: *Tegenaria parietina.* body length 11-14mm ($\frac{1}{2}$in).

Below: *Oonops domesticus.* Tiny pink spider 2mm ($\frac{1}{12}$in) in length.

Above: *Tegenaria gigantea.* Has a length of up to 18mm ($\frac{2}{3}$in).

Above: *Herpyllus blackwalli.* Reaches a body length of 11mm ($\frac{1}{2}$in).

Above: Five fairly common house spiders. Males are usually less obvious and smaller than the females.

Below: *Tegenaria* house spider. It has just moulted its skin (you can see the shrivelled old skin to the left of the spider). Spiders moult a number of times before becoming adult a year or so after hatching. Long-lived adults, like *Tegenaria,* may also moult once a year.

legend that Cardinal Wolsey was frightened by them when he lived at Hampton Court. One would have expected more spiritual fortitude from so eminent an ecclesiastic!

Long-legged spider The 'daddy long-legs' spider *(Pholcus phalangoides)* is still fairly common in the south of England, but its numbers have been reduced by the increase in central heating, which produces an atmosphere too dry for its existence.

The cephalothorax in *Pholcus* is small and rounded and the abdomen cylindrical, while the legs are extremely long and slender. The web consists of a sort of scaffolding of threads so fine as to be invisible to human eyes, spun in a ceiling corner. When an

insect becomes entangled in them the spider bundles it up in a parcel of silk before killing it and feeding on it. Sometimes the spider rapidly shakes the web, which increases the entanglement of the small insect, while shaking free an unsuitably large one. The ends of the long legs are used in manipulating the silk, so the spider keeps its body well out of range of injury from the victim's struggles. The female is less predatory in her attitude towards the opposite sex than most spiders, and the male may remain in her web for a day or two after mating.

The late Dr Bristowe conducted a special survey in southern England, to determine the northern limit of *Pholcus* in Britain. On the

The daddy long-legs spider

Above: The daddy long-legs spider *(Pholcus phalangoides)* spins a scaffolding-like web in a ceiling corner. The female carries her egg sac, held together by a few threads, in her chelicerae. The first batch of eggs is laid in June, followed by second and third batches in July and August.

pretext of seeking accommodation he gained entrance to a variety of lodging houses and carefully inspected as many rooms as possible for evidence of spiders' webs before departing with polite expressions of dissatisfaction. He found that the line south of which *Pholcus* is commonly seen runs roughly east and west a little south of London. The spider is entirely confined to houses.

The mouse spider Dr Bristowe suggested the name 'mouse' spider for *Herpyllus black-walli* on account of its glossy grey abdomen. This spider is widely distributed in Britain and Ireland and mainly, but not entirely, confined to houses. Since it hides by day and hunts by night, the mouse spider is not very often seen, but it sometimes falls into the bath-tub and is found there in the morning since it cannot climb up the slippery sides.

The mouse spider's method of hunting is simply to creep about at night on walls and ceilings, pouncing on any flies or moths that it encounters. This would seem to be a precarious mode of subsistence, but possibly *Herpyllus* has some sensory perception, not yet explained, that aids its hunting. It can go without water for months and eats dead insects – even butterflies left on lepidopterists' carelessly exposed setting boards. There is usually sparring and even fighting when a male woos a female mouse spider.

Pink prowler The least noticed of all the common house spiders is *Oonops domesticus*, a tiny pink or orange-brown spider only 2mm long. It is confined to houses and, like the mouse spider, hides by day and hunts by night, so it is hardly surprising that most people are quite unaware of its existence. Its prowling walk has been described as a 'slow, smooth, groping progress' so charac-teristic that it can be recognised several feet away, but it can dart forward when necessary.

Oonops hides by day in a small silk cell; its eggs are wrapped in a silk cocoon con-cealed in the cell. Some species of spider wrap up batches of several hundred eggs in each cocoon, others lay clutches of 20 or less, but one of the oddest features of *Oonops* is that it lays its eggs in clutches of two at a time.

The spitting spider The least common of the house spiders is the remarkable spitting spider *Scytodes thoracica*. It is related to the daddy long-legs spider and has the same features of a rounded cephalothorax and slender legs, but the latter are not so dis-proportionately long. The coloration is distinctive – yellow with a pattern of black dots. In Britain it is confined to houses in the southern half of England. It is a long-lived spider, taking two to three years to mature and living another year or two as an adult.

Like the last two species, *Scytodes* hunts by prowling at night. When a victim is located the spider approaches to within a centimetre (about ½in) or less and appears to jerk its head. The insect is instantly immobil-

ised. What actually happens is that the cephalothorax is rapidly vibrated from side to side and, at the same time, a jet of gum is squirted from the chelicerae. This results in a network of sticky threads falling on the insect, rather like a fisherman casting a net, and completely pinning it down. The spider then advances and bites its victim repeatedly, retreating after each bite. Finally the spider drags its victim free of the threads and devours it. The threads that immobilise the prey are wholly distinct from the silk spun by all spiders which is drawn from the spinnerets at the hind end of the body. The eggs that a *Scytodes* female carries under her body are put aside when she catches an insect.

Above: *Amaurobius similis* is a common spider often found on the walls of a dry shed or outhouse; in autumn it wanders into houses, but is not an all-year round house dweller. The female lays eggs in June and July, and the males mature in late summer of the following year.

The spitting spider's fly trap

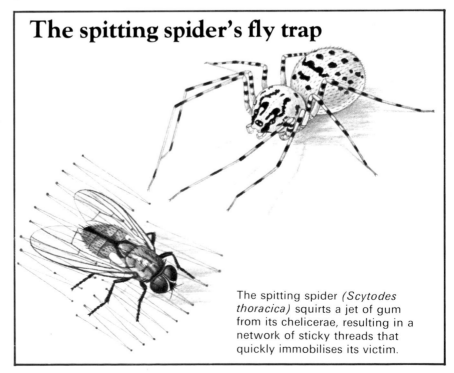

The spitting spider *(Scytodes thoracica)* squirts a jet of gum from its chelicerae, resulting in a network of sticky threads that quickly immobilises its victim.

INSECTS IN THE GARDEN

Look around your garden and you will be amazed by the abundance of insects. Some are a positive advantage, pollinating the flowers, but others can be serious pests.

Most kinds of insects can be found in gardens at some time or other. Some are merely casual visitors from the surrounding countryside, but many are actually resident. Northern gardens support fewer species than southern gardens, and new gardens also have fewer species than established ones–many insects cannot take up residence until the garden plant life is reasonably mature.

Spring Some insects are present all year

Above: The summer generation of small tortoiseshells can be seen feeding on lavender in the garden.

Below: The honey bee is one of the earlier insects in the garden, putting in an appearance as soon as the days warm up.

round. Bluebottles and various other flies, fo example, can be seen basking on sunny wall even in the middle of winter. Most specie have definite seasons, however, and insec populations change markedly between sprin and autumn.

Among the first to stir in spring are thos insects that hibernate as adults. Brimstone peacock and small tortoiseshell butterflies fl on warm days even in February, seekin

The ants' wedding

Ants are extremely common in the garden, but they are generally unobtrusive for much of the year. The commonest species is the black *Lasius niger* which feeds on a variety of small insects and also 'milks' aphids for honeydew. This species breeds under paths and rockery stones, and the nests 'explode' in July or August when thousands of winged ants take to the air for their mating flight. The winged ants are males and new queens (right) which have been nurtured by the workers for several weeks. When the weather conditions are right—reasonably still, warm and humid—the workers open the nests and allow the winged forms out for their mid-air matings. All the nests in one area tend to erupt at the same time, thus encouraging inter-marriage between the different colonies.

The great majority of the ants fall victim to swallows and other birds, but of those which return to the ground, the males soon die while the queens break off their wings and search for suitable places in which to start their new colonies.

Above: Unwelcome visitors in the vegetable garden include the large white butterfly. The females lay their eggs on brassicas, where they hatch into caterpillars which gorge themselves on the leaves.

nectar from any flowers that happen to be open, but not until the aubrietia and polyanthus come to flower later in the spring do these butterflies become particularly busy. They are soon joined by the first broods of large and small whites, which emerge from their pupae early in April.

Honey bees put in an appearance as soon as the days warm up, mingling with the drone-flies on the snowdrops and crocuses. Bumble bee queens emerge from hibernation and are active as soon as the temperatures begin to rise. Several species are common in the garden, with *Bombus pratorum* being one of the earliest to appear. Other garden species of bee include *B. lapidarius, B. pascuorum, B. lucorum* and *B. hortum.* The bees all find plenty of nectar in deadnettle flowers and sallow catkins, and build up their strength in readiness for nesting.

When the aubrietia opens on the rockery the fascinating bee-fly is never far away, hovering over the plants or rising and falling like a miniature helicopter, all the time emitting a high-pitched whine.

Queen wasps, like queen bumble bees, pass the winter in hibernation, and when they wake they need a plentiful supply of energy-rich food. Nectar provides most of this, and the wasps can be seen buzzing around cotoneaster and other early flowering shrubs. If the flowers are not yet open, the wasps bite through their bases to reach the nectar. (Apple blossom is commonly damaged in this way.) When not feeding the wasps can often be seen, and even heard, scraping wood from sheds and fences; this they chew and mix with saliva to make the paper for their nests.

As you get busy in the garden, digging and weeding in readiness for spring planting, you may well uncover many ground-dwelling insects. As gardeners you can do without the root-eating leatherjackets (cranefly larvae) and wireworms (click beetle larvae), but you should look kindly on the predatory ground beetles, such as the violet ground beetle, that scuttle rapidly over the surface feeding on harmful insect larvae.

During May many garden plants become decorated with blobs of white froth known as cuckoo spit. People once thought this really was cuckoo spit as it seems to appear from nowhere at a time when cuckoos abound. It is in fact produced by the nymphs of frog hoppers which feed on the plant sap. The froth protects the nymphs from desiccation and also from predators, to a certain extent.

Summer As spring passes into summer the aphids multiply rapidly on many garden plants, exuding large quantities of honey-

Right: The aphids which you find in the garden in summer are females, all of which can give birth to several offspring in one day—no wonder populations build up so rapidly. Fortunately we have our allies to fight them. Ladybirds, like this 7-spot, and their larvae are great aphid-eaters, sometimes consuming as many as 100 individuals in a single day. Other insects which help control aphid populations are the delicate green lacewings and hoverfly larvae.

Above: Gardens, with their extremely varied mixture of foreign plant species, represent an artificial habitat, yet a surprisingly large number of insects can be found in them.

Left: Common wasps find ripe fruit particularly attractive in late summer. By then they have finished rearing their broods and the workers now spend the last few weeks of their lives gorging themselves. Half a dozen wasps can soon reduce an apple to a few pips and some pieces of skin. Other insects attracted to ripe fruit include the red admiral—which can become so drunk on the fermenting juices that you can easily catch it—and earwigs which can be found curled up asleep in crevices in the fruit.

dew, eagerly sought by ants and many other insects.

Garden insects reach a peak in high summer when every flower has its attendant hoverfly and often many other insects as well. The summer generations of small tortoiseshells, peacocks and brimstones feed on lavender and buddleia nectar, and may be joined by the wall brown and comma butterflies. The large and small whites join the throng when they are not busy laying eggs on the brassicas, together with their harmless relative, the green-veined white.

Wander around the garden at night with a torch, or better still, shine a reading lamp out of the window, and you will soon be aware of the large numbers of moths in the garden, feeding at the flowers or simply flying about in search of mates. They include the yellow underwings, whose shiny brown pupae you may well have dug up in spring, and the tiger moth and its cousins, the white and buff ermines.

Several day-flying moths also occur in the garden during the summer and autumn. Bes

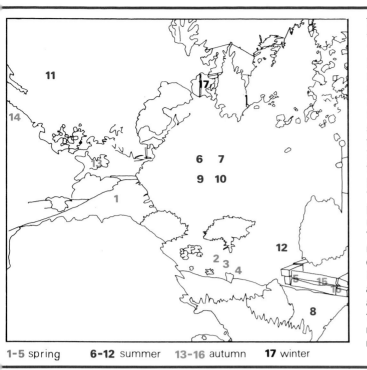

Insect niches

1 Mining bees make mines in the lawn for the females to lay their eggs in. **2 Leatherjackets** (cranefly larvae) feed on roots in the soil. **3 Wireworms** (click beetle larvae) also occur in the soil where they feed on plant roots. **4 Violet ground beetles** scuttle over the flowerbeds looking for stones to hide under. **5 Bee-flies** bask in the sun on brickwork. **6 Aphids** occur on garden plants in very large numbers, where they exude honeydew. **7 Ladybirds** are also present on garden plants, where they feed on aphids. **8 Garden ants** emerge from cracks in the path when it is warm. **9 Hoverflies** visit garden flowers. **10 Leaf-cutter bees** occur on roses, where they cut off pieces of leaf with which to line their burrows. **11 Lackey moth** caterpillars feed on the leaves of birch trees. **12 Bumble bees** visit a number of flowers, but especially rockroses, collecting nectar. **13 Earwigs** can be found curled up in the seed capsules of columbine. **14 Green lacewings** occur on viburnum. **15 Wasps** can be seen almost anywhere in the garden, but if there is rotting fruit around they are particularly abundant. **16 Green bottle flies** like basking in the sun on stones. **17 Winter moth** males can be seen on window panes right through the months of winter.

1-5 spring   **6-12** summer   **13-16** autumn   **17** winter

Left: While digging up the garden in spring, you are highly likely to come across wireworms–click beetle larvae–in the soil. These worm-like grubs are the gardener's enemies since, like leatherjackets, they feed on plant roots.

Below: Drone-flies, which busy themselves visiting garden flowers, look remarkably similar to honey bees, but have only two wings, a faster darting flight and the ability to hover. Well-established gardens obviously attract more insects than gardens which have just been made, and gardens in the south of the country abound with more insect life than those in the north.

nown are the hummingbird hawkmoth and he silver-Y. Both are migrants, arriving here ı late spring and producing a new generation ı late summer, and both feed while hovering.

Autumn Earwigs can be found at all times of ear, but they are especially noticeable at pple-picking time. Found in all kinds of revices, they like curling up around the stalks f apples in daytime, from where they emerge t night to nibble holes in the fruit, ruining its eeping qualities. The oak bush cricket is nother common inhabitant of the apple tree nd of many other trees as well. Active mainly y night, it feeds on other small insects.

Dingy brown craneflies–also known as addy longlegs–abound in the autumn after pending several months as leatherjackets ibbling the roots under the lawn. These flies ke sunbathing on walls, but at night they ommonly enter houses and then buzz franti- ally around trying to find an escape.

Late autumn sees the last of the butterflies ith the small tortoiseshell usually the last to ibernate after feeding on nectar from the eplants and the Michaelmas daisies. Ivy blossom is also a rich source of nectar for many insects, including young queen wasps and bluebottles. At night the ivy blossom is a Mecca for such moths as the beaded chestnut and the green-brindled crescent.

Winter As the days become shorter, swarms of winter gnats come out in the afternoons. The males of these small, harmless, mosquito-like flies form dancing swarms to attract the females. The swarms usually take up station over a fixed object, such as a car, and remain there until dark. These performances go on all through the winter, in all but the very coldest weather.

The winter moth is another hardy species, whose males can be seen on window panes throughout the winter. The females are wingless and occur on the trunks and bran-ches of various trees. Several other moths share the winter nights, including the mottled umber and the drab grey November moth, and when the spring usher makes its appear-ance–usually in February–we can be sure that spring, with its longer, warmer days, is not far away.

HONEY BEES

Man has kept honey bees for thousands of years, but research is only now revealing details of their complex lives – including the extraordinary 'dances' used by workers to signal the whereabouts of food.

Although people have kept honey bees for thousands of years, it was not until recently that these insects could really be called domestic. Throughout their association with man, honey bees have behaved exactly like their wild ancestors, man's only contribution being to provide artificial homes in the form of various kinds of hive. In recent years, however, bee-keeping experts have perfected some delicate techniques for artificially inseminating female bees, and it is now possible to control their breeding. By selecting insects with desirable features – such as high honey yield and a reduced tendency to sting – man can modify the behaviour of future honey bee populations.

A social life The honey bee is a social insect, living in colonies of perhaps 80,000 individuals. Each colony is a huge family group headed by a fertilised female known as the queen. All the other bees are her offspring; most of them are subordinate females known as workers, but during the spring and summer there are also a few hundred males (drones), in the colony.

The queen does nothing but lay eggs, which she can produce at a rate of over one thousand per day. Except when she leaves on her marriage flight or in the middle of a swarm, she never leaves the nest. She has no pollen-gathering apparatus and she cannot make wax. She has a larger body than the workers because she produces the large number of eggs, but her brain is smaller since she does not have to carry out such complex tasks as the workers. The latter do all the nest-building as well as food collecting and looking after the young. The sole function of the drones is to mate with the new queens.

Unlike the bumble bee colony, the honey bee colony is permanent, continuing from year to year. The population fluctuates a good deal during the year, numbers increasing to a summer peak before falling again in autumn. Individual workers born in the spring and summer normally live for about a month, while those emerging from their pupae in the autumn live through the winter. Bees emerging in late autumn may survive

Above: The western honey bee, *Apis mellifera*. This is a worker. The native British race is a dark brownish-black in colour, but interbreeding with other races has resulted in several different colour strains.

til June. The queens have much longer lives and normally head the colony for two or even three years.

Chemical messengers The smooth running of the honey bee colony is controlled by various chemical 'messengers' (pheromones) which are produced by the bees themselves and distributed throughout the population. They ensure that all the bees 'know' what is going on and react accordingly. The queen produces several different pheromones in glands around her mouth, and these are picked up by the throng of workers who lick her and feed her and surround her wherever she goes. The workers continually feed each other and the larvae, and so the pheromones reach all members of the colony.

One of the best known group of pheromones produced by the queen is 'queen substance'. All is well as long as a certain level of queen substance is maintained throughout a colony, but if the level falls the workers know that their queen is ailing and they immediately set about rearing a replacement. Another important pheromone is produced by the larval bees. The workers pick up this 'message' as they feed the brood, then pass it on to other bees so that it stimulates the foragers to go out and collect more food.

The nest and brood The western honey bee occasionally builds its nest in the open, but the normal natural nesting site is in a hollow tree or cave. Within the nesting cavity, the honey bees build the nest entirely of wax produced on the bodies of the workers. It consists of several vertical sheets called combs, both sides of which are covered with hexagonal cells that are used for eggs, larvae and pupae and also for storing pollen and honey.

The queen starts egg-laying in spring, laying one egg in each cell. The egg hatches in

Communication by dancing

In order to collect food efficiently, worker bees must know where to look. A forager communicates the whereabouts of a nectar source by means of 'dances' – a system first discovered by the German biologist Karl von Frisch. A bee indicates a source within 90m (100yd) of the nest by the 'round dance': it circles rapidly clockwise and anticlockwise, on the combs. The richer the source the more vigorous the dance.

To communicate a source further from the nest than 90m (100yd), the worker performs a 'figure-of-eight' dance, waggling her abdomen while making a straight run across the figure. The direction of the straight run shows the direction of the source. Inside the nest the bee indicates the source by directing her straight run at the correct angle from the vertical.

An indication of the distance of the source of food is given by the length of the straight run and the number of abdominal flicks.

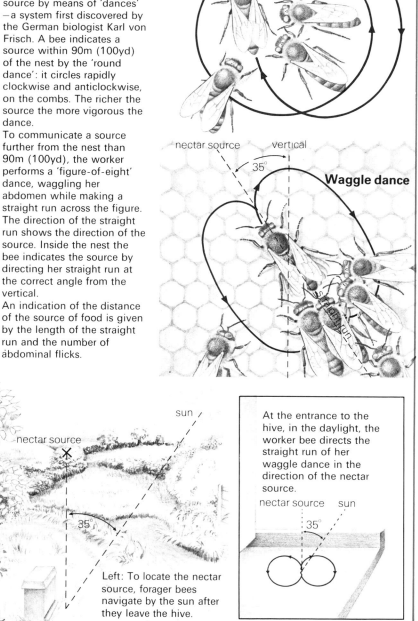

Round dance

nectar source   vertical

35°

Waggle dance

sun

nectar source
X

35°

Left: To locate the nectar source, forager bees navigate by the sun after they leave the hive.

At the entrance to the hive, in the daylight, the worker bee directs the straight run of her waggle dance in the direction of the nectar source.

nectar source   sun

35°

Left: A honey bee worker on a flower head. Pollen from the flower brushes on to the branched hairs that cover the bee's body. The bee periodically combs the pollen grain into the 'baskets' on its back legs. When it has a full load, the bee flies back to the nest and dumps it into empty cells where it is then packed down by other workers. Pollen provides almost all the bees' protein requirements and is particularly important for feeding the grubs and young adult bees.

about three days and the larva then receives constant attention, being visited by workers every few minutes and receiving as many as 30 feeds a day. For the first two days the larva is fed with secretions from glands around the workers' mouths. One secretion is a clear, protein-rich material known as brood-food, and the other is a white fatty material. Together they are often called 'royal jelly'. Larvae destined to become new queens receive this food throughout the five days of larval development, but worker and drone larvae get a change of diet on the third day. The white secretion is withdrawn and replaced by honey and pollen, although brood-food is still provided. The larvae are fully grown

Life in the comb

The honey bees' nest is built with wax produced by the workers, and consists of several vertical sheets called combs. Both sides of the combs are covered with six-sided cells that fit together perfectly. The hexagonal pattern means that no space is wasted. The nest is never empty as shown here—workers are always about. The large acorn-shaped outer cells of the comb (1) are queen cells. The larvae that hatch here receive special treatment, being fed on an ample supply of 'royal jelly' so they develop into queens.

Other cells in the comb are used to store honey (2); these cells are capped with wax. Nectar still being processed into honey is stored in uncapped cells (3) while chemical changes proceed and much of the water content evaporates.

The queen bee roams over the combs, laying eggs in empty cells. Fertilised eggs, which produce workers, are laid in the smaller cells that are about 5·3-6·3mm ($\frac{1}{5}$-$\frac{1}{4}$in) in diameter. Here the worker larvae (4) develop. The worker larvae become full-grown in about five days; at this stage the cells are capped with wax (5) and the larvae pupate inside. The queen also lays unfertilised eggs which develop into drones. These eggs are laid in the larger cells (6) which are about 6·3-7mm ($\frac{1}{4}$in) across. Like the workers, the drones pupate inside capped cells (7).

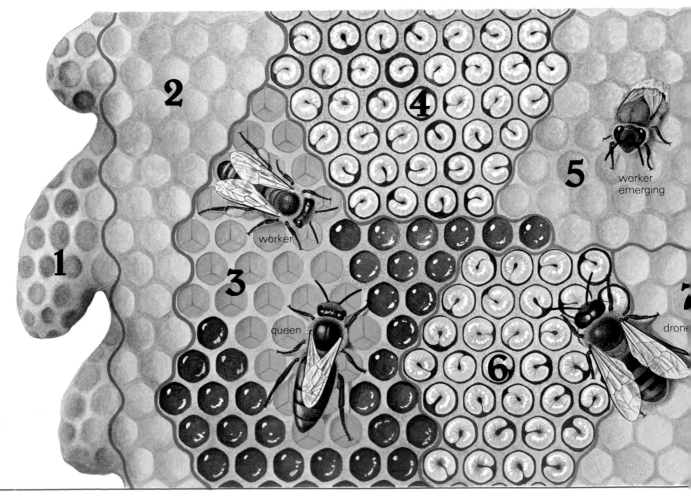

worker emerging

worker

queen

drone

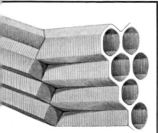

Above: The hexagonal cells in a comb fit together perfectly. The cell walls are slightly tilted so the honey can't run out.

Distribution of cells

□ **worker cells**

■ **drone cells**

▨ **honey stores**

■ **queen cells**

Left: An adult worker bee emerging from its cell. Up to this moment its whole life has been spent inside the cell. In the larval stage it is fed and tended by workers, being given about 125mg of honey in all and about the same amount of pollen. Drones are given slightly more.

Left: A queen bee and drone on the comb. The queen spends most of her life laying eggs in the cells. She can distinguish the different sizes of cell by measuring them with her sensitive fore-feet. She starts laying in early spring, using the central cells first and only coming to the drone cells near the edge of the comb in late spring.

in five days; at this stage the workers cap the cells with brownish wax, the larvae pupate inside and new workers emerge in about eight days.

Division of labour Young bees normally start work by doing 'household chores'. The youngest are usually engaged in cleaning out brood cells ready for more eggs. They actually control the population through the number of cells that they clean, for the queen will not lay in a dirty cell. The glands around the workers' mouths become active after about three days, and the bees can then feed the brood for about two weeks. The wax glands on the abdomen become active when the workers are between one and three weeks old. The bees can then build cells, although they continue to feed the brood as well. They also begin to accept nectar from returning foragers and spend a lot of time converting it into honey. The next stage is for the workers to leave the nest and become foragers.

Honey Forager bees collect pollen and nectar from flowers to feed the colony. Nectar, the sugary liquid produced by flowers to attract bees for the purpose of pollination, is made into honey. On returning to the nest the worker regurgitates the nectar and passes it to a 'household' bee. This bee 'chews' the blob of fluid in her mouthparts for about 20 minutes, during which time she adds enzymes which convert the sugar into glucose and fructose.

Swarming

Swarming is the bees' method of starting a new colony. Overcrowding and a fall in the levels of the queen's pheromones probably help to 'trigger' this off. Prior to swarming, the workers build several queen cells and begin rearing new queens. They also fill themselves with honey. Just before the new queens are due to emerge, the old queen flies off with a large group of workers. The swarm usually settles on a tree (see right) while scouts search for a suitable nest site. Returning scouts 'dance' on the surface of the swarm. They persuade other workers to inspect the sites and, after a good deal of 'discussion', the swarm accepts one of the sites and moves in. The honey that they carry from their old nest keeps them going until they settle down and begin foraging again. Meanwhile, one of the new queens takes over in the old nest— the bees have split into two completely separate colonies.

The semi-processed nectar is then dumped into a cell for a while, during which time the chemical changes proceed and much of the water is evaporated. After a further period of manipulation in the bees' mouthparts, the fluid, which is now true honey, is packed into cells and capped with wax.

New queens When a queen becomes old her pheromone production falls and the workers prepare to rear a new queen. They build a number of large, acorn-shaped cells on the edges of the comb. The eggs laid in these cells are no different from those that produce workers, but the larvae are fed on an abundance of 'royal jelly' throughout their lives and thus become much larger than the less well fed worker grubs. The first new queen to emerge from her cell normally tears open the other queen cells and kills their occupants. She then goes off on her one and only marriage flight, during which she mates with several drones and receives enough sperm to fertilize the thousands of eggs she will lay over the next few years.

The successful drones die soon after mating, but the queen returns to her nest to take over as ruler. The old queen soon dies, and may even be stung to death by her royal daughter. Unsuccessful drones also return to their nest, and remain in the colony until the autumn, but they are then denied food and are evicted by the workers.

THE FAMILY LIFE OF THE EARWIG

Earwigs are immediately identifiable by the pincer-like forceps at the end of the body. The female is unusual among insects for the maternal care she gives to her young.

Most people are familiar with earwigs, but not many know what interesting insects they are and most shudder at the mention of the name. While resembling some rove-beetles (which also have wings folded under short wing-cases), earwigs are readily recognisable by the forceps or pincers at the end of the body. These are almost straight in the female, but strongly curved in the male.

Wings The front wings of the earwig are reduced to small mahogany-coloured flaps on the thorax, and the transparent hind wings are intricately pleated and folded under them when not being used in flight. They are remarkably large when unfolded and each is rounded rather like an ear, possibly giving

rise to the name earwig–corrupted from earwing. This is at least as plausible as the suggestion that the name is derived from the insect's supposed habit of entering the human ear. Doubtless, on extremely rare occasions this can happen–the earwig will seek out and enter any small crevice where protection can be found. An alternative suggestion for the origin of the name earwig is the likeness of the pincers to the old-fashioned instrument used to pierce ears for earrings.

Fliers A number of species have been recorded in the British Isles, but only five are native. The familiar common earwig is the only widespread one. The lesser earwig is much rarer and probably not so widely distributed. Both are able to fly, but the lesser earwig does so far more readily than its larger relative. These two species are able to tolerate quite low temperatures. Others, less tolerant of the cold, are confined to the southern counties; these include *Forficula lesnei* and *Apterygida albipennis*. Occasionally you may find a temporary colony of foreign species in or around warehouses; these are introduced with produce brought in from abroad, but they cannot survive here in the wild.

Life cycle Earwigs belong to that group of insects whose members have an incomplete life cycle. They go through three stages only–egg, nymph or larva, and adult. The chrysalis or pupa stage familiar in butterflies and moths and beetles, for example, is not present, and

Above: A male and female common earwig (*Forficula auricularia*) on a chrysanthemum flower. You can easily tell them apart by the forceps at the end of the body: the forceps of the male (left) are strongly-curved. This species is about 12mm ($\frac{1}{2}$in) in length.

Above: The wingless common earwig nymph looks similar to the adult, but is white in colour at first apart from the darker jaws and eyes. It will go through four stages of moulting until it assumes the full adult characteristics.

he nymphs resemble wingless adults.

The common earwig is the only species to have been studied in great detail. The male and female live together as a pair in a small cavity in loose earth or leaf debris or, during winter, behind the bark of an old log. Pairing is said to take place before and during hibernation. The male usually leaves the nest early in the year – about February – when the female is ready to lay eggs; these normally number about three dozen, but can be considerably more.

The clutch of small oval yellowish eggs is carefully looked after by the mother. If the eggs are scattered she will gather them up again and stand guard over them. You can watch this happening if you have a captive female in a suitable container such as a jam jar. If she lays eggs, scatter them with a stick or pencil.

This maternal care, most unusual among insects, is extended to the young after they hatch. The brood is protected and even fed until the young are ready to leave the winter quarters and can look after themselves. Some females rear a second brood in late spring.

The newly hatched earwig is quite white except for the darker jaws and eyes. There are no wings and the forceps are straight, but otherwise the nymph bears a general resemblance to the adult. There are normally about four moults, during which the skin begins to darken. At the last moult, which takes place anytime from June to August, the adult stage is reached. The young earwig has its full set of wings and 14 segments to the feelers, together with fully formed forceps and mature sex organs. The adult proceeds to mate and then seeks out hibernating quarters; so the life cycle begins again.

Diet Earwigs are probably largely vegetarian, but are quite prepared to accept any kind of food and in this respect can be called true omnivores. The common earwig's liking for petals, particularly of dahlias, is well known to gardeners, who invert straw-stuffed flower pots on the ends of sticks to trap them. In this way they take advantage of the earwig's thigmotaxic nature – that is, its preference for being in contact with a solid surface, and

hence its seeking out of crannies and tunnels. In nature this is a useful response to the danger of being eaten by a bird or other predator. The speed with which an earwig drops to the ground when disturbed is another useful survival reflex.

Earwigs also damage the flowers of garden nasturtiums as well as apples both on the tree and the ground. Their excavations into fruit are probably made where two fruit touch or where there is previous damage, which enables them to make their initial entry. They will also take advantage of the space between cabbage and Brussels sprout leaves; although they make a mess with their droppings, they rarely do much damage through eating the leaves.

Earwigs are also found in animal carcases, usually those in a fairly advanced state of decay when the rotting parts are beginning to dry out. If earwigs are kept in large numbers, they may start to eat each other.

Minor pest Earwigs cannot be regarded as a major pest of farm or garden. Their scavenging habits are undoubtedly useful in helping to dispose of natural refuse and they provide food for some of the larger insect predators such as the violet ground beetle.

Various internal parasites, including the ichneumon fly whose larva develops inside the host and at first eats the non-vital organs, have been recorded in earwigs. But none of these seems to be a major controlling factor in earwig populations.

Above: The lesser earwig (*Labia minor*) is half the size or less of the common earwig, at about 5mm ($\frac{1}{4}$in) long. It flies quite readily and can be found in lighted rooms or the moth collector's light-trap during summer. You may also see it in the sunshine inhabiting or flying over rich organic matter such as farmyard manure.

Above: The common earwig in an aggressive mood. The forceps are raised forward over the body like a scorpion's sting, as a defence when the insect is disturbed.

Packing wings

The earwig's large hind wings are thin and skin-like and their folding is an elaborate process often aided by the forceps. It can take an earwig as much as half a minute or so to fold a hind wing. Anyone who has difficulty folding up a road map will appreciate the earwig's problem. The hind wings are folded under the front wings on the thorax.

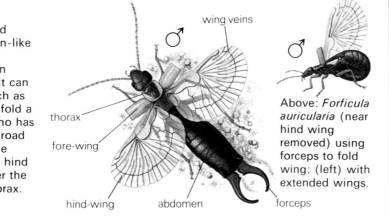

wing veins

thorax

fore-wing

hind-wing

abdomen

forceps

Above: *Forficula auricularia* (near hind wing removed) using forceps to fold wing; (left) with extended wings.

LADYBIRDS: WELCOME BEETLES

Ladybirds, always popular for their bright colouring, are also one of the few insects welcome in the garden for the work they do in keeping down destructive aphids.

Above: The 7-spot ladybird, our commonest species, making a meal of an aphid. Ladybirds are voracious feeders and will turn up almost wherever there are aphids; a garden rose bush is a good place to search for them.

Below: 7-spot ladybirds mating. The male is the one on top; externally male and female ladybirds look alike.

The familiar black and red ladybird is most people's favourite beetle. In the Middle Ages it was associated with the Virgin Mary and called 'beetle of Our Lady'; all our present-day names for this insect—ladybird, ladybug or sometimes ladybeetle—are derived from this medieval title. Today, ladybirds are welcomed by farmer and gardener alike for the valuable work they do in keeping down aphids.

Warning coloration The colouring of most insects is designed to help them remain concealed from predators, but the bright markings of ladybirds make them startlingly conspicuous. Strange though it may seem, this coloration is a protective device. Ladybirds have a very unpleasant taste and they advertise this fact to their enemies through their coloration, which makes them instantly recognisable. A predator such as a house sparrow only has to eat a ladybird once to discover the unpalatable taste; thereafter it will leave others alone. Most species of ladybird are fairly similar in colour—they all gain blanket protection from looking alike. However, a few species, such as the red marsh ladybird (*Coccidula rufa*) and *Rhyzobiu litura* which are a dull red-brown in colour and more elongated in shape than other ladybirds, seem to be the exceptions to this rule. No one really knows why this should be.

If you handle a ladybird, you'll find it exudes a few drops of yellow, strong smelling liquid—actually blood—which stains the hand and smells pungent for quite some time. This, an example of defensive 'reflex bleeding', is designed to alarm and warn off enemies. Occasionally ladybirds will also bite and are quite capable of giving a sharp nip.

Common or garden species There are 4 different species of ladybird in the British Isles. Apart from their colour, you can distinguish them from other beetles by their short clubbed antennae and 3-jointed feet. With one exception, they are all carnivorous, feeding on a variety of insects, especially aphids. The exception to this rule is the vegetarian 24-spot ladybird which eats the leaves of clover.

The ladybird you'll find almost everywhere—fields, gardens, woods—is the 7-spot, which is red in colour with three bold black spots on each wing cover and an extra spot in the centre of its back where the wing cases meet. You should also be able to find 2-spot and 10-spot ladybirds fairly readily; both these species are red with black spots, but both can be very variable. In some individual 2-spot ladybirds, for example, the black marks 'run' to form patterns rather than spots, while in others the colours may be reversed so the insect is black with red spots. Some show melanism—darkness of colour—which is curious since in some other insects, particularly moths, it is a camouflage condition that

Spot that ladybird!

2-spot ladybird in flight with wing cases fully raised

2-spot *(Adalia bipunctata)*

10-spot *(Adalia 10-punctata)*

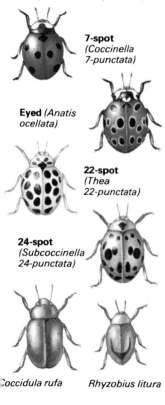

7-spot *(Coccinella 7-punctata)*

Eyed *(Anatis ocellata)*

22-spot *(Thea 22-punctata)*

24-spot *(Subcoccinella 24-punctata)*

Coccidula rufa   Rhyzobius litura

above: Some of the 45 different species of ladybird found in Britain. Most are instantly recognisable as ladybirds for their rounded shape and their spots. *Coccidula* and *Rhyzobius* are, however, exceptions to this rule. One factor to bear in mind when identifying any species of ladybird is that their colour and patterns vary enormously. The number of spots referred to in their name, in particular, is misleading – the 24-spot never has 24 spots!

appears to have developed in heavily industrial areas where dark forms could not easily be seen on soot-grimed trees and buildings. Ladybirds do not normally require the protection of camouflage colouring. Again, this is something which continues to puzzle researchers. Some 2-spot ladybirds even have extra spots, or can be black with yellow spots; these can be confused with the 22-spot ladybird which is always yellow with black spots.

Avid aphid-eaters Ladybirds often overwinter in communal groups. You can find them sheltering beneath loose bark on trees and in similar protected places, even indoors in the corners of window frames and doors. In spring, they fly in search of plants such as nettles or rose bushes which are infested with aphids. Here they feed, mate and lay their eggs. The eggs, usually deposited in batches of up to 50, are laid on the undersides of leaves.

The larvae which emerge from the eggs are quite unlike the adults; they are long, thin, grub-like creatures, generally dark grey with yellow or orange markings. In common with the adults, they have a voracious appetite for aphids; each larva can devour several hundreds of these unfortunate insects. After about three to four weeks of intensive feeding, the larvae moult to become pupae. The pupa case, similar in colour to the larva, is attached to a leaf by the tail. After one or two weeks in this transitional stage, the adult ladybird emerges from the pupa.

In Britain, ladybirds normally have only one generation a year. Eggs are laid by overwintered females which have mated either in the autumn or, more usually, after hibernation. Young adults spend the summer feeding or in a state of dormancy before hibernation. The complete life cycle takes seven to eight weeks.

The year of the ladybird During the hot, dry summer of 1976 there was a ladybird population explosion in Britain. Swarms of 7-spot ladybirds were reported in towns and on beaches, with complaints that people were being bitten. Tests showed that some ladybirds were actually imbibing human blood, but most were drinking sweat to obtain water. The irritations were probably caused by reaction to the ladybird's own bitter blood, which gave some people a pricking sensation.

The build-up in numbers in fact began in the warm summer of 1975. Aphids were abundant in the spring and early summer but became scarce by mid-summer. This forced the ladybirds to travel in search of food. Many migrated to towns–increasing the population there by about 50 times its usual number–and remained there during the subsequent mild winter. They bred in huge numbers the following spring when, once again, aphids were plentiful. The population reached a peak in July 1976 when numbers were about 250 times the normal level.

Life cycle of the 2-spot

The eggs of the 2-spot ladybird are laid in batches on the underside of leaves. One female can produce several hundred eggs in her lifetime.

2-spot ladybird larva feeding on aphids. The larva will pupate after feeding for three or four weeks and undergoing three skin moults.

Pupae and one newly-emerged adult, whose wing cases take a few hours to harden and darken. The adult emerges from the pupa after about six days.

THE BLACK GARDEN ANT

Above: Black garden ants (*Lasius niger*) swarming. The two winged individuals are queens or males (in this picture they are too small to distinguish) which will take to the air to mate. The wingless forms are sexually underdeveloped females (workers).

Lift a paving slab or turn over a large stone in the garden, and the chances are that you will find a colony of black garden ants. This species takes to the air in swarms to mate on warm, humid summer days.

The black garden ant is widely distributed in the British Isles, but is most common in the southern third of England. It is a dull black, rather hairy ant and occurs in fields as well as gardens.

If you look into the black garden ants' nest at any time from late July to the end of September, you'll find three different types of ant. The largest individuals are queens; they have four thin, transparent wings. The smallest ones–also winged–are males, while the slightly larger wingless individuals are workers. For most of the rest of the year the workers are the only easily seen ants in the nest.

Mating swarms The black ants' mating flight takes place in summer in warm, humid weather. Males and queens emerge from the nests in swarms–those from nests in the same neighbourhood all appearing at much the same time (usually about mid-day). They take to the air in vast numbers, then disperse. Many fall victim to predators such

as swallows. Mating takes place in flight; afterwards, the queens settle on the ground, tear off their wings and either return to their original nest or find a suitable place under a log or stone to overwinter. The males die soon after mating.

Colony life In spring the mated queen starts laying eggs. These develop into workers which build up the nest. Later in the summer new winged queens and males are produced, the males from unfertilised eggs.

Life in the ant colony centres on the queen. She is carefully tended by the workers who feed her a regurgitated sugar-rich fluid which was gathered as honeydew from aphids, or from the nectaries of flowers. The queen's eggs are taken to special brood chambers and guarded and the larvae, when they hatch, are fed and cleaned.

Foraging Apart from the honeydew and nectar, black garden ants eat flies and other small insects and mites, as well as crumbs dropped by people. They also gather the seeds of plants such as violets for the fat-rich body (elaiosome) they contain.

Black garden ants are themselves eaten by a variety of predators. The green woodpecker, for instance, scratches into the ants' nest and extracts ants with its long tongue. Some ground and rove beetles, spiders and centipedes also prey on ants, and even members of the same species attack their own kind if they come from a different nest.

Right: Black garden ant worker with larvae (the small white grubs) and pupae (the cocoons).

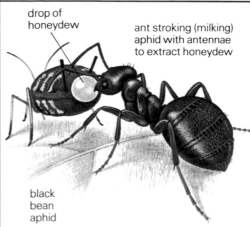

drop of honeydew

ant stroking (milking) aphid with antennae to extract honeydew

black bean aphid

Milking aphids
Ants are attracted by the sugar-rich fluid–honeydew–that is secreted by aphids. The ant 'milks' an aphid by stroking its rear end with its antennae; this appears to stimulate the aphid to secrete a drop of honeydew which the ant eats and regurgitates later in the nest to feed queen or larval ants. Sometimes ants appear to protect aphids from predators by squirting formic acid.

INDUSTRIAL MELANISM

Wildlife is threatened by industrialisation, but a few species have adapted to soot-covered environments by developing a darker colouring –industrial melanism.

Melanism is a term used to describe the occurrence of dark coloured or black individuals in a species which is normally a lighter colour. It is frequently seen in insects, often under natural conditions. In the north of Scotland, for instance, a dark coloured variety of the oak eggar moth occurs on wet peaty moorland which produces a dark environment. Melanistic varieties of moths also occur in pine forests, probably as a response to the dark colours of tree bark on which the moths rest by day.

Industrial melanism, however, is a special case–the dark background on which the animals are trying to conceal themselves is produced by atmospheric pollution. Pollution affects trees in two ways; it kills lichen growing on their trunks, and it causes deposition of soot which blackens the bark of trunks and branches. The Industrial Revolution first produced this effect in Britain.

The peppered moth Already known to collectors in England in the 1770s, the peppered moth's name refers to the black

Above: Only a few woodland species of moth have successfully adapted to the spread of urbanisation. Among them is the waved umber moth, a member of the geometer family. As a species which rests by day on tree trunks, it has to adopt a suitable colouring to conceal itself from birds. The normal form (above), found in rural areas, is pale with brown wavy markings, but the melanic form (below) is distinctly darker to blend with the soot-blackened tree trunks of urban areas. This black form occurs plentifully in north and east London.

speckling on its wings. In 1848 specimens of a black variety were reported from Manchester and these rapidly replaced the speckled form in this area. By 1895, 98% of the Manchester peppered moths were black, and this variety quickly established itself in areas where the coal-burning industry was polluting and transforming the environment.

This pollution also affected areas to the east of London and the Midlands–because of the predominantly westerly winds–and the moths also responded here by developing mainly black populations. In south-west England and the north and west of Scotland, however, the black form remained absent, and along the south coast the speckled form was, and still is, much more common than the black.

Researching melanism Throughout the first half of this century the association of the black peppered moth with smoke-polluted areas became clear, and the rather obvious explanation of this–that black moths were protected from predation by birds when they rested on a black background–was suggested.

In 1952 Dr Kettlewell–a geneticist from Oxford–began a long, painstaking and entirely successful programme of research. It was based on the theory that the establishment of black peppered moths was due to natural selection of an originally black mutation in an environment where the normal speckled form, resting on sooty tree trunks and branches, was conspicuous, while the black form was well concealed. (In unpolluted rural areas the speckled form is well protected when at rest on lichened bark.) The selective agent was assumed to be predation by birds, which hunt their prey by sight.

In one of his best known experiments Dr Kettlewell chose a wood near Birmingham in which the trees were blackened by industrial pollution. While collecting in the wood he established that 90% of the naturally occurring moths were black. He also found an unpolluted wood in Dorset in which 95% were speckled. He then bred large numbers of both

forms and released half of the black and half of the speckled varieties in each locality.

A few days after releasing them he operated illuminated moth traps in order to recapture as many of the moths as possible. In the Dorset wood the percentage recaptured of the total of released black moths was just half that of the speckled ones. In the Birmingham wood, however, the percentages were almost exactly reversed. Black moths resting on the lichen-covered trees in Dorset had been found by their predators twice as readily as speckled ones, but on the soot-blackened trunks near Birmingham the pale speckled ones were at an equal disadvantage.

Selective predators Dr Kettlewell's experiment, however, gave no indications of what predators were involved in this selective elimination of black and speckled moths. To discover this he placed moths of both types on lichened and blackened trunks, and watched to see if any insectivorous animals found them. This required a great deal of patience, but he was rewarded by observing birds finding and devouring the moths. The birds took them selectively, mostly finding moths which were resting on the 'wrong' background.

Dr Kettlewell's research on the peppered moth is of great importance since it provides a demonstration of evolution by natural selection, actually in the course of taking place, and doing so much more rapidly than is usual in nature. The speed of this evolutionary change is due, of course, to the very rapid environmental change (industrialisation) which brought it about.

Black genes Dr Kettlewell also bred peppered moths in captivity on a vast scale in order to investigate their heredity and genetics. He found that there are two genetically distinct dark forms: the melanic form *carbonaria*, which is abundant and fairly black, and the other form *insularia*, which is less common and black with faint pale speckling.

He also found that both black forms are

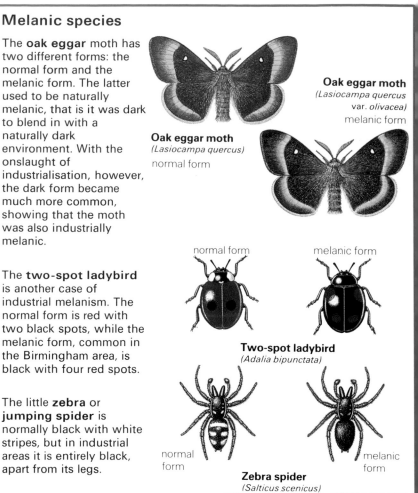

Melanic species

The **oak eggar** moth has two different forms: the normal form and the melanic form. The latter used to be naturally melanic, that is it was dark to blend in with a naturally dark environment. With the onslaught of industrialisation, however, the dark form became much more common, showing that the moth was also industrially melanic.

Oak eggar moth
(*Lasiocampa quercus* var. *olivacea*)
melanic form

Oak eggar moth
(*Lasiocampa quercus*)
normal form

The **two-spot ladybird** is another case of industrial melanism. The normal form is red with two black spots, while the melanic form, common in the Birmingham area, is black with four red spots.

normal form   melanic form

Two-spot ladybird
(*Adalia bipunctata*)

The little **zebra** or **jumping spider** is normally black with white stripes, but in industrial areas it is entirely black, apart from its legs.

normal form   melanic form

Zebra spider
(*Salticus scenicus*)

Right: Two maps showing the occurrence of melanic peppered moths and two-spot ladybirds in Britain. The melanic forms are predominant in the industrial regions—the London area, the West Midlands, Lancashire and the Scottish Lowlands.

Below: A melanic figure of eighty moth.

Distribution of melanic peppered moth
% of melanic form
● 75–100%
● 50–74%
● 25–49%
● 0–24%

Distribution of melanic two-spot ladybird
% of melanic form
● 75–100%
● 50–74%
● 25–49%
● 0–24%

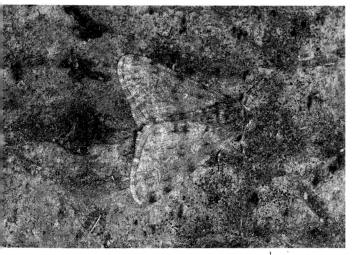

genetically dominant to the normal speckled form; that is to say, a moth that has inherited a 'black' gene from one parent and a 'speckled' gene from the other will be black, not intermediate in coloration.

Other melanistic moths As many as a hundred British moth species have been reported as showing signs of industrial melanism. One such species is the pale brindled beauty, normally a pale brownish-grey moth. It has more than one melanic form, and its distribution differs from that of the black peppered moths. Although both species are black in urban areas, you can also find black pale brindled beauties in the rural parts of Scotland and South Wales where no melanic peppered moths occur. In East Anglia most peppered moths are black, but pale brindled beauties are their normal colour.

Little seems to be known of the black pale brindled beauties before the Industrial Revolution, but this species may have a natural tendency to melanism, which becomes established by natural selection in industrial areas.

The oak eggar has a northern natural melanic (it is naturally dark in Scotland), although it also has a black form on the Yorkshire moors, where the ground surface and heather are heavily polluted by industrial smoke. It does not live in urban districts, but the Yorkshire moorland dark form can be regarded as an industrial melanic (unlike its Scottish counterpart).

The case of the figure of eighty moth is interesting, as the melanic form seems to have migrated to this country from Continental Europe. It appeared in Holland in about the second quarter of this century, but was not seen in England until 1945. The normal brownish-grey colour is replaced by black.

Although the spread of urban conditions threatens most species of woodland moths, a few adapt to it well, feeding as larvae on trees in parks and suburban gardens. Among them are the brindled beauty, the waved umber and the sycamore moth. All these species rest by day on the bark of trees and, not surprisingly, have evolved melanic forms.

Black ladybirds Among insects other than

Above: The normal form (left) and melanic form (right) of the pale brindled beauty. This moth is on the wing in January, February and March, but you are only likely to see the male because the female is wingless.

Below: Peppered moths resting on a wall. The one in the top left hand corner is melanistic while the other two are normal forms. The peppered moth is probably the best known example of a species which has adopted melanism in urban areas. The first melanic peppered moths were reported in Manchester in 1848, and by 1895 nearly all of the city's peppered moths were melanic. This black variety soon established itself in all the large industrial areas, and also in the regions to the east where the westerly winds were blowing the smoke, and polluting the environment.

moths, the best known case of industrial melanism is that of the two-spot ladybird. The normal form is red with two black spots, but the amount of red and black is naturally variable. However, in the industrial Midlands the prevalence of a black form ranges from 60% or 70% to 90%, and surely must be a case of industrial melanism.

It is difficult to see how the beetles gain any advantage from being camouflaged though. They are protected by distasteful body juices and their normal bright pattern is an example of warning coloration. It is possible that shiny black is also effective as a warning, so that the melanic ladybirds enjoy the double advantage of being difficult to find, and recognisable as nasty if they are discovered.

Zebra spider Outside the scope of insects, cases of industrial melanism appear to be rare. One example is the zebra or jumping spider. Normally clearly marked with black and white stripes, it lives and hunts its prey on walls and tree trunks. Insectivores take this spider if they see it, and it is obviously to the spider's advantage not to be conspicuous. Just as in the peppered moth, a black and white normal form has been replaced by a black one in urban areas, so that the spider is almost invisible on the soot-stained walls and trees.

Birds of urban habitats

It comes as a great surprise to most people to learn that Britain's most common birds are town and city dwellers. Blackbirds, robins, song thrushes, starlings, house sparrows, greenfinches, blue tits and many others are all a familiar sight in built-up areas, and most of them are more common in these places than in the open countryside.

Birds need a good supply of food, available all year round (unless they migrate), somewhere to nest and somewhere safe to roost. If these requirements are met, then the birds are likely to withstand the problems of daily life, even in the city environment. For birds that use trees and shrubs, or nest on and in buildings, there are at least as many nest sites in towns as in the countryside, and frequently many more. There is plenty of food to suit a wide variety of preferences, especially for omnivores like the blackbirds which eat anything from worms to redcurrants, and for aerial feeders like the swifts and martins which feed on the abundant 'aerial plankton' of insects and young spiders rising from the land below. And safe roosting sites – such as playing fields, garden trees and shrubs and the roofs and ledges of buildings – are plentiful enough. In such favourable circumstances many birds can often produce several clutches of eggs a year.

Nevertheless, though they may have escaped the weasels and sparrowhawks of the countryside, the birds have exchanged them for other problems. Domestic cats, man (particularly in the form of boys), grey squirrels, magpies, rats and other predators all take their toll, and the higher density of birds means that disease spreads more rapidly. But, as with most things in nature, a balance is struck and the net result is that our towns and cities all have very high populations of birds, of many different species, particularly in the suburbs but also in city centres and industrial areas. Visitors in winter only serve to swell the numbers even more.

Left: The pied wagtail is one of the liveliest birds you will see anywhere: its tail in non-stop flicking motion, it leaps and dances in the air after the insects which are its staple diet. It is perfectly at home in cities, especially where water is close at hand, and it has even been known to roost in heated commercial greenhouses in the winter.

CHECKLIST

This checklist is a guide to some of the birds you can find in towns, cities, parks, houses and gardens in Britain. Although you will not see them all in the same place, you should be able to spot many of them throughout the changing seasons. The species listed in **bold** *type are described in detail.*

Barn owl
Black-headed gull
Black redstart
Blue tit
Bullfinch
Chaffinch
Coal tit
Collared dove
Coot
Feral pigeon
Great spotted woodpecker
Great tit
Greenfinch
Goldfinch
Herring gull
House martin
House sparrow
Jay
Kestrel
Magpie
Mallard
Mandarin duck
Moorhen
Mute swan
Nuthatch
Pied wagtail
Robin
Song thrush
Starling
Stock dove
Swallow
Swift
Tawny owl
Tree sparrow
Tufted duck
Woodpigeon
Wren

Left: Almost no garden in town or country is complete in winter without the visits of the blue tit to the bird table, where peanuts are always the main attraction. But in spring and summer this acrobatic little bird feeds mostly on the tiny caterpillars that are so plentiful in the foliage of trees.

123

ROBINS: FRIENDLY GARDEN VISITORS

The robin is a particular favourite among bird lovers; everyone enjoys the attentions of this familiar redbreast in the garden during winter. But despite all the efforts made to feed this bird in the harsh weather, thousands perish each year.

The robin enjoys a popularity with man unrivalled by any other species. A familiar visitor at the bird-table in winter and constant gardening companion, even nesting in the toolshed, it is a year-round bird. This close association with man is a special feature of the robin's relationship with the British. Robins of exactly the same species nest over most of Europe, but a tendency on the continent to shoot and eat small birds has made robins there generally shy and retiring woodland birds.

The bird's popularity in Britain has built up over the years and legends about the bad luck incurred by anyone harming a robin go back to the 16th century. A Christian link has been

attached to the legend because the robin's red breast was supposedly stained by blood after the bird had been pricked by Christ's crown of thorns. This is why the robin features prominently on the earliest Christmas cards.

Pairing and nesting The adults get together as pairs in early January. As they look exactly alike, the sexes can only recognise each other by display and posture. An unmated male singing loudly in his territory will, at first, behave aggressively to any intruding robin. If the intruder is a male it either retreats or tries to oust the occupier. If the new bird is a female seeking a mate, she persists in approaching the resident male, apparently unimpressed by his threats. Over a period of some hours, sometimes as much as two days, the bond between the two is built up so that they accept each other.

In many species this pair-bonding is directly followed by nest-building and egg-laying. With the robin, pairing is accomplished weeks or even months before any nesting attempt is made. During this time the birds occupy the same territory and recognise each other as mates but do not pay much attention to each other. As the weather improves the hen bird starts to build her nest, using moss and dead leaves and lining it with hair. In the natural state she may choose a rocky crevice or hollow of a tree, most often, a bank or an ivy-covered tree—usually well concealed and difficult to find.

However some robins select the most unlikely sites. One nest was found in a chest of drawers in a toolshed. The drawer was half-closed and the nest at the back was only discovered when the drawer was opened.

When she begins to build the nest the female also starts to receive food from the male. This so-called 'courtship-feeding' was initially thought to be a ritual designed to reinforce the pair-bond between male and female. In fact it is an important source of food for the female—one that she almost completely relies upon during incubation.

The clutch of white eggs with pale reddish freckling is laid, one egg each day, and the complete clutch is generally five or six eggs, although up to nine have been recorded. The

Robin (*Erithacus rubecula*). Also called redbreast; 14cm (5in) from beak to tip of tail; 5-9cm (2-4in) high. Distribution nationwide.

Below: Hungry fledglings wait to be fed in their nest, which is usually made up of twigs, grass and moss. Robins are well known for making their nests in such unlikely places as kettles, old buckets—even the pockets of jackets left in garden sheds.

incubating female loses the feathers from her breast and belly and the blood vessels just under the skin enlarge greatly. The bare skin and increased blood supply allow her to transfer heat more efficiently to the eggs.

Greedy chicks After two weeks the eggs hatch out and the blind chicks, covered in thin dark down, increasingly dominate the parents' lives with their enormous appetites. Both adult and young robins feed on insects, spiders and worms. They do not generally eat seeds or berries. About 15 days after hatching these young robins, now weighing more than their parents, leave the nest.

Two particularly attentive parents were reported by naturalist David Lack. They

Five or six eggs—12mm (½in) long—are laid and incubated for two weeks. Eggs generally have a whitish background and orange/brown freckles.

Nests vary in size. They are made of dead leaves, grass, moss and hairs; very few feathers are used as lining.

built their nest in a cart which had to go on a 200-mile round trip just after the young hatched. Undaunted, the adult birds accompanied their offspring, feeding them on the way.

When the young birds leave the nest they face two or three days of great danger since they cannot yet fly well. At this stage they have a soft speckled brown plumage with no trace of their parents' red breast. By the beginning of June they start to lose their body feathers and to develop their red breasts —growing from the bottom upwards. The wings do not moult but continue to develop until July of the next year when they reach their full size.

Second brood Once the young are fledged the adults build a new nest within the same territory and, unless they are prevented for any reason (disturbance by a cat, flooding of the nest in bad weather or thoughtless hedge-cutting), will raise another brood in May. During the summer for a period of five weeks, the adult robins replace their old feathers with new ones. They stay in the same area, but make themselves less obvious and less active, concealed in shrubberies and thickets. During this moult the adult robins also fall silent—the only time of the year when the robin song is not a feature of the British countryside.

As the second brood of young birds acquires its red plumage and the adult birds their replacement plumage, the autumn song starts up. The rich and fruity spring song of the males gives way to the thinner, more piping song of young and old, cock and hen, as each claims its own territory; this is kept, with a few local alterations, through the winter until pairing takes place. In times of real food shortage, territoriality breaks down as all the birds concentrate on feeding.

Population control Although some British robins migrate each autumn, most stay within a mile or two of their birthplace. So what happens to all these robins? If each pair of adults raises two broods with five or six young in each, there are six times as many robins at the end of the breeding season as at the start. A single pair would become almost ten million pairs at the end of ten years—about twice the total British population of robins. In fact the majority of them die. As many as a million robins may be killed by cats; while owls, cars, plate glass windows and harsh winters also take their toll. Sadly, but naturally, of the original pair and their offspring, on average only one adult and one youngster survive to breed the following year. Harsh winter weather often provides the greatest danger; so millions of people who feed birds leave out all sorts of titbits—even mince meat and grated cheese—to ensure that 'their' robins are the ones to survive. This feeding also encourages the robins to stay in backyards and gardens.

Left: A spotty juvenile robin, speckled brown and with no hint of a red breast which develops later in the summer. In its first year, the robin has a one-in-six chance of survival.

Below: Proudly displaying its red breast and singing its rich spring song, this robin lays claim to its territory and warns off other birds.

Competing for space

Almost all birds are territorial. It is generally during the breeding season that each bird defends a home area, and will not tolerate any bird of the same species apart from its mate within its territory. Robins are no exception, and like other song birds (such as blackbirds and song thrushes) they stake out quite large claims by their presence at strategic songposts. Other birds restrict themselves to much smaller areas—gannets, for instance, only defend the immediate nest area.

The blackbird singing on your television aerial may seem full of the joys of spring but, much more important to itself and other blackbirds, it is saying: 'This is part of my territory—keep off'. If the message is not understood it may still have to chase off the encroaching birds—a sight often seen when disputing birds dart at each other along a lawn or hedgerow without actually making contact. It is both these aggressive flutterings and song patterns that prevent actual fighting—unless large numbers of birds are competing for a very small territory.

SPARROWS OF TOWN AND COUNTRY

The house sparrow is a species closely associated with man, sharing his environment and sometimes even becoming a pest. Another less numerous species – the tree sparrow – leads a relatively hidden life in our woods and orchards.

he house sparrow is always seen in close ssociation with man, his buildings and his vestock. It might be possible to describe uch an association as 'commensal', except at this would imply some form of mutual enefit, or at least no detriment to either artner in the association. Short of enjoying s presence, we derive little benefit from the ouse sparrow. The bird, on the other hand, hile gaining access to plenty of good nest tes (at no cost to us), oversteps the bounds f commensalism in its attacks on our garden ants. This becomes more serious when it tacks our cereal crops: the sparrow ceases be commensal and becomes a competitor r, in plain terms, an agricultural pest.

House sparrows are not normally birds of en environments such as hillsides or moors. the vicinity of farm buildings, however, pecially those with livestock, a colony of ouse sparrows is likely to be present. The rds are also common bird-table visitors, ting almost everything that is put out for em. They even feed on scraps of meat, if it is er available to them.

Above: The house sparrow's nest, made of coarse grass or straw, is roughly domed.

Below: The male house sparrow (right) can be distinguished from the female (left) by its black bib and grey crown.

Variations in plumage In spring, the male house sparrow is an attractive bird, with a grey crown bordered in rich chestnut brown. His back is a mixture of rich browns fringed with golden buff, his breast is greyish fawn and beneath the chin is a fan-shaped black bib. In winter he is drabber, since many of his body feathers have broad buff fringes which gradually wear away to expose the colours beneath in early spring. The upper plumage of the female (both in summer and winter) is a mixture of sandy or greyish fawns and pale browns, and she is greyish beneath. Until they moult in their first autumn, young birds of both sexes resemble the females.

If you travel about in Britain and Ireland, you may notice that house sparrows living far from towns have much brighter plumage than those living in the industrial conurbations, where the sparrows seem particularly dark. In such circumstances, some species of animals have adapted by changing colour to improve their camouflage. Best known is the peppered moth, normally white with a black peppering of spots. By the process of natural

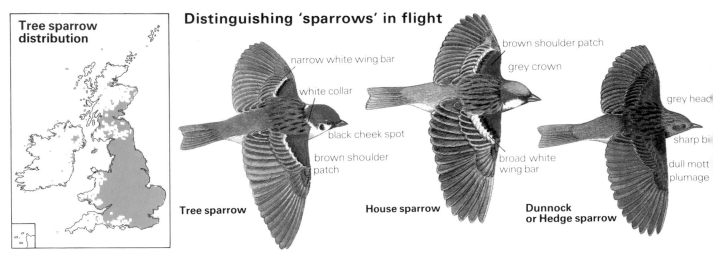

Distinguishing 'sparrows' in flight

Tree sparrow distribution

narrow white wing bar

white collar

black cheek spot

brown shoulder patch

Tree sparrow

brown shoulder patch

grey crown

broad white wing bar

House sparrow

grey head

sharp bi

dull mott plumage

Dunnock or Hedge sparrow

selection, this moth has gradually evolved darker and darker colours, which improve its camouflage on the grimy trunks of city trees. Recently there was some debate as to whether house sparrows, too, were exhibiting this change (which is called 'industrial melanism'). Samples of sparrows of various shades were examined by experts. A strong superficial correlation was indeed found between darker plumages and more industrialised areas. Washing the feathers of all colour types with strong detergent, however, revealed that the darker ones had been contaminated with soot and other industrial grime, and thus their sombre shades were only 'skin deep'.

Feeding habits The house sparrow is an opportunist feeder, taking what food is easily available in greatest abundance at the time. The diet includes seeds, buds, leaves, shoots, flowers and a huge variety of human food waste and leftovers. Our sparrows are representatives of the largely African weaver-bird family, some members of which are as devastating to crops as plagues of locusts. It is not surprising, then, that our house sparrows flock into the corn at harvest time. Although each bird eats only a few grams of grain in a day, the house sparrow has an extremely wide distribution, and flocks often contain some hundreds of individual birds. The nationwide total of house sparrows is so high that the species is a serious pest, causing many millions of pounds worth of damage each year.

Many gardeners are incensed by house sparrow attacks on their flowering plants. We put out food for them, which they take greedily, only to start to tear apart the crocus and primula flowers when they appear. Although it may be of little comfort to the gardener, there is at least an explanation for this. Notice how often it is the yellow flowers that are attacked. Yellow coloration is associated with flowers that have a particularly strong attraction for pollinating insects, and tends to occur together with a rich supply of nectar. Yellow crocuses, for example, have far more nectar than purple ones. It is this nectar at the base of the flowers that the sparrows are seeking.

Formation of flocks Flocks are very much a part of sparrow life. They are an effective means of exploiting local abundance of food (as in cereal fields) and offer considerable protection from predators. They start to form in late summer, and are often composed largely of juvenile birds. These flocks roam over a distance of several miles. In winter, they join with other species, particularly finches and buntings, on stubble or weedy ground, or around places where livestock are fed.

From late summer onwards, roosting, too, is often communal. Sometimes the roosts are within buildings, and sometimes in the dense shelter provided by rhododendron, hawthorn

House sparrow (*Passer domesticus*). Resident near human habitations. Length 14.5cm (5¾in).

Tree sparrow (*Passer montanus*). Resident in many lowland rural areas. Length 14cm (5½in).

Below: A tree sparrow at its nest site on a cliff. Eggs are laid all through spring and summer, starting in March and continuing into August. Some pairs raise as many as three broods in a season.

two thirds the weight of its larger relative. The sexes are similar in plumage; the all-brown cap, the small black bib and the characteristic black spot in the centre of a white cheek distinguish them from the house sparrow. Their call, a rich, fruity chirrup, once heard and learned is an excellent way of separating the two species at a distance or in flight.

Tree sparrows are just as catholic in their food choice as house sparrows, but tend to shun the presence of man, usually feeding and nesting at a distance from human habitation.

The display pattern and the breeding season are closely similar to those of the house sparrow. The tree sparrow lays from two to eight eggs, usually about six, densely flecked with grey-brown. The nest is often in a hole in a building or a tree. In the latter case, the hole may be a natural one, or else the disused nest of a woodpecker. Tree sparrows readily occupy nestboxes, and are pugnacious in their tenancy of them, even evicting other birds such as blue or great tits, and building their own nests on top of those of the first occupiers. Incubation lasts 12 days, sometimes less, and the brood fledges after 10 days, or sometimes more.

Tree sparrows are nowhere as numerous as house sparrows, and have a much less widespread distribution in Ireland, northern and western Scotland, the Hebrides, and southwest England.

r blackthorn thickets, or ivy-clad trees or uildings.

Nesting sparrows House sparrows can be en around their nest sites in almost any onth of the year, though attendance is at s lowest in late summer and early autumn. ttendance remains low through the winter, creasing as days lengthen and the temperaure rises. Most nests are under the eaves of ouses, or in some other cavity in a building. ome are in haystacks and more natural sites ch as crevices in cliffs or in thorny or dense hrubs like hawthorn. Usually, several pairs uild nests in a loose colony.

The song of a territorial male house arrow is a monotonous, repetitive 'chirrup', familiar noise to us all as he sits close to his hosen site, often adopting a squat, fluffed-up osture. Just as familiar is the sight of the male, perched on roof or guttering, wings rooped and shivering, soliciting the male's ttentions. Sometimes there is a communal isplay, which becomes more and more xcited, sometimes even out of hand, developg into a rough-and-tumble chase. Often a ngle female is the centre of attraction for veral males.

Eggs are laid from March through to ugust, with each pair attempting two or ree, sometimes four broods in a season. heir colours vary from off-white to dull rown, and all are flecked with rich brown. our or five is the usual number, but clutch zes range from two to seven. Incubation kes about 12 days, but the time is more ariable than in most birds. The young y after 11 to 18 days, depending on weather onditions and food supply.

The tree sparrow In many ways, the tree arrow can be considered as the house arrow's 'country cousin'. It is a slightly naller, more muscular looking bird, about

Above: A male house sparrow in full breeding plumage.

Below: A tree sparrow in full summer plumage (the sexes are alike). It differs from the male house sparrow in having a brown cap and nape, and a black cheek spot.

BLACK-AND-WHITE WAGTAILS

Pied wagtails are far commoner than the two other species of wagtails in Britain and Ireland. On almost any area of turf, shingle or rock, in towns or in the countryside, they can be seen hunting insects, with quick dashes, swerves and dramatic leaps into the air.

Above: A female pied wagtail at the entrance to her nest in a rock crevice. Unaided by the male, she builds the nest of mosses, grasses and dead leaves, and lines it with feathers or wool. Her clutch normally consists of five or six eggs, which are greyish-white and freckled with black or brown. She also undertakes most of the incubation, which lasts for two weeks; but she hands over responsibility for feeding the young to her mate when the time comes for her to lay again.

The pied wagtail is a familiar, lively and popular neighbour of man. Its bold black and white plumage, conspicuous habits and loud, distinctive 'chis-ick' call are easy to recognise and help to make it so well-known. It is surprisingly widespread, too: as widely distributed as any British bird, it breeds throughout our islands (but only occasionally on the Shetlands) and is thoroughly at home in city centres and on riversides, meadows, farms and seashore – in fact, almost anywhere except the open mountains and in woodland. One of its commonest vernacular names, water wagtail, is not as applicable as it might be, for it is not as closely associated with water as its relative, the grey wagtail. It is predominantly a bird of moist places, but not necessarily of the very margins of open water.

The pied wagtail is a truly British and Irish species, for its breeding range is virtually confined to these islands. It is replaced on the Continent, and as far north as Iceland, by the grey wagtail race referred to–somewhat confusingly–as the white wagtail. Birds belonging to this Continental race migrate through Britain in spring and autumn to and from their northern breeding areas, which are in northern Scandinavia and Iceland. Some occasionally stay to breed in Scotland and on the northern and western islands. These birds are noticeably whiter than our pied wagtails and in spring it is easy to distinguish them from the British race. In autumn the task is much more difficult, as the young of both races are very similar.

Chasing after a mate As April arrives each year, the wagtails prepare for another breeding season. Males begin to establish territories, and several of them may pursue a single female in erratic and excited chases, each displaying to her when on the ground by throwing back his head and displaying his bold black gorget (throat patch). The competition of courtship eventually results in a successful pairing; then the newly paired birds spend some days together strengthening the bond between them, and establishing their breeding territory and nesting site.

Pied wagtails nest in a wide variety of sites

wherever an adequate crevice will conceal the nest. As well as choosing holes in banks, ivy-covered trees or cliffs, they often favour man-made objects: farm machinery, outbuildings or woodstacks are common sites.

A partial migrant All wagtails are insect-eating birds, but only the yellow wagtail migrates completely to warmer latitudes when the British winter reduces the abundance of its food. The pied wagtail demonstrates an interesting half-way stage between migration and year-round residence.

The appearance of increasing numbers of pied wagtails on school playing fields, in town parks and sewage farms in August and September is evidence of the fact that at least part of the population is migratory. In the south of Britain young birds predominate among those that migrate, but from further north there is a greater percentage of adults. All these birds flying south from Britain are bound for south-west France and Iberia, as is shown by the recovery of ringed birds. Birds from the south of England tend to travel further than those of more northerly origin; some of the southern birds fly as far as Morocco.

The other part of the population remains in Britain, one of the few species of insectivorous birds to gamble on finding an adequate supply of insects through the winter months as an alternative to facing the hazards of a long two-way migration. Through the British winter, the pied wagtail's secret lies in the ever-replenishing supply of insects to be found at the edge of water. Individual birds establish themselves in a winter territory along a river bank (sometimes a lake or other stretch of water) and defend it resolutely against others of their kind.

They feed along a fixed route near the water edge, returning each time to the starting point by the time the waters of the river or lake have delivered another supply of tiny insects and other invertebrates. To share the territory with another bird would be self-defeating for

grey back of head ♀

black cap

White wagtail

light grey back

grey back may have an olive tinge

whitish grey flanks ♂

♀

Pied wagtail

black throat

black crown and back

lower breast white ♂

smoky grey flanks

Pied wagtail (*Motacilla alba yarrelli*); the British and Irish subspecies. Some individuals are resident and others are summer visitors. Length 18cm (7in).

White wagtail (*Motacilla alba alba*); the Continental subspecies, seen in Britain occasionally as a passage migrant.

Right: The white wagtail is similar in appearance to the female of the pied wagtail, but its back is a lighter shade of grey.

Below: A female pied wagtail stands on a log in a typical jaunty attitude. Pied wagtails forage energetically, running jerkily on short turf, shingle or rock. With tails flicking non-stop, they make rapid dashes and swerves to catch their insect prey. Sometimes they leap into the air in dancing flight, to catch insects on the wing.

both, and would tip the balance between survival and failure. Defence of the territory is therefore crucially important.

Communal roosts At most times of the year outside the breeding season (except when winter is at its severest), pied wagtails roost communally, normally choosing reedbeds, scrub or bushes. An interesting development of this has been an increasingly common adaptation to the urban environment – roosting on buildings and trees in city centres. Here the winter temperature can be a little higher than in the open countryside.

In a further adaptation to man's presence, they have been recorded as roosting in commercial glasshouses, sometimes in large numbers. Heated glasshouses obviously have enhanced survival value for them in cold winter months, and may also be thought of as giving security from predators. On the other hand, however, little owls and cats have sometimes discovered these roosts, and as there is small chance of escape the results can be disastrous.

GARDEN VISITING GREENFINCHES

The greenfinch is the largest of a trio of British finches with partly green plumage (the others are the siskin and the rare serin). It is one of our more numerous birds, being well suited to our lowland countryside with its mosaic-like pattern of woods, farmland, hedgerows, thickets and gardens.

Above: A pair of greenfinches (the male is on the right) with four young. In the past, these birds were often caught and caged—such birds used to be called 'green linnets'.

Below: A male greenfinch (right) with a juvenile (left) at water. The juveniles are much less highly coloured than the adults. Many have brown streaks on their plumage, like sparrows.

The greenfinch is one of the most widespread and abundant visitors to bird-tables in Britain and Ireland. It is sometimes disparaged by birdwatchers who are captivated by the acrobatic feats of the blue and great tits as they hang on to strings of nuts. The greenfinch, being a relatively large finch, is not a particularly acrobatic feeder although, in many areas, it has learned to feed on hanging nuts. Some people actually overlook its presence since it is similar in size to the ubiquitous house sparrow, and many greenfinches have rather little yellow or green on their plumage, which strengthens the resemblance.

The adult male greenfinch is a handsome bird, with brilliant yellow flashes on the wings and tail—most obvious when in flight—and washes of green and greenish yellow over the rest of the plumage. The females, and the young of either sex, are less highly coloured, with much brown streaked plumage—like a sparrow's. (In recent years another much smaller finch, the siskin, has also taken to

feeding in gardens, mostly at the end of winter, but there is little chance of the two being confused.)

Habitat and range As with many of our garden and farmland bird species, greenfinches are naturally birds of the woodland edge, finding hedges in arable land, and shrubberies in parks and gardens, ideal places for breeding. They can be found over most of Europe, spreading into Asia in the east and to north Africa in the south, but they are absent from the far northern parts of Europe and Asia, which lack trees or shrubs. Many areas in Britain have reported recent spreads in the breeding range and local increases in numbers.

Seed eaters Greenfinches feed on seeds for almost all their lives. In the autumn the flocks of young birds, which are soon joined by the adults, may become very numerous, with some numbering in the thousands. These large flocks are sometimes seen feeding on ripening corn, gleaning the stubbles or feasting on weed seeds in root crops or on waste ground. Their weight generally precludes feeding from seeds still held on the plants, but they are adept at finding seeds on the ground. They can live well on open ploughed land, finding dormant seeds which may, in some cases, be several years old.

The weeds particularly favoured include charlock, persicaria, groundsel, chickweed and fat hen. When a large flock has found a good feeding site, it is quite possible to hear the birds from thirty or forty yards away – not from their calls but from the cracking of seeds in their bills. All the food is first manoeuvred in the bird's beak to remove the husk, for greenfinches only eat the central nutritious part.

Autumn and winter The autumn flocks frequently contain other finch species, but during the evening the greenfinches tend to roost on their own. The roosting site is often a clump of rhododendrons, laurels or an old hedge with plenty of holly or ivy. The birds prefer roosting sites which are not particularly high, but have plenty of thick cover. Ringing results have shown that the birds move regularly from roost to roost and that, in general, they are a mobile and 'nomadic' species. There are not many indications of movements over 200 or 300km (120-180 miles) within the British population, but many birds from the northern part of the European range travel 1000km (600 miles) or more each autumn and spring.

Cold winter weather is not a serious threat to survival – provided that the feeding grounds are clear of snow. If the weather is very cold and the day-length is very short, they may find it difficult to take in sufficient food to see them through the night. In such circumstance, and during snowy weather, many more may join the flocks feeding in gardens.

Human help Greenfinches visiting gardens take almost any sort of seed. Hemp, peanuts (loose on the ground or hanging) and par-

olive green head and back

yellow tail flashes

♂

yellow edges of primaries

summer plumage

brownish green head and back

♀

wing and tail markings are less vivid than in male

grey wings with yellow flashes

yellow underparts

♂

ticularly sunflower seeds are favourites. As with many species observed at feeding stations, the numbers seen at any instant in a garden are a tiny proportion of all the individual birds using the site through the whole winter.

As many garden bird feeders know, the number of greenfinches seen in gardens reaches a peak in March and April, and many are still present in early May. Ringing returns show that this is the period when more greenfinches die in the wild than at any other time of year. This is easily explained, for the birds have been exploiting a stock of seeds which has not been replenished naturally since the autumn. The food supply has thus

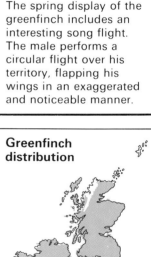

The song flight

conspicuously beating wings

The spring display of the greenfinch includes an interesting song flight. The male performs a circular flight over his territory, flapping his wings in an exaggerated and noticeable manner.

Greenfinch distribution

Greenfinch (*Carduelis chloris*). Resident in Britain and Ireland; partial migrant on the Continent. Habitats include woodland edges, gardens, shrubberies and farmland. 14.5cm (5¾in).

Left: Nesting begins in late April or early May. With six eggs, this is a good clutch for greenfinches; many have only four.

Above: A male greenfinch in flight. The two flight (and contact) calls are 'chup, chup, chup' and 'chit-chit-chit-chit-chit'. When the bird is seen in flight the yellow wing patches and tail edges are conspicuous.

Below: A greenfinch bathing in a stream. Note the stout body (even allowing for the fluffed-out feathers) and the clear pink beak.

run out, and continued feeding—by people who put out food for birds in their gardens—is particularly important.

The breeding season During the spring, the males start to give their 'dreeeez' summer call. When displaying, they precede this by a rather weak, chattering song. Displaying males may sing and call from the top of a tree or bush, or may advertise their presence in a characteristic song-flight. In most cases several pairs take up territories close together, each male defending only a small area round the chosen nest site.

The nest is built of twigs, roots and moss in late April or early May, and is lined with fine grass, roots, hair, wool or feathers. Four to

six eggs are generally laid in each clutch and incubated for two weeks. The chicks are fed on insects for the first few days, but soon the diet is changed to regurgitated seeds. Two or three broods are often raised by a single pair, and young may sometimes be found in the nest as late as September.

Countless hazards In ideal conditions, the two or three broods raised by a single pair of greenfinches could be expected to produce a total of about 20 birds where there had been only two at the beginning. Nature is not in fact so profligate, for although a highly successful pair may be able to produce three large broods, the great majority of breeding attempts actually fail.

Failure arises in many ways—lack of food may cause starvation, one of the adults may die or be killed, or a predator may find the nest and eat the eggs or young. Apart from these dangers, the eggs might be infertile, the nest may be blown out of its bush or the bush may be destroyed during agricultural or gardening work.

In any case, the production of eggs and the successful fledging of young is not the end of the parents' responsibility, for they also have to look after the young birds, out of the nest for a period of ten days or more, while they learn about the world and how to find food for themselves.

Resilient population Besides all the difficulties that they have to face at breeding time, greenfinches are affected by wide variations in winter weather conditions from year to year. Despite this, the British breeding population, as shown by the Common Birds Census farmland index, has remained constant over the last 25 years. The two cold winters in 1961-62 and 1962-63 probably halved the population, but it had returned to an average level by 1966.

Since then it has varied by less than 10% either way, except in 1975 when it was rather higher than normal. These figures are based on observations made on farmland—probably the habitat holding the most stable populations. The figures relating to woodland are based on a smaller sample and show a rather greater fluctuation. The highest woodland population they indicated was in 1966.

The prospects for this attractive bird look excellent, with range expansions being reported during the present century. These have occurred in western areas, where the birds were formerly absent, and also in city centre areas. The most serious problem which they are likely to face arises from the increasing use of herbicides in cereal growing and other farming. If the trend continues, the range of species of weeds which are able to seed and thus produce natural winter feeding for the birds may be reduced. On current evidence, it seems likely that human bird-lovers will more than make up for the deficiency, with the plentiful supplies of seeds and peanuts that they put out for the birds in their gardens.

SWIFTS ON THE WING

Swifts spend their lives in the air – feeding, sleeping and even mating on the wing. Once fledged, they do not set foot on the ground – not even on a perch – for two years or even more.

The swift is the most aerial of our birds. Every aspect of its anatomy and biology underlines its commitment to this mode of life. The swift rarely breeds until it is at least two years old, and entering its nest hole is its first contact with anything solid since it fledged. If a swift is accidentally grounded, its legs are so short and its wings so long, that the bird has little chance of getting airborne again.

Wing design The most obvious outward indication of specialisation is the wings – slender, sickle-shaped and extremely long. Much of this length comes from the unusually long primary feathers – the outer section of the wing.

The primary feathers provide the forward power for flight and – in most birds – are roughly equal in length to the secondary feathers which produce aerodynamic lift. But the swift's extra long primaries give greater power and make it one of the fastest birds, capable of speeds of over 60mph and perhaps even twice this in dives or if pursued by a falcon such as hobby.

Aerodynamics The streamlined body is shaped like a torpedo, with a blunt, rounded head and a body gradually tapering to a short, forked, tail. You might expect the bird to have a slender pointed head which would penetrate the air better, instead of the blunt front that appears to act as a buffer against the wind current. But the swift's shape is actually in perfect agreement with the engineering principles involved. The tapered rear end reduces the turbulent eddies of air *behind* the bird which would otherwise create a partial vacuum, or 'drag', and so slow the swift down.

The swift has few body projections interfering with airflow: the feet are tiny, and tucked into the feathers; the visible part of the beak is pointed, and extremely small; and the eyes, though large, are deep-set in slots – similar to the headlights of a sports car which are recessed in the smooth fibreglass body shell. The swift's body feathers serve a similar function in producing an unimpeded airflow over the body.

High-flyers In flight, swifts are capable of climbing up to 3000m (10,000ft). At these great heights they seem to spiral on set wing positions, certainly for long enough to obtain the necessary 'catnaps' of sleep. Sometimes swifts ascend to such altitudes in pursuit of their insect prey. They are highly specialised feeders, taking only flying insects and spiders drifting on gossamer-thin threads.

Behind the minute beak lies an enormous gape: the mouth literally opens from ear to ear, and when wide open occupies a large proportion of the front of the bird. The swift is ideally adapted to effective feeding on the wing, sweeping back and forth through the air, with its mouth gaping open, collecting small insects ('aerial plankton'), in much the way a whale scoops plankton from the sea.

Above: The swift grips on to brickwork, aided by four needle-sharp claws (below) which all point forwards. Its legs and feet, though small in proportion to the rest of its body, are very muscular.

Where to watch them One of the best places to watch swifts is over reservoirs in early summer as they feed on insects. Another good viewing site is marshland–here, using high speed passes, the swift catches the myriad midges that dance in smoke-like columns. In summer, insect abundance is controlled by the weather. In long, cool, rainy periods flying insects can become scarce, and in fine spells they may be at a great height, often accumulating at the junction of cold and warm air fronts.

Radar tracking Mobile and speedy, swifts may travel hundreds of kilometres daily in search of food. Striking evidence of this is provided by some remarkable film (taken by Marconi Ltd) of a radar screen in south east England. Many birds, swifts included, are large enough to leave a blip or 'echo' on modern radar; this spectacular film – covering a summer afternoon and the following night – shows the radar screen covered by a mass of blips caused by London swifts rising high into the sky at dusk. The blips show a rapid movement north to the Wash, where the birds congregated. Here they fed on the insects massing at a cold/warm front junction over the North Sea, before returning to their nests in the city.

Acclimatised young Nestling swifts are as well-adapted as their parents to the vagaries of the British summer which affect their food supply. Since their food is so specialised, they are more vulnerable than most young birds to shortages which may last several days. The young swifts have a survival mechanism that allows them to go gradually into a torpor – a sort of short-term hibernation.

Their body temperature falls, pulse and breathing rates are reduced to a minimum and growth ceases. The nestlings survive on a tick-over metabolism (using as energy their stored body fat), in a way not possible in

long primary feathers

sickle-shaped wi

short forked ta

Above: With long slender wings and body built to much the same design as high-speed, high altitude reconnaissance aircraft, swifts have difficulty manoeuvring in confined spaces. You can distinguish swifts from martins and swallows which have much lighter bellies when viewed from below.

Right: In common with many other birds that nest in dark cavities, the swift's eggs are white and rather spherical. In a new site the nest may be composed of no more than a few bits of mortar arranged in a rough circle.

Below: Occasionally both adults roost in the nest hole, sharing the cramped quarters with the eggs or, more uncomfortably, with well grown young.

other birds. With the return of better weather, and a restoration of food supplies, the body temperature rises again, the nestlings become active and normal growth is resumed.

Mid-air mating 'Screaming parties' of adult swifts are a common sight in many towns and villages throughout the summer. Gangs of birds, all uttering their high-pitched call, whistle through the air on rapidly flickering wings. They seem to have narrow escapes with traffic and overhead wires, but in reality they are well in control of their manoeuvres. Following such mass displays, you may see the birds mating – the male alighting gently on the female's back while both are in mid-air. The birds may glide briefly on wings upheld in a narrow 'V' while actually mating. The pair then break apart and resume normal flight.

Nest sites In the British Isles swifts now nest under the eaves of houses in the older parts of towns and cities. In the past they may have depended on natural cavities in cliffs and caves, perhaps even trees. Related species in other parts of the world still nest in trees.

Swifts have benefited from the expansion of human populations which have provided more nesting sites. But this must be set against the adverse effects of aerial pollution – particularly sulphur dioxide – on their food supply. Moreover, modern houses and blocks of flats have smoother outlines which are not suitable for nest holes or for the swift's

method of getting in and out. The bird approaches its nest entrance from below, landing briefly on the rim and scuttling in, and leaves by simply dropping out of the entrance and flying off. The nest hole usually faces downwards.

The nest itself is a spartan affair inside the roof of the building. As the birds cannot gather nesting material from the ground or trees, they rely on bits and pieces scattered about on roofs. They shuffle these loosely together using liberal quantities of droppings. They may even line the nest with a few feathers caught in mid-air.

There are usually one or two (sometimes three or four) dull white and rather rounded eggs. The parents share a 20-day incubation period and the young take five to eight weeks to fledge, depending on the weather. The short stay of the swift in Britain allows no time for more than one brood.

Travelling abroad Most swifts leave the British Isles in August for their winter quarters in the central regions of Africa. They do not return until mid-May. Despite their highly specialised and apparently risky lifestyle, the results of intensive ringing studies show that swifts are successful birds. Many may live for ten years or more – unusually long for a small bird. At a rough calculation, the oldest swift on record, at 16 years, may have exceeded four million flying miles in its lifetime.

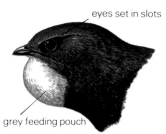
eyes set in slots

grey feeding pouch

Above: The adults catch food for their young by gathering 'aerial plankton' which they hold in their throats. This creates a 'food ball' that often exceeds 1cm ($\frac{1}{2}$in) in diameter, and produces a conspicuous, bulging grey patch – the only relief to the swift's sooty plumage.

Swift (*Apus apus*), 16.5cm ($6\frac{1}{2}$in) from beak to tail. Distribution throughout the British Isles, though scarcer the further north they go. Summer visitor.

Flight silhouettes

Flight silhouettes are useful indicators of a bird's way of life, and a great help when it comes to identifying unfamiliar birds in the countryside.

Swift, hobby The swift's silhouette shows an adaptation to fast flight. Though unrelated to the swift, the swallow, sand and house martins have similar silhouettes. This is due to 'parallel evolution', by which two unrelated groups arrive at the same evolutionary solution to their problem. The best example of design for speed is the hobby, a falcon that can outfly even these birds, and in fact specialises in feeding on them.

Hoopoe, grey partridge At the other end of the scale from speed is manoeuvrability. This makes opposing demands on wing design, and the hoopoe, with broad rounded wings with 'fingered' ends, is an excellent example of an agile bird able to twist in and out of the trees. The partridge has a similar pattern to give high lifting power, and an instant take-off to escape predators.

Greenfinch Most small birds, such as the greenfinch, fly between these two scales – not exceptionally fast nor exceptionally mobile, but just as successful in their less specialised habits.

Razorbill Other specialists include those seabirds – particularly the auks – that spend a lot of time hunting fish beneath the sea surface. Their short, stiffened wings give poor flying ability, but excellent underwater propulsion – like a penguin's flipper.

Buzzard, Manx shearwater You can see energy-saving designs in the buzzard soaring at high altitudes on thermal upcurrents, using broad wings and a broad rounded tail. In contrast the Manx shearwater uses its long, narrow, rigidly held wings to glide swiftly at low level. Shearwaters are adept at exploiting sea winds and upcurrents close to the waves.

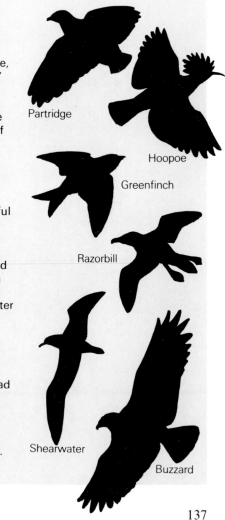
Partridge
Hoopoe
Greenfinch
Razorbill
Shearwater
Buzzard

Swift
Hobby
Sand martin
Swallow
House martin

SWOOPING HOUSE MARTINS

House martins, among the most aerial of all our birds, feed and even roost on the wing, coming down to earth only to collect mud for their nests.

The house martin is a familiar summer visitor to nearly all parts of Britain and Ireland. It is an almost entirely aerial species and is often confused with its close relative, the swallow. However, house martins' tails are more shallowly forked than those of swallows, and house martins also lack the chestnut colour seen on swallows. The crucial field mark of the house martin is the white patch on the rump, which is very prominent when the bird is flying. The sand martin, our third member of the hirundine family, is brown, in contrast to the metallic blue of the house martin. (The swift, though superficially similar to the hirundines, is much larger and lacks the white rump: also, it has an even smoother, narrower 'sickle' shape in flight than any of the hirundines.)

Both the swallow and the house martin build nests of mud, plastered on to the walls of buildings or the ends of rafters. The structure of these two birds' nests is quite different, however. The swallow's nest is a simple cup, generally placed inside a building rather than on the outside. The house martin produces a rather more elaborate structure, generally on the outside of a building: when complete, this forms an almost complete quarter globe with a narrow slit entrance on the outside top edge.

Spring arrival The first sightings of house martins each spring generally occur in early April, but most birds do not arrive until the end of this month, or early May. Stragglers continue to appear until the end of May and even during June. They are therefore later in arriving than both sand martins and swallows, but a little earlier, on average, than swifts. The first migrants search out areas where food is in good supply, and often congregate around the shores of lakes or reservoirs, for there they are able to find newly hatched insects.

The house martin's flight is not as acrobatic as that of the swallow, nor as direct and speedy as that of the swift. House martins are frequently seen hawking very high in the sky, but if the weather is cold they fly very low in the shelter of a hedge or bank. Because of their startling white rumps they are often much more conspicuous under such circumstances than the other hirundines and the swifts, all of which often feed together with them. A wide variety of aerial insects are taken, as are many species of gossamer spiders floating about in the air on threads of silk.

Mud collectors In order to build their nests, house martins must abandon their aerial life temporarily and come down to the ground to collect mud. Here they are not very agile, and walk with a pronounced 'waddle'. The mud may be gathered from the fringes of a pond, a muddy gateway or, most often, from a

Above: House martins start their nests about 7cm (3in) below the eaves and build steadily upwards. A nail in the wall is a useful keying point from which to start.

Opposite page: A multitude of house martins roosting on telephone wires before migration. They are smaller than swallows, with whiter undersides.

House martin distribution

Left: House martins are not timid and often allow a close approach, particularly if you are in a car and they are collecting mud from a roadside puddle. Seeing them at close quarters, you can appreciate the fascinating tiny white feathers that cover their legs. If dry weather removes the supply of mud, some people do the house martins a kindness by leaving out a bowl full of a mixture of earth and water.

Above: A crowd of young house martins on telephone wires: their plumage is more mottled than that of adults. Being aerial birds, their instinctive reaction to any approaching danger is to escape into the open sky, where their speed and endurance serve them best. The wires are a perfect aerial perch, giving them a clear view all round and an easy launch into fast flight.

Left: The nest, made of many hundreds of beakfuls of mud, forms a neat quarter globe. The entrance is a slit at the top.

Bottom right: This cliff colony of house martins is one of the few instances where the birds manage to nest successfully without resorting to house walls. The birds here are sunning themselves; their nests are in holes within the cliff.

Below: House martins waddle on very short legs when walking on the ground to collect mud.

roadside puddle. In really dry weather nest building may be held up for weeks through lack of mud, and birds may have to fly long distances to fetch it.

Observations of nest-building house martins have shown that it takes the birds roughly a fortnight to complete a nest. Many blobs of mud tend to be lost at the very start, in the process of keying the nest to the wall. Often the birds use a nail in the wall, a gutter bracket or a window hinge as a support. The complete nest may contain roughly 500cc (30 cu in) of mud, comprising more than 2500 beakfuls. The bare mud is then lined with feathers, grasses and straw. Much of the lining material is caught in the air, but some is picked up off the ground.

The brood in the nest The female lays a clutch of four or five white eggs, which are incubated, with the help of the male, for about two weeks. The young are fed in the nest, by both parents, for 18 or 19 days before they fledge. Most pairs are able to rear two broods, and three broods are not uncommon. The young from the first clutch often help their parents to feed later young, and the whole of this extended family may live crammed into one nest. There have been records of 13 birds living together in this way. Alternatively, a new nest may be constructed as a dormitory for the fledged young.

Man's dependant? In recent years, house martins have been recorded breeding much nearer the centres of many British cities than before. This is a measure of the success which the various Clean Air Acts have been able to achieve. Earlier this century, so much smoke was emitted that there were few if any of the insects needed by house martins in inner city areas.

Going back further in the history of the species, it is interesting to speculate how many (or how few) pairs of house martins there may have been in Britain and Ireland before man built dwellings on a large scale. There are certainly a handful of natural house martin colonies on coastal cliffs, in quarries and along river banks, but over 99% of all British breeding pairs now nest on buildings.

Feeding flocks of house martins

House martin (*Delichon urbica*). Aerial bird making an elaborate mud nest, usually on walls. Summer visitor. Sexes are alike. Length 12.5cm (5in).

'plump' body shape

forked tail

pure white underside of body

dark brown underwing

slender wing adapted for fast flight

dark blue upperparts appear black

white rump

long flight feathers make a 'sickle' shape

insects hovering over water

insects carried by wind

reservoir

birds fly back and forth catching insects

insects caught in circulating air currents

hedge

In cold weather birds very often hunt for insects near water. If there is a fairly strong wind, the newly hatched insects are blown downwind and, if there is a convenient patch of relatively still air, their numbers become concentrated. Here the birds can feed much more efficiently than they can in the open. Insect numbers in the sheltered air beside the hedge are augmented by those blown off the reservoir. Here house martins (as well as swifts and swallows) often feed.

Quite apart from nesting sites on the walls of houses, man provides the birds with two useful kinds of perches. Telephone wires are an ideal perch for such a truly aerial species, for they allow a good look-out in all directions, and also an unimpeded take-off. Small song birds react to a predator's arrival by dashing for cover, but the house martin needs the freedom of the sky.

The other man-made luxury is provided by houses whose roofs face both south-east and towards the rising sun. They absorb the early morning heat and, thus warmed, attract hundreds of sunning house martins.

Autumn departure Like other aerial feeders, house martins are forced to migrate from Britain and Ireland by the cold weather of the winter, which denies them sufficient insect food. The first movement of autumn passage birds through Britain is seen in August. Some roost in unoccupied nests at colonies which they pass, but it is almost certain that most of them roost on the wing—while their flight muscles are active, much of the rest of the bird is at rest. By September, large gatherings of house martins are seen on telephone wires and south-facing tile roofs. These continue to form until October in mild years, for some adults are still able to raise and feed late broods even in autumn.

Rather little is known about the house martins' migration routes, for few have been found abroad with rings from Britain or Ireland. The early stage of the journey, through Europe, is routed through France and (in general) Spain, later reaching North Africa. There are no records of British house martins south of the Sahara, but Continental birds reach tropical West Africa and may possibly fly even further south. In their wintering habitat, not being dependent on houses for nesting, the birds are less frequently in contact with man than in the breeding season. This is the principal reason for our lack of knowledge about this stage of the house martin's life.

ACROBATIC BLUE AND GREAT TITS

The colourful, agile little blue and great tits which frequent our gardens in winter are a delight to watch as they cluster round a bag of peanuts.

Blue and great tits, both colloquially known as tomtits, are popular garden birds which visit bird tables regularly in winter. Both are widespread throughout the British Isles and you'll see them in deciduous woodland, scrubland, hedgerows and farmland everywhere. The blue tit is an agile, aggressive, always excitedly active little bird which specialises in hanging at awkward angles to feed, while the great tit, larger than the blue and twice as heavy, often prefers to feed on the ground like a finch. Male and female blue tits are very similar in appearance. Among great tits a distinguishing feature between male and female is the black line which runs down the centre of their primrose-yellow breasts. This is faint in the female but very bold and wide in the male.

Seasonal foraging In summer blue tits feed mainly on insects, searching for them at the tips of twigs and shoots. In winter this diet is supplemented with occasional nuts and seeds. Since insects are neither active nor easily visible in winter, blue tits have to spend considerable time peering and probing round buds and under flakes of bark to find hibernating adults and larvae. If you observe the apparently aimless acrobatics of a blue tit through binoculars, you'll see that it is in fact purposefully searching every potentially rewarding nook and cranny.

In the garden the boldness and agility of blue tits as they attack peanuts hung in a plastic mesh sock is a delight to watch. They feed on almost everything put out on a bird table except bird seed, but above all they prefer nuts and fat.

Great tits eat much the same food as the blue, but take more vegetable food in winter – particularly seeds and nuts which have fallen to the ground.

Feeding for breeding The breeding season for great tits begins in late March and for blue tits in early April. To get into peak condition for egg laying as early as possible – earlier broods tend to be larger and healthier than later ones – the female must eat prodigiously. In the three weeks before laying begins, she puts on weight at an extraordinary rate, increasing her normal weight by at least a half and sometimes more. Then, over 10 or 12 days, she produces almost her own weight in eggs, laying one each day. This remarkable feat cannot be achieved by the female unaided; the male must feed her. You may well see a pair of tits side by side on a branch, the male offering his mate a beakful of caterpillars which she accepts with rapidly fluttering wings. This behaviour – called courtship feeding – may be essential if breeding is to be successful.

The female tit does all the nest-building, choosing a hole or crevice in a wall, tree or garden nestbox. The nest – a cup of moss, grass, wool, leaves, roots and spiders' webs – is lined with hair or feathers.

All eggs in one basket In summer, in deciduous woodland, both great and blue tits often rely heavily on just one species of insect as food for themselves and their young. In oak woods this is the winter moth which frequently produces huge numbers of caterpillars. The parent birds need to synchronise the maximum food demands of their young with the single, short-lived peak in the caterpillar food supply. They therefore produce a single large brood each year. This is unlike most other small birds which rear two or even three broods a year and thus have two or three chances if anything goes wrong. It is almost literally a case of the tits putting all their eggs in one basket!

great tit

Great tit *(Parus major)*; 14cm (5½in); widespread; resident.

blue tit

blue tit

Blue tit *(Parus caeruleus)*; 11cm (4½in); widespread; resident.

Left: A glossy black crown and white cheeks clearly identify the great tit.

Left: Tit attacks on milk bottles, first reported as isolated incidents in the 1930s, are now common all over the British Isles.

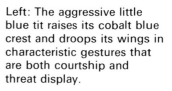

Above: Peanuts, which have high nutritional value, are a favourite food of garden-visiting tits.

Left: The aggressive little blue tit raises its cobalt blue crest and droops its wings in characteristic gestures that are both courtship and threat display.

One in ten survive In spring each breeding pair of tits is generally composed of one adult bird which bred the year before and is at least 21 months old, and one young bird which is about nine months old and breeding for the first time. One half of each breeding pair dies each year. For the population to remain steady, only one youngster would need to be reared per pair to replace the dead adult. On average, however, ten youngsters leave each nest in summer. This means that nine die by the following spring – a staggering 90% mortality rate. Gruesome though it sounds, this is an insurance against catastrophe and is quite usual in the bird world. Indeed, if one extra youngster per brood were to survive each year, the whole countryside would soon be overrun by hordes of tits eating up all available resources and precipitating a disastrous drop in the population.

Plenty of predators The high mortality rate is largely the result of natural causes, especially starvation, since inexperienced young birds have difficulty finding enough food in winter. Also, at the start of the season, competition for nesting holes is fierce. Larger birds such as the starling may oust tits from the bigger holes, and tit may oust tit from smaller ones. The larger great tit does not always succeed in evicting the smaller but more aggressive blue. Tree sparrows can squeeze through an entrance apparently only

Above: A parent blue tit bringing a caterpillar to its young. The nest is only relatively secure from predators. Weasels and woodpeckers take a large toll of eggs and young chicks every year.

Left: A clutch of great tit eggs. The blue tit's eggs are slightly smaller but very similar in colour. In both species the female incubates the eggs by herself for 12-16 days, often fed by the male while she is sitting on the nest.

Right: A brood of blue tit chicks in their down and feather-lined nest. The youngsters are fed by both parents and fledge in about 15-23 days.

just large enough for a blue tit, and often build their untidy nest on top of a clutch of tit eggs or, as tree sparrows are late nesters, even on top of a flourishing brood of chicks.

Predators also play a significant part in the high mortality rate, and may account for a third or more of the deaths. Great spotted woodpeckers have a taste for tit eggs and young and can easily open up a nest hole with their strong beak. Woodpeckers capitalize on the fact that well-grown tit chicks are alerted by a shadow falling across their nest hole and jump up to the entrance to grab the expected food from a returning parent. As soon as the unfortunate chicks appear, the woodpecker catches them. In the early days after fledging, the inexperienced youngsters may fall easy victims to hunting sparrow-hawks.

Strangely enough, wood mice and some-times voles climb trees readily and enjoy any eggs they happen to find. The prime predatory mammal, however, is the weasel, which can squeeze through the nest hole without much difficulty. Often the weasel will gorge on young birds to such an extent that it has to sleep off the meal until it slims down enough to squeeze out again. Weasel predation is particularly high in summers when the weather is poor and the young tits are underfed. The hungry chicks squeak noisily for more food and are heard by patrolling weasels on the look-out for prey.

Irruptions The general trend in tit numbers is more or less steady, but there are some fluctuations from year to year. Often, after a series of good summers and mild winters (especially on the Continent), mortality is lower than usual and consequently tit num-bers far higher than average. In this situation, the sudden onset of a severe winter, or a shortage of natural food, produces a massive westward movement—called an irruption—as hungry birds move about in search of food. When these hordes cross the Channel, autumn numbers in the eastern counties of England reach spectacular levels. Strange reports sometimes appear of tits eating the putty round window frames and even entering houses and tearing strips of wallpaper off

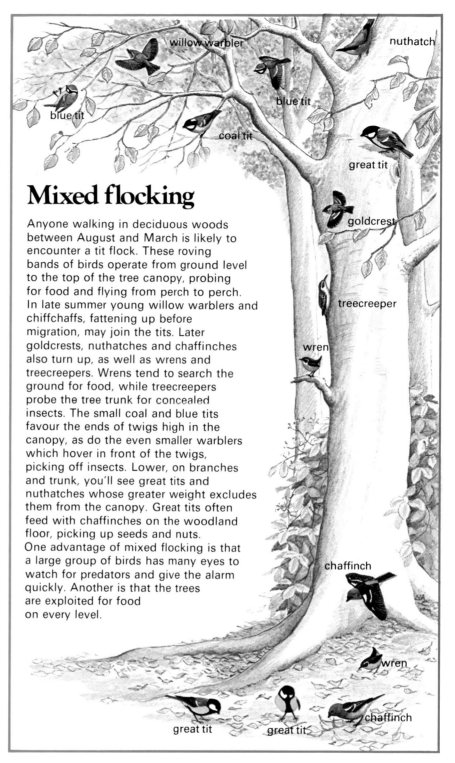

Mixed flocking

Anyone walking in deciduous woods between August and March is likely to encounter a tit flock. These roving bands of birds operate from ground level to the top of the tree canopy, probing for food and flying from perch to perch. In late summer young willow warblers and chiffchaffs, fattening up before migration, may join the tits. Later goldcrests, nuthatches and chaffinches also turn up, as well as wrens and treecreepers. Wrens tend to search the ground for food, while treecreepers probe the tree trunk for concealed insects. The small coal and blue tits favour the ends of twigs high in the canopy, as do the even smaller warblers which hover in front of the twigs, picking off insects. Lower, on branches and trunk, you'll see great tits and nuthatches whose greater weight excludes them from the canopy. Great tits often feed with chaffinches on the woodland floor, picking up seeds and nuts. One advantage of mixed flocking is that a large group of birds has many eyes to watch for predators and give the alarm quickly. Another is that the trees are exploited for food on every level.

the walls. Irruptions occur irregularly, per-haps only once a decade.

Ringing results show that most of the birds in an irruption are of Continental origin, coming from as far away as eastern Poland. Winters in mainland Europe are generally more severe than in much of Britain and Ireland, so Continental blue and great tits migrate south and west in autumn to escape climatic hardship and to find easier feeding. British birds, on the other hand, tend to stay close to home, and, although they may roam around several parishes, rarely make journeys of more than 30 miles. Many establish a circuit of known good feeding spots and visit each in turn.

THE BLACKBIRD: A JAUNTY SONGSTER

The blackbird–one of the most familiar and best loved of our garden birds–is often regarded as uninteresting because of its very familiarity. In fact, because it is so easy to study, more is known of its life-style than of almost any other bird.

Above: A male blackbird with jet black plumage and bright orange bill. This bird is easily recognisable by its jaunty, hopping gait and also by its habit of standing with head cocked to one side, listening for worms underground. The melodious, fluting song of the blackbird–the one heard most often in our dawn choruses–is also easily identifiable. The blackbird has a danger note as well –a harsh, persistent 'pink-pink-pink-pink' call.

The blackbird, a bird familiar to everyone, is a successful and adaptable species whose natural habitats, before man started to make his mark on the British countryside several thousand years ago, were woodland edges and natural clearings. Now it not only frequents gardens in town and countryside but also most of the hedges over the millions of acres of British farmland.

The blackbird's very numbers allow it to be studied in much greater detail than most species; thousands are ringed each year and nest-recorders are able to find and record nests in great quantities.

Male, female and juvenile The adult male is quite literally a 'black bird', with a wholly black plumage relieved only by a bright orange bill and an orange eye-ring. The younger males, hatched the previous summer retain their old flight feathers and some wing coverts, giving their wings a peculiar 'patch work' effect where the old brown juvenile feathers contrast with the newer ones grown during the post-juvenile moult in their first autumn. The females are much browner, with a pale throat and speckling on the breast. Juvenile birds of both sexes have rich brown centres to many of their body feathers, but these are retained only for a month or two.

Territorial song and combat The blackbird's year, in Britain, may be said to start in February when the singing males begin to define their territories for the coming breeding season. This is not only accomplished through the exceptionally melodious medium of their song–used by the birds to announce their presence and continuing occupation of their territories–but also by physical displays.

These displays are particularly visible on a lawn, where two males may posture at each other for periods of ten or twenty minutes at a time. Often they never come to within a metre of each other but, just occasionally, physical warfare breaks out. Later in the season, when the adjacent males are both paired, such posturing (and even fights) may have extra protagonists–three or even four territories may meet on a lawn and the females may join in.

A long breeding season It often seems as if the blackbird breeding season extends from early April through to the end of May. This is indeed the time when they are at their most conspicuous, but many pairs already have a nest with eggs in the middle of March (or even earlier), and may continue with breeding attempts right through to July or even early August, provided the weather is suitable. Early broods are often quite successful for the predators, such as cats, jays, magpies and crows, which take such a toll on nests, are not yet active.

During April, when most species have started to nest, the blackbird's success is at its lowest (although clutch size is then at its highest); success is higher in May and June when there is plenty of cover for the birds to nest in.

The clutch of three to five (sometimes six) eggs is laid in a nest which, although it contains a layer of mud, is lined with grasses. The blackbird's eggs are a dull blue-green with reddish-brown speckling.

Incubation, carried out mainly by the female bird, lasts for about a fortnight from the laying of the penultimate egg, and the young are then fed–on worms and other animal food–at increasingly frequent intervals by both parents for two weeks before they fledge. This is their most vulnerable period for they are still unable to fly for up to 36 hours after fledging and are at the mercy of cats or any other predator able to withstand the brave and noisy attentions of the parent birds. The youngsters may be fed by their parents for a further three weeks–first by both and then later only by the male, as the female will already be sitting on her next clutch.

The annual moult At the end of the breeding season–which may be as early as mid-June in a dry year when the blackbirds are unable to find their food easily, or as late as mid-August in a wet summer–the adults undergo a complete moult to replace all their feathers. At the same time the partial moult of the juveniles takes place and, for a few weeks, the blackbirds, although still present, are not at all easy to see.

However, a little later they become much more conspicuous, particularly to anyone with an orchard and windfall apples or with ornamental shrubs bearing a good crop of berries. Although worms are readily taken at all times of the year, most of their food during the autumn and winter is fruit (where bird-table food is not being exploited).

Urban versus country populations Our own breeding blackbirds are mostly fairly sedentary, although ringing has shown some movement, particularly from northern and upland areas in winter. Indeed, it is certain that the majority of blackbirds hatched in Britain move no more than a kilometre or two from their natal territory throughout the whole of their lives. This has enabled detailed research to unravel the different pressures on different

Identifying the blackbird family

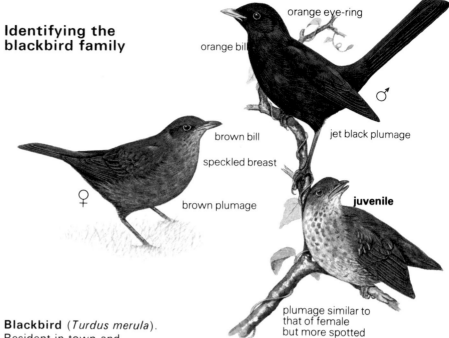

orange eye-ring

orange bill

brown bill

speckled breast

jet black plumage

♂

brown plumage

♀

juvenile

plumage similar to that of female but more spotted

Blackbird (*Turdus merula*). Resident in town and country gardens, hedgerows, woodland edges throughout the British Isles. 25cm (10in).

Right: An albino blackbird. This species seems to be prone to albinism, as many records show. The birds may be partially albino, with just a few white feathers here and there, or pure white, as here.

Below: A female blackbird sunbathing, with wings spread wide. Note the speckling on the breast. Blackbirds are one of the most common bird species of British gardens, on a par with the robin and the acrobatic blue tit.

Above: A juvenile blackbird –the body feathers of the young birds often have rich brown centres.

Left: A blackbird's nest (close to the ground) and the eggs. Unlike the nest of the song thrush (a close relative of the blackbird), which is just made of bare mud, this nest is lined with grasses. A clutch of three to five eggs is usual.

Below: A young blackbird in first-year plumage, with brown primary feathers.

populations of blackbirds.

In urban habitats it appears that adult blackbirds survive very well indeed–the food provided for them on bird-tables keeps them fit and healthy through even the coldest weather, and the experience of their first few years of life teaches them, as it does most urban birds, to avoid cats and cars. Their nests and eggs are, however, much more likely to be preyed upon or fail for other reasons and the few young that they raise have a difficult time surviving all the hazards of city life.

In the country, on the other hand, more young are produced by each breeding pair and they are able to survive better–which is just as well, for the overall adult mortality is higher in the country than it is in urban areas. This seems to be due largely to shortages of food during the winter–urban birds, which have access to more food, put on a greater amount of fat in hard weather to keep them going.

Since they are easy to observe, blackbirds are among the best species to keep notes on. For instance, if the birds in your garden are territorial, or possess distinguishing features, it is possible to list the feeding preferences of particular individuals.

Communal roosts During the winter, in particular, blackbirds spend their nights together in communal roosts. These are often at traditional sites and it has been shown that they choose areas which offer them shelter and safety from predators. The shelter enables them to conserve heat most efficiently, and gathering together in one roost may even serve the birds as an information exchange, so that those with sub-standard feeding sites are able to follow out those who know of the best feeding areas.

These roosting birds are not just the home-grown British population, for vast numbers of blackbirds from Germany, Denmark, Norway, Sweden, Poland and Finland come to Britain for the winter and join our own birds. Many British birds stay in their own home territories but, although some remain territorial, many tolerate visits from the foreign migrants. In the spring, when our own birds are just starting to breed and have already acquired their bright orange beaks, many of the migrants still sport their dull brown winter beak colour.

Albino blackbirds One feature of the blackbird species is that it is prone to albinism. There have been many records of pure white male blackbirds which still show the orange (or yellow) beak and eye-ring (and, in the albino, legs). Often the birds just show a few white feathers flecking the plumage, but this is sometimes neatly symmetrical and progressive–becoming more and more apparent year after year. The whiteness does not seem to put the birds at such a disadvantage that they get caught by cats or other predators, however. In some areas the albinism is transmitted genetically within the population, and pockets of partially albino birds persist for several years.

STARLINGS: SAINTS OR SINNERS?

In both town and country the starling is so familiar that birdwatchers all too often ignore it. Yet, if it were as rare today as it used to be, its superb iridescent plumage would rank it as one of the most beautiful of British birds.

Starling (*Sturnus vulgaris*). Resident; numbers swell in winter with the arrival of Continental migrants. Very common in both rural and urban areas, forming large flocks. Length 22cm (8½in).

The starling is one of our most common birds. More than four million pairs breed in Britain every year, and in the winter they are joined by at least 30 million more individuals that migrate here from northern and eastern Europe. Yet, up until the middle of the last century, the starling was relatively uncom-mon in Britain. The rise in the British popula-tion is part of a general pattern throughout Europe in which starlings have increased in numbers and spread westwards.

Omnivorous eaters The reasons for this population increase are not completely under-stood but an important factor is the bird's ability to live on a wide variety of foods. Fruits, seeds, flying insects, caterpillars, grubs, earthworms and household waste are all eaten, although the amounts taken of these different foods vary with the season. In spring the starling's diet consists mainly of insects and their larvae; in summer fruits become important; by winter these are replaced with seeds. Throughout the year, however, animal foods remain an important source of protein.

Another reason for the starling's success is that, during the last century or so, large areas of Europe's indigenous forests have been cleared to create grassland for farming. Close-cropped grassland is the starling's favourite habitat and you can often see them probing

male
blue base
white-tipped
breast feathers

winter

summer

iridescent
plumage

male

winter

female
pink base

Above: Starlings are so familiar that their beautiful iridescent plumage is too often overlooked. In autumn they develop white-tipped feathers on the breast; these remain until spring when they grow new feathers. Males and females can be distinguished by their eyes—female eyes have a distinctive brown ring—and, during winter and spring, by the colour at the base of their bills.

juvenile

Right: Juveniles are grey-brown with white chins until summer, when they develop adult white-tipped plumage.

grass roots for invertebrates such as caterpillars, earthworms and leatherjackets (the larvae of craneflies and a serious agricultural pest).

During the breeding season starlings spend most of their feeding time in grassland but at other times of the year they spread out into new habitats—a necessity if they are to take full advantage of their omnivorous nature. Bushes, hedgerows and trees are visited by starlings for fruits such as cherries, elderberries and sloes; they also search stubble fields, newly sown cereal fields and farmyards for seeds.

Forming flocks People often ask how starlings gather so quickly and in such numbers when food is put out into a garden. Starlings have an excellent memory, especially when it comes to remembering places where food appears regularly and in abundance. These places are always under observation by at least one bird. When food appears, one starling flies down to investigate. If it begins to peck, then all the other starlings nearby recognise this as a sign of food and fly down to join in. Within a very short time a feeding flock has formed.

The formation of a flock for feeding is advantageous for the flock members in that they can feed much faster than when they are on their own. There are many more eyes on the look-out for predators such as cats and sparrowhawks. Against this, however, is

Right: A flock of starlings searching for food. The starling's remarkable increase in numbers during the last century is, in part, the result of its omnivorous habits. Its diet ranges from seeds and fruits to insects, grubs and earthworms, and includes household waste as well.

the problem that a flock can grow too big for the food source, with the result that bickering and fighting ensue.

The starlings' omnivorous diet means that, depending on what they are eating, a large flock can either inflict great damage or be of great benefit. The starlings' consumption of large numbers of leatherjackets is an obvious boon to the farmer but, on the other hand, they can devastate cherry orchards that are in fruit.

Roosting by the million As well as feeding in flocks, starlings also roost in flocks. Sometimes more than a million birds gather together in night roosts, attracting large numbers of predators. In places such as Trafalgar Square in London, huge flocks can be seen wheeling around and darkening the sky at dusk.

Quite why starlings roost in such numbers is not yet known, but the advantages must be considerable since they outweigh the attentions of predators. It may be that roosting presents a good opportunity for poorly fed birds to learn from their better-fed neighbours the location of good food supplies.

Nesting in letter boxes The starling's choice of nesting site shows again how well it takes advantage of opportunities presented by man. Its most typical nest site is a natural hole, usually in a tree but also in a cliff. However, any hole of the right size and situation will do: cavities in the roofs of houses and farm

Mimicry in birds

The starling's song is not particularly musical but it is remarkable for its mimicry. Sometimes it mimics phrases from the songs of neighbouring starlings, but it can also mimic the calls of other birds, including bullfinches, curlews, tawny owls and green woodpeckers. It can even imitate mammal noises—as well as inanimate sounds, such as telephones ringing.

Ornithologists have discovered that, with some species, if a male possesses a wide repertoire of songs it has a better chance of breeding successfully. This explains why starlings make such a variety of noises but not why they mimic 'foreign' sounds rather than create their own distinct sounds. That remains a mystery.

Starlings are closely related to those master-mimics, the mynah birds. Unlike the mynahs, however, starlings cannot imitate human speech. Mimicry is not confined to the starling family: parrots and jackdaws reproduce words, and many species imitate other birds.

buildings are especially popular, and on occasions it even nests in letter boxes.

The breeding season begins in April. The male chooses his nest site and starts to build the nest – a bulky affair of dried grasses decorated with fresh green vegetation and the petals of spring flowers. The breeding season is the only time of year when starlings are territorial. The male defends a small territory around his nest site, but other breeding pairs are tolerated only a few yards away.

Once the male has built his nest he tries to attract a female by flying inside the nest hole and singing. Once the male has a mate, she completes the nest, lining the cup with material that can range from fine grasses and feathers to string and cellophane.

Eggs and young Between three and six eggs may be laid, though the usual clutch is five. The eggs are small, about 3cm ($1\frac{1}{4}$in) long, and clear pale blue or blue-green with no markings. Incubation is carried out mostly by the female and takes about 11 days.

At first the young chicks are blind and without any feathering, save for a few tufts of down. But the chicks grow quickly since they are fed by both parents on a protein-rich diet of invertebrates; in the first 12 days their weight increases from 5g ($\frac{1}{6}$oz) to 60g (2oz). After the twelfth day they virtually cease to add weight, but their feathers begin to develop rapidly and by the time the chicks are 21 days old they are ready to leave the nest.

In most years the parents begin a second clutch of eggs. Between the first and second broods starlings often swap partners, the females moving on to join males at other nests, and the situation is further complicated by the fact that a few male starlings are polygamous, having two females occupying nearby nests.

Above. Large flocks of starlings gathering together to roost is a common sight in both the city and the countryside. Flocks can contain as many as a million individuals.

Right: A starling feeding its young. The chicks grow very quickly and leave the nest when they are about three weeks old, though they continue to follow the parents and beg food from them for a while afterwards.

Below: A typical clutch of starling eggs is five. Incubation takes about 11 days and is carried out mainly by the female. Starlings usually manage to raise two broods in a season.

BLACK-HEADED GULLS: LIVING OFF THE LAND

The black-headed gull—its head is in fact chocolate brown in summer and mainly white in winter—forms breeding colonies inland more often than on the coast. Thus it is so often seen that it appears to be our commonest gull, despite the fact that the kittiwake and the herring gull are both more numerous.

Above: Black-headed gulls leaving the colony briefly in a mass flight known as a 'dread'. This is thought to be a part of the process of mutual stimulation, which ensures synchronised egg-laying. This increases security, for the colony is at its most vulnerable when the chicks are young.

Below: A black-headed gull chick. Still unfledged, it is largely dependent on its parents.

Since the beginning of this century, the black-headed gull has increasingly become a terrestrial, even agricultural, bird rather than a marine one. Although several gull species follow the plough, it is the black-headed gull that is most often seen forming lines of squabbling birds competing with one another for worms in the fresh-turned furrows behind the tractor. In some places it could now even be described as an urban species, so frequently is it seen in winter on playing fields and rubbish dumps.

Changing plumage The variety of black-headed gull plumage is such that it often causes confusion. The 'black' head is in reality chocolate brown, forming a hood

Black-headed gulls: the first two years

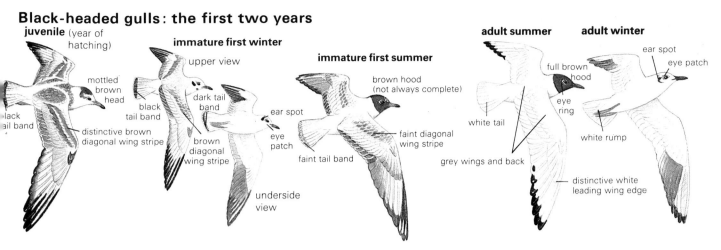

juvenile (year of hatching)
- mottled brown head
- black tail band
- distinctive brown diagonal wing stripe

immature first winter
- upper view
- dark tail band
- black tail band
- brown diagonal wing stripe
- ear spot
- eye patch
- underside view

immature first summer
- brown hood (not always complete)
- faint diagonal wing stripe
- faint tail band

adult summer
- white tail
- full brown hood
- eye ring
- grey wings and back

adult winter
- ear spot
- eye patch
- white rump
- distinctive white leading wing edge

Black-headed gull distribution

Below: Black-headed gulls roosting in a car park in winter. Even in the urban habitat, they can find spaces giving a clear view of any approaching danger.

stretching down the nape and broken only by a white ring round the eye. It is seen only in summer; at this time, the beak, legs and feet are a deep blood-red, contrasting with the impeccable silvery white plumage of the body. The wing-tips are black, with a triangular shaft of white along the leading edge of the primaries (a most useful characteristic for identification purposes).

This white leading edge remains as a good field character in winter, when the brown hood is lost and replaced by a small grey-brown smudge behind the eye. In winter, the beak and legs are a much muddier red while the beak usually has a black tip. Sometimes the hood may start to reappear shortly after Christmas, so intermediate stages are frequently seen.

Young birds, when they leave the colony, share the small size and relatively delicate shape that help to separate black-headed from larger gulls. Seen from above, when in flight, the young birds have a distinctive

diagonal brown stripe across the inner half of the wing, giving a 'W' pattern.

The specific name of the black-headed gull is *ridibundus*, which means 'laughing'. This is derived from its summer calls, which are varied forms of laughing yelps. Some are long and drawn out, others short, but all are detectably higher-pitched and less harsh than those of the larger gulls.

Widespread species No birdwatcher should have difficulty finding black-headed gulls: during winter they are widespread both on the coast and inland over much of Britain and Ireland. At this time of year our own birds are augmented in numbers by many thousands of black-headed gulls from the Continent, escaping the harsh winter in northern Europe. In summer, too, they are more widely distributed than the other gulls, with many inland colonies. With a breeding population which observers estimate as numbering about 300,000 pairs, black-headed gulls are not as numerous as herring gulls or

153

kittiwakes; but their distribution both inland and on the coast ensures that they are the most commonly seen gulls in summer and winter alike.

Location of colonies The species breeds in a broad belt right across western, central and eastern Europe and into the Far East. In Britain and Ireland, colonies in the south tend to be near to the coast, and in the north they tend to be both coastal and inland.

Although the black-headed gull is always a colonial breeder, the sizes and sometimes the locations of the gulleries vary considerably from year to year. The commonest coastal sites are among sand dunes and on saltings, or on islands in estuaries; inland, typical sites are beside lakes and moorland tarns on boggy ground, often at a considerable altitude.

More recently, black-headed gulls have begun to exploit a range of man-made sites, particularly those resulting from mineral extraction where subsequent flooding has left a series of exposed islands. Other colonies can be found on sewage farms.

Colourful courtship Black-headed gulls begin to reassemble in their colonies in March and April. During winter they show a preference for wide open spaces with a clear view of approaching predators, but at the start of summer they begin to look for areas with sufficient ground cover to conceal nests and young.

Within the colony, males establish small territories, and strike an aggressive pose if any other bird approaches. This is followed by a 'stretching' posture, in which the male tries to appear as tall as possible. He turns his brown-hooded head towards the intruder, pointing his beak downwards in defiance. Accompanying this behaviour are head movements ('flagging') which emphasise the contrast between the white nape and the brown face as the head is suddenly turned sideways.

Such measures usually serve to frighten off a male intruder without actual strife, and help to space out nests so that there is adequate room for the broods. The response of an intruding female differs: although partly frightened, she is driven on by greater sexual urges, and continues to approach. Gradually she adopts a submissive, head-down posture. Once she is accepted, the courtship ritual continues with both sexes making vigorous head movements simultaneously ('head tossing'). The male leads his female to a nest site which he has chosen in the territory, and there the pair build a nest.

Raising the brood The usual number of eggs is three, but one, two or four are sometimes laid. The usual colour is olive green, with darker blobs, but in any large colony a range of colours is likely to be encountered, from pure sky blue to almost black. Incubation lasts just over three weeks, with the sexes sharing the duties, and the youngsters take

about five weeks to fledge. The birds usually raise one brood per season.

The young hatch covered in down, with their eyes open. The down is yellow, with brown camouflage markings, and the young remain in the nest for a day or two before moving off to shelter under nearby vegetation. They emerge when a parent returns with food.

With such a variety of gullery sites, food for the young varies from place to place. In many areas, insect larvae and earthworms feature prominently in the diet. Elsewhere, the young are fed on gleanings from rubbish tips, fish or fish offal, small crustaceans and other marine animals.

Above and opposite page: Nests vary from little more than a saucer-shaped scrape in the ground to a substantial pile of grass, reeds or seaweed. The usual number of eggs is two or three.

Black-headed gull (*Larus ridibundus*). Resident small gull; widely distributed. Length 36-38cm (14-15in).

Below: At the time of courtship, the two birds perform ritualised head-shaking displays to strengthen the pair bond.

Mammals of urban habitats

Mammals are the most timid of all our native animals. It is possible to see birds, insects and even reptiles and amphibians regularly, but wild mammals are very much scarcer. It is all the more surprising then, to discover that many mammals have adapted to life in built-up areas, where the likelihood of disturbance is much higher than in the open countryside.

Foxes, and to a lesser extent the more timid badger, have moved into cities in a big way, drawn by the many ready sources of food in such areas. At first these mammals made cautious night-time forays into towns just to find food, but this habit has burgeoned to such an extent that most towns and cities now have resident populations, some supporting as many as five fox families per square kilometre (about half a square mile) – much more than in the surrounding countryside. Badgers are more choosy about where they live, but even so they may be as common in favoured cities (such as Bristol) as in the best badger countryside. During the day the grey squirrel is probably the most frequently seen town mammal; it does particularly well in heavily wooded town parks.

Some mammals have come to rely largely or wholly on man and his stored foodstuffs during their association, and such species naturally tend to be common in urban areas. House mice and rats (nowadays usually the brown rat) thrive in the warmth and protected environment of homes and other buildings as long as there is food available, despite concerted attempts to remove or reduce them. But perhaps the most surprising associates of man in towns are the various species of bats. Although bats must once have relied heavily on caves and hollow trees for their roosts and homes, some species have taken happily to houses. Pipistrelles, serotines and long-eared bats roost in any house that is to their liking and are as likely to choose brand new houses as old ones.

Besides these species that associate closely with man, there are also the field mice, shrews, voles, hedgehogs and others that make use of the wilder, quieter parts of towns, often quite unknown to the human inhabitants. At night, especially, city mammals – a remarkably large and varied population – come alive.

Left: The brown rat is a most adaptable animal and thrives wherever man grows food and stores it. Cracked brickwork or damaged air bricks enable it to enter houses, warehouses, sheds, barns and factories with ease – to the great detriment of man since this mammal damages food and can carry disease.

Left: The grey squirrel is bold and determined when it comes to finding food. In parks it is quite at home, ignoring nearby people as it scurries about searching for nuts or cones, and it will even sometimes rob bird tables in private gardens, reaching them by scrambling along a washing line if there are no trees near enough.

157

TWENTIETH CENTURY URBAN FOX

Urban foxes are increasing in numbers, according to studies in Bristol and other areas. For many people they are welcome visitors.

Urban foxes are now well established in many towns and cities in the British Isles, particularly in Glasgow and Edinburgh in Scotland, and in most towns and cities in England from Nottingham southwards. They are rare in the north of England.

Their appearance in our urban areas has been a relatively recent phenomenon; the rapid development of low density housing suburbs in the inter-war years provided an ideal habitat for the fox, and by the end of World War II several towns had foxes living on their fringes. In fact, by the early 1950s foxes were considered to be a pest in the Kent and Surrey suburbs of London and the Ministry of Agriculture was shooting over

Above: A pair of foxes sunbathing on the roof of a shop in Bristol and (below) a fox taking a day-time stroll. In the 1950s and early 1960s foxes spread rapidly in many towns and cities and urban foxes have been a common sight for the last 20 years.

100 animals each year. In the 1950s and early 1960s urban foxes spread rapidly and they continue to be a common sight.

Fox populations In many areas foxes attain higher densities than in the surrounding rural areas. Up to five fox families per square kilometre have been recorded in Bristol, parts of the West Midlands conurbation and Bournemouth and Poole. These high densities are always found in the areas of inter-

formed 34.8% of the adult diet, the foxes instead taking more wild mammals and birds, particularly small garden birds and feral pigeons. These birds were particularly important to young cubs, forming about 45% of the diet. Why foxes in two apparently similar situations should exploit such very different food sources is uncertain, but it may be a reflection of the attitudes of the local residents. In Bristol the foxes are not officially regarded as pests by the local Council, whereas many London boroughs undertake fox control. These differing attitudes by the local authorities may be reflected in the willingness of the residents to feed and encourage foxes.

It is difficult to understand why some people and some local authorities should be so strongly anti-fox. As the surveys in Bristol showed, even in an area where foxes are very numerous, losses of pets and tipping out of dustbins are relatively unusual events, and keeping small pets in properly constructed cages or putting a clip on the dustbin lid easily eliminates such problems.

Cubs under the garden shed Town foxes may create more of a nuisance during the breeding season. Peak mating time is in January, when the foxes are at their most vocal. Their barking and screaming calls carry long distances, particularly on cold, clear nights. Pregnancy lasts an average of about 53 days, and in the latter part of pregnancy the vixen

war housing. Smaller towns and cities generally seem to have lower fox densities, but at present no-one knows why this is the case.

Foxes live in family groups and these usually consist of a dog fox, a breeding vixen and, in some cases, perhaps one or two non-breeding vixens which are related to the breeding vixen. Usually these barren animals are daughters, but occasionally they may be a sister or, if the original mother reaches old age, she may cease to breed and be replaced by one of her daughters.

In Bristol research showed that for every three vixens that breed each year, one does not, and so one in three fox families will have a barren vixen living with them. A detailed survey showed that there were 211 families living in an area of 116 square kilometres (45 square miles); these consisted of 211 dog foxes, 211 breeding vixens and 74 barren vixens–496 adult foxes in all. Since the average litter size is 4.8 cubs, these 211 families could produce 1013 cubs each year. For comparison, similar densities were recorded in the West Midlands conurbation, where there were 683 fox families in an area of 589 square kilometres (227 square miles), and Bournemouth and Poole which had 144 fox families in an area of 83 square kilometres (32 square miles).

Urban fox menus The diet of these urban foxes consists mainly of scavenged food from rubbish heaps and food put out specially for them. The survey showed that the diet of the Bristol foxes was supplemented by small birds, a few wild animals such as squirrels and short-tailed field voles, windfall fruit, insects and earthworms. Predation on pets was comparatively rare. For example, foxes killed only 0.7% of the cats found dead; this works out at 0.17 cats per adult fox each year. Since most foxes may encounter several cats each night while out foraging, this number is incredibly low. In most encounters foxes and cats treat each other with total indifference and in the fights witnessed from start to finish all were started by the cat and all resulted in the fox turning tail and running.

By comparison, the diet of foxes in London was very different. Scavenged food only

Above: A six-week old fox cub in a suburban garden. Adventurous fox cubs get themselves into a variety of predicaments and often have to be rescued.

Below: This traditional view of the urban fox was not borne out by a survey in Bristol. In over 5500 households 81% of the occupants never had their dustbins touched, and in only 2.7% of the households were foxes a regular problem.

will select an earth in which to rear her cubs.

One of the most popular sites for the earth is under a garden shed that is raised off the ground on a single row of bricks. The vixen squeezes under the shed and her cubs are born on the bare soil. Unlike badgers, foxes do not collect any bedding. Sometimes the vixen digs an earth in a flower bed, a rockery or in a railway bank. She may even bear her cubs under the floor-boards of an occupied house.

In many old houses there are broken air bricks through which the fox can squeeze and, once in, it is an ideal site for the vixen to bear her cubs. In early May, when the cubs are about five weeks old, they start to play and then there is mayhem under the householder's feet as the cubs chase, fight and growl at each other. This activity raises clouds of dust that may rise through the joints of the floorboards and settle throughout the house. Just to add to the general effect, the adult foxes are busy bringing food back to the earth for the cubs, much of which may remain uneaten and slowly decompose. So the house fills with flies and the smell of both rotting food and accumulated urine and faeces. Not surprisingly, most people who have suffered such an experience make sure that they repair any missing air bricks before the onset of the next breeding season.

The cubs normally move out of their natal earth in early June and from then onwards they lie above ground in dense vegetation, or

Above: A fox outside its earth overlooking a railway line near Bristol, and (right) a fox resting under a garden seat. Since there are so many foxes in some towns, there must be ample food to support them. In Bristol, for instance, the majority (61%) of food is 'scavenged': lumps of meat, fat and bones that people put out in their gardens to feed their foxes. One person alone puts out 11kg (24lb) of best meat each week! Foxes also take potato peelings and similar items obtained from compost heaps, and sultanas, bread and bird seed left for garden birds. The foxes rarely touch dustbins or prey on pets. The survey showed that of the households that keep such animals as rabbits, guinea pigs, ducks and chickens, only eight per cent annually suffered any loss. As most of the pets were kept in poorly constructed cages, the foxes could have taken them all if they had wanted.

under piles of rubbish. The whole family group meets at these play areas and the young cubs chase and play with one another, already showing many of the behaviour patterns seen in the adult foxes. The cubs pounce with their fore feet to pin imaginary mice to the ground, or stand on their hind feet and push each other with their fore legs in mock fights.

The adult foxes also bring various play items back for the cubs. Tennis, rubber and golf balls are particularly favoured, as are food wrappers, and outside one earth in Bristol there were over 40 Kentucky Fried Chicken boxes. Playful fox cubs have been known to pull washing off lines, chew or steal shoes and boots left outside the kitchen door, jump on to and break the glass tops of seed incubators, and chew plastic plant cloches. They also like to chase each other around vegetable patches, and several get hung in garden netting each year. Some fall down inspection pits in garages, others enter houses through cat-flaps and once inside panic and cannot find their way out.

The cubs disperse in autumn. Dispersal may start in late September, but late October until the end of January is the main period for dispersion. Many cubs move away from the city centre and some may leave the city entirely. For instance, two fox cubs born in Bristol moved 18km (11m) to settle on the wind-swept tops of the Mendips. As a general rule, the higher the population density the lower the dispersal distance, and so foxes living at high population densities in cities tend to move short distances. In Bristol dispersal distances of over five kilometres (3 miles) are rare, and many are less than one kilometre. Also cubs born in the city centre tend to move shorter distances than those born near the edge of the city, and they also

Above: A fox in a garden in Birmingham. In towns foxes face a number of population pressures and about 60% die each year. At first sight this may appear a very high mortality rate, but for foxes it is comparatively low. In many rural areas up to 80% die each year. In towns the major cause of death is the motor car.

Below: A fox has found its way into a chicken coop.

start to move later.

In towns foxes face a number of population pressures and about 60% die each year. Many are run over, particularly during winter when the cubs are dispersing and the adults mating. Research in London showed that 27.5% of all the foxes had healed bone fractures which were probably the result of car injuries. Foxes also suffer from more direct man-induced mortality. Even in towns they are snared, dug out or caught with dogs, mainly for the price of their skins. Some town Councils still shoot or trap them as pests, although fortunately most take a more enlightened view and leave them alone.

Living in close contact with domestic pets means that foxes are in an ideal position to contract a number of canine diseases. For instance, many town foxes carry antibodies to canine parovirus, which was very prevalent a couple of years ago. In Bristol many are also infected with *Leptospira canicola*, a bacterium that causes chronic renal disease, and in older foxes there may be extensive kidney damage.

In some towns, particularly parts of London and in the south-east, the foxes suffer from mange, an extremely unpleasant disease. It is caused by the sarcoptic mite, which burrows into the skin, causing severe irritation. The fox may lose up to half its body weight, and invariably dies within three to four months. It is widely believed that this disease is so prevalent in urban foxes because their diet is deficient in a number of vitamins as a result of scavenging. This is not true. It is just that since the foxes can live at such high densities in towns it is easier for such diseases to spread. Even then mange is not seen in all urban fox populations. In Bristol, for instance, the disease is totally absent, and the animals look at least as healthy as rural foxes.

BRISTOL BADGERS: AN URBAN SUCCESS

Unlike foxes, which are now common in many of our towns and cities, urban-dwelling badgers are relatively rare. They frequently forage in gardens on the edge of built-up areas, but only a few towns have well-established badger populations.

There are established badger populations in Edinburgh, Bristol, Bath, parts of London and the West Midlands conurbation, Basildon and Southend-on-Sea in Essex, and some of the south coast towns. Of these, Bristol far exceeds all the others in the number of badger setts per square kilometre; in some areas there are over 20 badgers per square kilometre–densities comparable with some of the best badger country in rural England.

Urban survivors Badgers are large, rather obtrusive animals, and at first sight it is difficult to understand how they have managed to survive in some of our built-up areas. For, unlike foxes, which are relatively recent colonists of many towns and cities, the

Below: A badger tackles the scraps round a dustbin. In Bristol there are badger setts in steep-sided river cliffs, railway cuttings, rubbish tips, golf courses, allotments, factory sites and cemeteries. In the north-west setts are common in private gardens. Some of these are old setts that survived the inter-war period of house building; others have been dug recently under such places as summerhouses and garden sheds or in flowerbeds.

badgers tend to be relict populations that have survived urban encroachment. The cities that do contain badgers are in areas where badgers are common in the surrounding rural areas, and where it would appear that the city developed in a locality in which the geology and general habitat were already eminently suitable.

In Bristol, for example, the badgers and their setts have managed to survive in three areas where there are river cliffs or sloping land and a diversity of geological deposits. In the two parts of the city where badgers are rare today they were probably always rare: the south is built on clay soils which are poorly drained and unsuitable for digging setts; similarly in the north, where clay soils predominate, badgers are rare.

Occasionally a badger may even live under the floorboards of an occupied house, entering through a broken air brick. In one instance a badger was living under the floorboards of a house undergoing renovation, where several floorboards had been removed to lay new piping. At night the badger would come up into the house to eat the cat's food, leaving dusty footprints all over the furniture and along the top of the piano. This caused some consternation, both to the old lady in the house and her cat, which was a somewhat nervous animal. The badger finally outstayed its welcome when one night the lady was awoken to absolute bedlam: the badger

was chasing the cat round and round her bed!

Urban diet Besides stealing food from cats, urban badgers find a wide range of different food items from other sources. In rural areas earthworms constitute the major part of a badger's diet, but in towns these are of much lesser importance. In Bristol earthworms formed only 18% of the diet of badgers studied, whereas 20% consisted of insects and snails, fruit constituted 30%, scavenged food and food put out by householders 24%, vegetables—mainly garden crops—5%, and vertebrates—predominantly garden birds—nearly 3%. Fruit is clearly the most important food item for the Bristol badgers, and in autumn when windfall apples, plums and pears are available in abundance, nearly two-thirds of the diet is fruit. The range of foods taken is amazing, including blackberries, mulberries, gooseberries, strawberries, medlars, raspberries, and red and black currants.

While no-one would begrudge the badgers their windfall fruit, unfortunately they are very partial to strawberries, gooseberries and raspberries and cause considerable damage both to soft fruit crops and fruit cages. Badgers are also very keen on new potatoes and carrots, and where badgers are common most people just give up trying to grow carrots. The moment the crop is ready the badgers take it all—overnight an immaculate vegetable garden is devastated as the badgers root out every carrot. In the hot dry summers of 1975 and 1976 damage to garden crops was particularly severe.

Badgers can certainly make their presence felt in towns. In one area of Bristol where they are common 16% of householders had their dustbins regularly rifled by badgers—they were even more persistent than foxes which can easily jump garden fences. Instead, the

Above: In Bristol it is quite a common occurrence for people to be woken in the middle of the night by the sound of a badger tearing a big hole in the garden fence. Badgers are creatures of habit and follow regular tracks between gardens. Any attempts to block these runs are vigorously resisted by the badgers, and many people resign themselves to having one or more permanent holes in the garden fence.

Below: A badger visiting a garden to take table scraps left out for its benefit. Many people put out food for badgers, but they also take garden produce, fruit, insects and snails.

badgers simply knock a hole in the fence; 10% of the householders questioned reported badgers breaking fences. Not surprisingly, therefore, to some people the badger is an unwelcome addition to our urban fauna.

Urban behaviour The behaviour of badgers living in urban areas is different from that of those in rural areas. The badgers emerge from their setts about an hour later than animals in the country, and are rarely out before it is completely dark. Where the roads are busy, activity may be further restricted until the traffic dies down, after which the animals readily move about on the roads—the sound of their long claws clattering on the tarmac as they run along is clearly audible from some distance. In the morning town badgers do not return to their setts any earlier than those in rural areas, and in mid-summer can sometimes be seen trotting home in broad daylight.

The badgers are not active throughout the whole night; periods of activity are interspersed with periods of sleep when the badgers may either return to their setts or crawl under a shed to sleep. Sometimes a fox and a badger sleep under the same shed. Badgers will even build a couch of dry grass or leaves under a garden bush on which to rest during the night. One has even been seen asleep in the middle of a school field. In July badgers spend the greatest proportion (65%) of the night active, this dropping to as little as 8% in January when they are rarely active above ground and move only small distances from the sett. They do not hibernate, and are often active underground, but they do live off their fat accumulated in autumn when windfall fruit is available in abundance.

Badgers have adapted many aspects of their behaviour to life in our cities. In lowland areas of rural Britain they live in well-defined social groups, each of which defends a territory, and the boundaries of these territories are marked with large latrines. In towns the territorial system is far less rigidly defined. Instead of clear-cut territorial boundaries with conspicuous boundary latrines, the fringes of each group's foraging area are poorly defined and may overlap with those of adjacent social groups. In rural areas most badger latrines are

found on the boundaries of the group's territory, with relatively few sited near the setts. In towns the pattern is exactly the reverse: the area around the sett is heavily marked with latrines, with half the latrines less than 50m (165ft) from the sett, and there are relatively few latrines towards the periphery of the foraging area.

This change in behaviour is a response to the diverse nature of the urban habitat and the wide range of food sources available. In rural areas the badgers specialise in feeding on one main type of food–earthworms. Their territory is designed to encompass several potential sources of earthworms, and these feeding areas are predictable and worth defending. In towns the food sources are more varied but less predictable, so the badgers in towns forage in a more random manner than in rural areas, checking many potential food sources and often travelling long distances criss-crossing a small area. Hence, although it may be foraging in an area of less than half a square kilometre, the badger may travel over 8km (5 miles) on a summer night, thoroughly searching this small area.

In most towns the habitat is diverse and in Bristol badger home ranges vary according to the type of area where they live. So animals whose range consists mainly of gardens have large home ranges and the badgers eat a diversity of food types; in smaller home ranges the habitat is more varied and the animals take a smaller variety of food types–the situation is similar to a rural area where the badgers specialise in obtaining one particular food.

Although town badgers modify their behaviour to suit their environment, they are not permanently adapted to urban life. In Bristol some badgers born in the town move out into

Above: Bedding which has been dropped by a badger.

Above left: Badger prints in a soft garden lawn.

Opposite page: Young badger in daylight.

Below: Urban badgers are only really safe in gardens.

the surrounding countryside, and animals from the countryside probably still move into the town. Clearly the urban and rural badger populations are not living as distinct populations. There are a number of problems for urban badgers. The major cause of death is road accidents. Some die in swimming pools; cubs particularly are killed by large pet dogs; and some get entangled in garden netting. Quite a few are also trapped by humans.

THE GARDEN HOME OF THE HEDGEHOG

Search your garden or back-yard at night with a torch and you may find several hedgehogs (when you thought you had none) pursuing the plentiful garden pests. They are determined foragers, burrowing under obstacles and even climbing over wire fences.

The hedgehog is a familiar inhabitant of town parks, gardens, cemeteries, railway banks and waste ground. Suburban gardens in particular provide the hedgehog with an ideal summer and winter home under compost heaps, behind sheds, below hedges and tucked away in odd corners. Its small size and nocturnal movements make it inconspicuous, so much so that many people have these spiny creatures in their gardens without even realising it. There is plenty of invertebrate food in gardens such as worms, slugs and beetles. The hedgehog also plunders bread put out for birds and bowls of milk left for cats.

Friend or foe Hedgehogs may cause some

irritation to game keepers–by eating game bird eggs for example; but their presence in urban areas is wholly beneficial. They may even be the cheapest and most effective form of pest control, because they prefer to eat those animals that gardeners are glad to be rid of–beetles, slugs, worms and caterpillars. Hedgehogs also eat millipedes which many predators find distasteful, and snap up earwigs when they can. Strangely, however, they avoid the numerous and easy-to-catch snails and woodlice.

Poisoning problems Gardeners may be doing themselves and the hedgehogs a serious disservice by using artificial means to get rid of pests, rather than relying on the natural

resources of the hedgehog to do the job. The use of various pesticides results in the slow poisoning of invertebrates, which are then eaten by hedgehogs. They in turn accumulate small doses of poison which build up in the fat deposits laid down during the autumn in readiness for hibernation. As the animals eke out their fat reserves over winter, the poison is released and many hedgehogs must surely suffer as a result.

Slug pellets are another potential hazard. These are much more poisonous to slugs than to mammals, and are therefore regarded as relatively safe. Hedgehogs, however, are likely to eat any sickly or poisoned slugs they come across, even if not the pellets themselves. Although not a lethal dose of poison, the small quantities (along with other garden chemicals eaten accidentally) may be enough to cause serious internal damage to the hedgehog.

There is a high probability that both types of poisoning lead to death; but nobody seems to have studied this danger for hedgehogs, whereas the effects of pesticides on birds and pets are well-publicised. Hedgehogs accumulating poison may account for the sickly ones found wandering about gardens in a dazed fashion in broad daylight. It could explain such curious hedgehog behaviour as the running in circles that is often reported, or the staggering gait that appears to be a prelude to death.

Breeding and birth You may come across courting hedgehogs in gardens, particularly on warm summer evenings. They make a loud repetitive snorting noise which you can hear from a considerable distance. The male continuously circles the female–perhaps for upwards of half an hour–often making a circular track in the soft earth of a flower bed or lawn. As in any other four-footed mammal,

HEDGEHOG (*Erinaceus europaeus*). Also called 'urchin'.
Size adult male weighs 800-1110g (28-40oz), body about 26cm (10in); female generally smaller and weighs 500-700g (17-25oz).
Colour brown; rarely albino. Spines on the back and sides dark brown with lighter tips; head and belly have coarse hairs.
Breeding season Young born May-July; late litters up to September.
Gestation period 31-35 days
No of young 2-7; 20% die before leaving nest.
Lifespan Average under 2 years, maximum 8 years.
Food Worms, caterpillars, beetles, carrion; almost anything available at ground level.
Predators Few because of spines. Fox, badger, dog take some (especially babies); tawny owl, pine marten, polecat. Gamekeepers and motor cars kill far more.
Distribution Throughout mainland Britain and Ireland, except wet places and mountain tops. Common on arable farmland, urban areas.

Opposite left: The mother looks after her babies for a month or so.

Below: Although the babies are born with only 100 or so pale spines, the adults have 3000 to 7000 spines.

the male mounts the female from behind. With so many spines around, both hedgehogs have to be very careful when mating; so the female spreads herself close to the ground, and her spines are flattened against her back.

This is the only time male hedgehogs get involved in breeding; the female performs all the chores of raising a family. In a secure nest she has built herself, she gives birth to a litter of usually four or five babies, which have only a few, pure white spines. Litters are born from May till September. It is thought that a mother that has an early litter may produce a second one, although this has not yet been proved.

Mother and young Tidying-up operations in the garden often accidentally uncover nests with babies. These should not be disturbed if at all possible; if the mother is alarmed at this time, she may often eat, or partly eat, her offspring or abandon them. This is less likely to occur when the babies have grown a few brown spines after a week or so. Should the nest be disturbed at this stage, the mother often carries her family one at a time, by the scruff of their necks, to a new home.

About 20% of baby hedgehogs die before they leave the nest. Those in large litters are particularly at risk–presumably because the mother cannot feed them all adequately. The mother looks after her young for four or five weeks, after which she may lead them from the nest on feeding excursions–a charming procession of prickly little litter mates. From here on the individuals break away to live solitary lives.

Territory Nobody knows exactly what happens once the family has dispersed, because few studies have been made of hedgehogs in the wild–despite their numbers and familiarity. However, it is quite likely that some (especially females) stay put in favourable spots, while others wander widely, possibly spending much of their lives as nomads.

One way to study such behaviour is to mark hedgehogs, giving each an individually recognisable identity. This not only enables us to discover a little about where hedgehogs go, but also reveals something of their social activity. Once the garden hedgehog is marked 'it' frequently turns out to be six or more. An attendance register can be kept, noting which animals come to a feeding bowl each night. Many questions may be answered by observing marked hedgehogs, such as which is the dominant member in the feeding hierarchy. Some always eat their fill first, while others wait in the shadows until the rest have finished.

Mortality About one-third of the population dies each year; the mortality of juveniles is very high during their first winter. Not much is known about survival rates, but most hedgehogs probably do not live beyond three years, and maybe one in

300-400 survives seven years.

Nevertheless hedgehogs fare better than most small mammals because they are well-protected from predators by their spiny coat. Owls, foxes, badgers, weasels and other killers tend to leave them alone. Motor cars and game keepers kill more hedgehogs than any natural predators. But the greatest threat to the species results from the physiological stresses of hibernation.

Inner-city survivors Hedgehogs remain widespread and numerous despite these threats, plus the problems of pesticides. Their willingness to eat a great variety of food, and to live in man-dominated environments, means that they are not threatened

Right: Hedgehogs usually tolerate dim light, so you may spot them with a torch as they feed at night among the flower beds.

Below: Hedgehogs appear to have good memories for free food, such as bowls of milk, because many return after hibernation to where they fed the previous year. They have been known to dig under obstacles like fences or even climb over them – a 2m (6½ft) chain-wire fence presents no difficulty.

Sexing hedgehogs

To tell a male hedgehog from a female, you need to look at the underside (right). A hedgehog will curl up into a ball if it feels threatened; so to get the animal to unroll, first support it in both hands–wearing gloves. Gently shuffle the hedgehog until its forelegs are on your right hand and hind legs on the left. Then slowly raise your right hand and squeeze the animal's spiny back against your jacket, gently forcing the hedgehog to stretch out in your hands.

Its sex should then become obvious–either by the male's 5-8cm (2-3in) penis where you might expect its navel, or the female's two openings between the hind legs 1-2cm ($\frac{1}{2}$-$\frac{3}{4}$in) apart.

by the march of progress, characterised by the urban sprawl. Hedgehogs can in fact survive deep in the heart of our cities, not just around the suburban fringe. For example there are hedgehogs living in many Central London parks, spreading from there into adjacent streets and gardens.

The densely built-up inner suburbs of London (such as Streatham, Deptford, West Ham, Highgate, Willesden) have thriving hedgehog populations, even though they are only a few miles from the city centre. The same is true of residential areas of other major cities, including Bristol, Manchester, Norwich and Edinburgh.

The hedgehogs' stoic adaptability has helped them survive for over 15 million years – far longer than the woolly mammoths and sabre-toothed tigers that were once their contemporaries. When so many species are threatened with decline and possible extinction today, it's reassuring to know that hedgehogs will be an endearing feature of gardens and other man-made habitats far into the future, just as they are now.

The hedgehog flea

Garden hedgehogs are often blamed, unjustly, for passing on fleas to domestic pets. The hedgehog's reputation for being flea-ridden is well-deserved. But these fleas are all of one type – they are adapted to life among the thousands of hedgehog spines. The hedgehog's skin is such a difficult place to inhabit that only one species – the hedgehog flea *Archaeopsylla erinacei* – manages to live there. These fleas occasionally bite a human, or get on to another animal; but they soon drop off to find another hedgehog. If a dog or cat is plagued with a lot of fleas, it almost certainly got them from another dog or cat, because both animals have their own particular species of fleas, which are common enough – but never found on hedgehogs. So the often-made suggestion that fleas are exchanged between hedgehogs and domestic pets is not founded on fact.

Hibernation

In autumn the hedgehog carries the fallen leaves of deciduous trees to a sheltered place under brambles or a hedge. When a large pile has been collected, the hedgehog crawls inside and shuffles round and round until the loose leaves have become tightly packed against the bramble or hedge branches. This forms a secure, warm, weatherproof nest that will be its home during the cold of winter. This type of nest is called a hibernaculum. In the British Isles only hedgehogs, dormice and bats hibernate. Such mammals as badgers and squirrels may sleep in their dwellings for several days at a time in very severe weather, but sooner or later they emerge to forage in the open.

THE HOUSE MOUSE: AN URBAN SQUATTER

Britain's most successful mammal, and probably the most familiar, is the ubiquitous house mouse. It thrives in man-made environments and, in ideal conditions, may produce up to fourteen litters of a dozen or more young each year. Five to ten litters of five or six young are, however, more usual.

The most successful mammal in Britain, and probably the most familiar, is the house mouse. It is not a native: like the rabbit, grey squirrel, and many other species, it was introduced by man and, like house mice worldwide, it has shared his home ever since.

Excavations of fossil remains in Dorset show house mice to have been present in Britain at least since the pre-Roman Iron Age. The British subspecies is one of the most commensal races of house mice. (Commensal animals are those living in close association with another species–in this case, man.) Its ancestor, another subspecies, still lives wild in the Steppes of Central Asia. Since prehistoric times it has colonized vast areas of the world and today it is well adapted to a cosmopolitan existence: it can live for long periods on dry seeds and little or no water; it has a high reproductive rate, and is small, agile and alert; and above all it thrives in a man-made environment.

It is helped in this respect by man himself. On the whole we are wasteful creatures with untidy feeding habits, and we usually leave plenty of food lying around for the mouse to find. Our homes offer hiding and nesting places, and a warm environment for breeding.

Many variations Throughout its worldwide range the house mouse is extremely variable in appearance. In all, some 130 forms have been described, but only about 20 are thought to be true subspecies.

As with most of the commensal forms, the British house mouse is larger and darker than its ancestor, with a longer tail. The coat is greyish-brown above and slightly lighter greyish-buff below. Its eyes and ears are smaller than those of the wood-mouse, it has a thick, almost hairless, scaly tail, and a notch in the upper incisor teeth which is visible in side view.

Another subspecies of the house mouse, and one which has helped to pay for the activities of its destructive relatives, is the tame laboratory animal. First imported to Europe from Japan, the laboratory mouse has for many years been of great value to man in the studies of medicine and heredity.

Town mouse, country mouse House mice are social animals, living together in small groups dominated by a single male. Not all house mice live urban lives. There is also a thriving rural community. Others, the feral house mice, are found in fields and hedgerows in arable districts.

Urban mice make their homes in the many holes and cracks abounding in town build-

HOUSE MOUSE (*Mus musculus*)
Size of adult Max weight 30g (1oz). Max length head and body 9cm (3¾in), tail as long again.
Colour Dark brownish-grey above, greyish-buff below. Tail thick, almost naked, with conspicuous scaly rings.
Breeding season From March to October in countryside. In urban areas breeding may be continuous.
Gestation 19-20 days.
No of young 4-13 or more, but 5-6 is average. About 5 litters in urban areas and 10 in corn ricks is average.
Lifespan Few live longer than 18 months, most die in first winter.
Food Omnivorous, preferring grain, grain products· insects, man's food.
Predators Birds of prey (barn owls), mammals (stoat, weasel, man, rats, cats).
Distribution Throughout UK.

Left: Fourteen-day old house mice and (below) young mice and their mother in their nest. Town mice make nests of sacking, paper, fabric, clothes or string but in the countryside grass, leaves and straw are used.

Opposite: The house mouse common in north-western and western Europe is descended from a subspecies found in Central Asia. It has been associated with man since prehistoric times and its range has expanded as trading has increased.

example, whose forerunners are known to have been introduced between 250 and 1000 years ago, have diverged from mainland mice both in coloration—they are smoky grey with a cream underside—and in increased size.

In and out of doors Territorial aggression between males can become intense, especially in over-crowded conditions, and strange mice of either sex entering a territory are attacked. There seems to be more tolerance in mice found in buildings than in habitats such as corn ricks, where exceptionally dense populations can build up.

House mice are largely nocturnal, although they adapt to the activities of the human occupants of dwelling houses. They only stray into new areas when food is in short supply. They prefer grain and grain products such as bread. Rural house mice eat mainly grain and seeds, especially wheat, but their basic diet is supplemented with insects. Occasionally worms, arthropods and fungi are eaten. The average daily intake is 3g ($\frac{1}{16}$oz).

House mice can survive on little water, although animals feeding on dry seeds for long periods can have lower than normal fertility. In corn ricks mice obtain the balance of their water from dew or rain on the outside of the rick.

Fast breeders House mice owe much of their success to their high rate of reproduction. Females can breed at 40 days old and normally produce between five and ten litters annually, depending on where they live. Country mice tend to produce more litters. There is no breeding season as such, but feral mice living under 'natural' conditions bear their young between March and October. In favourable conditions in urban habitats and corn ricks breeding is continuous and up to 14 litters have been known.

Single or communal nests are made. In the crowded conditions of a corn rick, it is common to find nests of several young families. The average litter is five or six, and the young are weaned during their third week, by which time they are beginning to leave the nest for short explorations, and the female is pregnant with a new litter.

As the population density increases, so does

ings. Of all the house mice, those living in dwelling houses probably work hardest for a living. They are more disturbed by the movements of man and domestic animals and have to search more diligently for food than mice in warehouses or farms. The home range of individual mice is determined by the availability of food and cover. Urban house mice, which often have their hiding places and food source close together, usually have home ranges of five square metres.

The rural population is less localised and can be greatly influenced by farming practice. In summer, rural house mice that have been indoors during winter often leave for fields and woods, feeding on field crops, seeds and berries. In autumn they return indoors for food and shelter. Rural house mice are less markedly commensal than their urban relatives, and if evicted from corn ricks and farm buildings often migrate to fields and hedgerows.

The feral mice are more like their wild ancestors. They live independently of man, in subterranean burrows.

Island habitats House mice are also present on most British inhabited small islands. If the island becomes uninhabited, the mice revert to a feral existence. Isolated communities of house mice are particularly interesting to scientists because they show the rate at which new genetic characteristics can develop. The subspecies of house mouse in the Faeroes, for

Above: The urban house mouse is truly omnivorous, eating almost everything that man feeds on, and even on such strange items as plaster, glue, soap, candles and wood. If given a choice, house mice prefer grain and grain products, such as bread. They can remember tastes for a period of time, and avoid food that has disagreed with them—one that has been poisoned and made them ill, for example. They do not store their food.

Mice in cold storage

One of the most unusual places in which house mice have been found is the cold store where meat is kept for long periods. In these extreme conditions, where the temperature falls to −10°C (14°F), the house mouse thrives in almost total darkness, feeding on frozen meat and burrowing into the carcasses to make nests of the hessian material in which the meat is wrapped. The mice have adapted to these conditions by becoming larger and heavier than mice living in more normal circumstances, and by increasing their reproductive rate to an average of a little over 6.5 litters a year.

Scientists who have reproduced these conditions in laboratories discovered that of the 14 generations of mice they bred, only the first and second generations showed distinct abnormalities—heavier hearts and stomachs, shorter tails, longer fur—as a result of the cold. Later generations showed virtually no physical differences from the control mice reared in warmer conditions.

the fighting. Males tend to live with one or more females in territories that are vigorously defended, but at high population densities fighting can be intense and subordinate animals eventually lose their territories and breeding rights. If the population becomes too great, a natural 'birth control' becomes effective: reproduction is checked as many of the females become infertile and cease to bear any young.

During the year a female produces 30 to 50 young. Some fall prey to natural enemies, most die during their first winter, and few live longer than 18 months. The reputation of the domestic cat as a mice controller is much overrated. In some places, such as warehouses, cats used for mice control can be as unhygienic as the mice themselves.

House mice are agile and can scuttle away fast. Their senses of hearing and smell are acute, and they can see sudden movement near to them. By far their greatest predator is man, who has been trying to control them from the very beginning of the association. Excavations in Afghanistan have unearthed pottery mouse-traps about 6000 years old.

Mice damage The damage caused by mice is not as great as that done by rats. Reliable statistics for Britain are not available, but in grain stores where mice are present up to 16% damage has been suggested. Mice not only eat, but contaminate and damage grain, removing the outer husk to eat the white endo-

sperm contained inside.

Mice are also carriers of disease and parasites. They no longer carry plague fleas, but they are still a risk to human and animal health. They carry disease and infections such as food poisoning, caused by Salmonella bacteria, and leptospirosis, a bacterial infection that attacks the liver and kidneys. The anticoagulant poison, Warfarin, which prevents blood clotting, has been used against them since the 1950s, but during the late 1960s population increases were reported. Since then house mice have shown increasing resistance to this kind of poison, and other controls have been used with some degree of success.

Above: House mice advertise their presence by their distinctive black droppings.

Below: In the past, when harvested corn was stored in sheaves, rural house mice built up considerable populations in the corn ricks, finding food, shelter, nesting material, protection and an even temperature. 2000 mice at a time were commonly evicted from a single rick during threshing. Today the mice try to enter the granaries where the grain is stored.

THE OLD ENGLISH RAT IN A STEADY DECLINE

The steady decline of the black rat is one case which does not cause grief even among wildlife enthusiasts. Over the centuries it has carried plague and death on a massive scale, and it continues to do so in under-developed countries. Today in Britain it has to struggle hard for its existence.

Above: A black rat which was found near Kew Bridge, London. Today black rats are mainly confined to seaports.

Two species of rat occur in the British Isles, the brown or common rat, and the black rat. The black rat was introduced during the 11th or 12th century, and for 600 years was the common rat of the British countryside. When the more versatile brown rat was introduced in the late 1720s, the black rat was often referred to as the 'old English rat' to differentiate between the two species. Today the black rat is mainly confined to major ports such as London, Liverpool, Aberdeen and Southampton, a few city centres (including London's Oxford Street), the island of Lundy off the coast of Devon, and the Channel Isles. Its population is declining, however.

Arrival in Britain Traditionally the black rat arrived in the baggage of crusaders during the Middle Ages. Its original home was around Thailand where, several thousand years ago, it co-existed with early man, sharing his newly emerging settlements and eating his food. As trade routes were opened up, the rat followed, eventually reaching western Europe. By the 13th century, as the legend of the Pied Piper of Hamelin reminds us, black rats were firmly established in Europe.

The first black rats to arrive in this country thrived in the towns, villages and isolated farms of the period. By the late 13th century black rats were becoming a considerable nuisance in England, and attempts were made to eradicate them. According to Chaucer's

BLACK RAT (SHIP RAT, ROOF RAT, ALEXANDRINE RAT) (*Rattus rattus*)
Size Head and body 16-23cm (6½-9in), plus tail 18-25cm (7-10in). Adult weight 15-20gm (5½-7oz).
Colour Very variable. *Rattus rattus rattus* is pure black above, black or dark grey beneath; *R.r.alexandrinus* is grey-brown above, grey beneath; *R.r.frugivorus* is brown above, white or cream beneath. The three forms interbreed.
Breeding season All year, especially in summer.
Gestation 21 days.
No of young 5-10, average 7. 27 have been recorded.
Lifespan Maximum 18 months, most die in first winter.
Food Omnivorous. Fruit, vegetables, cereals.
Predators Man, domestic cat.

Pardoner's Tale, rat poison was available from apothecaries. In some areas 'ratoners' or ratcatchers were employed, and rats were sold in villages for a farthing each.

Black death The black rat is the main host of the flea that transmits the bacillus causing bubonic plague, and outbreaks of 'Black Death', as it was known, followed the rat's progress westwards. It reached Britain in 1348 and about one third of the population died. It reappeared several times and the last epidemic, known as the Great Plague, occurred in 1665, killing many thousands of people. The disease was destroyed in London in the Great Fire of 1666.

Medieval physicians, who knew nothing of germs, tried to treat plague symptoms—swellings, boils, tumours and delirium—by bleeding or fasting, both of which had a weakening effect and made the sufferer even more likely to die. Today plague still occurs, especially in under-developed areas of the world with poor housing and hygiene. A vaccine can now provide partial immunisation and the disease can be treated with drugs.

Three forms Colouring is an unreliable way to distinguish rats: some brown rats are almost black, while black rats have a variety of brown forms. There are three sub-species of black rat in Britain: *Rattus rattus rattus* has a black coat with a black or dark grey underside; the Alexandrine rat (*R.r.alexandrinus*) is brown above and grey beneath; and the tree or roof rat (*R.r.frugivorus*) is brown above and white or cream beneath. They can live together and interbreed, resulting in many colour gradations.

High life In the tropics and sub-tropics black rats often live in palm trees, fruit plantations and bushes. In Britain, too, they are less terrestrial than brown rats. Around seaports they are commonly found in warehouses and other waterside buildings where they inhabit rafters and wall cavities on the upper floors, while brown rats usually live in basements or in burrows outside.

Black rats are expert climbers, capable of ascending vertical wires, cables, walls and pipes, provided the surface is not too smooth. They cross between buildings and over streets along overhead wires and trees. They are more agile than brown rats, and move more rapidly, sprinting along, then pausing at a vantage point on a rafter or ledge for a moment before running off again.

Where rats have regular runways and their fur brushes against a wall or other object they leave black greasy smears. 'Loop' smears, semi-circular marks where the rats have had to swing under a rafter or pipe, are especially characteristic. Other signs of their presence are gnawed cables and pipes, a musty odour and damage to stored goods. They leave droppings anywhere, particularly at their feeding places. In grain stores droppings contaminate large quantities of food.

Black rats eat almost anything of nutritional

Which rat?

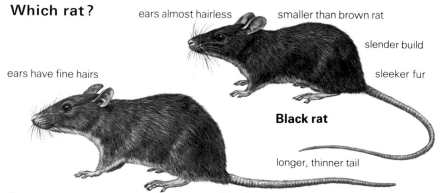

ears almost hairless   smaller than brown rat

slender build

sleeker fur

Black rat

ears have fine hairs

longer, thinner tail

Brown rat

tail is shorter than body
—one of the best ways of telling them apart

value. They are more vegetarian than brown rats, with a distinct preference for fruit. They forage within a range of 80-90m (262-295ft) for food, both inside and outside buildings, although some males may move farther afield. They are mainly nocturnal but some individuals, usually the less dominant, may forage in daylight.

Social life Black rats live in groups of up to several hundred animals. There are dominant and subordinate males, and females and juveniles in each group. Individuals recognise each other by smell, and within small colonies the social positions are well defined and there is little aggression. A newcomer is likely to be attacked. If he ignores the dominant

Black rat distribution

Aberdeen

Glasgow

Newcastle

Dublin   Liverpool   Hull

London

Southampton

Rat kings There is no adequate explanation for 'rat kings'—dead rats found with their tails mysteriously and elaborately knotted together, and recorded throughout the world over hundreds of years. Have the tails become soaked with urine and then frozen? Have the rats been frightened, tried to escape, and got knotted together? Or have they brought something sticky into the nest?

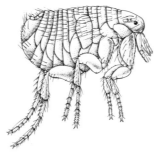

Above: Black rats are susceptible to bubonic plague which is spread by the rat flea (*Xenopsylla cheopis*). The flea feeds on an infected rat, then moves to another rat or human, so transmitting the disease. Bubonic plague is named after the swellings or 'buboes' of the lymph nodes in the armpits and groin. Today it is treated with drugs.

Left: The tree or roof rat, a subspecies of the black rat, most closely resembles the wild subspecies from which the other forms have arisen.

Below: A black rat grooming its tail.

rat's threat postures – an arching of the back with all four limbs extended and the flank turned towards the opponent, followed by mincing movements around the newcomer – the resident leaps at him and bites the ears, legs or tail.

Boxing, in which both animals stand on their hind legs and strike with their paws, sometimes occurs in the interval between more violent bouts of fighting. Fights are always between individuals, but a stranger may be attacked by a number of resident males in succession until it is ejected. Excitement can spread throughout the colony until all the animals are leaping wildly about. In larger colonies the social order occasionally breaks down and intruders may no longer be recognised.

Prolific breeders Black rats breed all year, reaching a peak in summer and sometimes in autumn. The female builds the nest with any available soft material in a wall cavity, among rafters, below floorboards or behind pipes. There are three to five litters of five to ten young each year. The male's involvement in rearing the young is actively discouraged by the female, for cannibalism by male rats is common.

The young are sexually mature at three or four months old, but by then many will have died from predation, poisoning and other causes. Man is the chief predator, but the domestic cat also catches rats. Few rats live

Ships' rats

Cones prevent rats from entering or leaving ship

More than 90% of rats found aboard ships are black rats. They boarded ships among stores, or climbed mooring ropes of ships in harbour and were unintentionally transported throughout the world. The vessels of explorers such as Captain Cook were heavily infested with black rats. Human populations have been devastated by them: in 1686, the 30 inhabitants of North Rona, between the Hebrides and the Shetlands, were eaten out of house and home by black rats that came ashore from a shipwreck. The entire population starved to death, and the rats soon after. There are now compulsory regulations to ensure that rat infestation on ships is minimised. Port Health Authorities are required to issue either 'de-ratting' or 'exemption' certificates, depending on whether a ship requires fumigation or is free from rats; permanent baits are common.

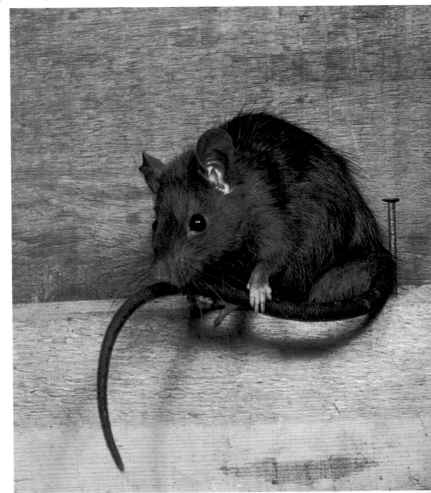

longer than 18 months, and the annual mortality rate is 91-97%.

Black rats have highly developed hearing and scurry into hiding if they hear an unfamiliar sound. Their sense of smell is also acute, but their eyesight is rather poor. Both species of rat tend to keep to familiar areas and runways, but black rats do not show such a marked avoidance of strange objects, such as traps, placed in their territory. Brown rats tend to avoid unfamiliar objects for 48 hours or more.

The black rat's decline By 1845 the black rat was thought almost to have vanished from London, and a ratcatcher of St Giles was able to sell specimens to naturalists from a stall in Trafalgar Square for three guineas each. In fact the rat was still common in some areas, and it is probable that observers were mistaking the brown forms–the roof rat and the Alexandrine rat–for brown rats.

It was not until this century that the black rat population began to decline rapidly. This is most likely due to our increased standards of hygiene and improved buildings, so that it is hard for rats to find warm homes. Where they do occur they are prime targets for control, and every effort is made to prevent them arriving from abroad.

A number of theories directly implicate the brown rat as a cause of the decline. One belief–that the brown rat kills the black and takes its territory–is certainly untrue. While it is a fact that in a direct confrontation between the species the heavier and more aggressive brown rat almost certainly wins, such an event seldom occurs. Both species live in and around the same buildings and there is often a considerable overlap in their ranges, but as brown rats often nest in the lower parts of buildings, or in burrows outside, and the black rat nests within the framework and in the upper stories, confrontation and competition is lessened.

Whatever the reason for the decline, it is likely to continue, and although black rats remain in several localities, even in small numbers and despite the precautions that allow little new blood to arrive from abroad, the future for the species looks very bleak.

Above: Although rats are generally considered to be dirty and unhygienic, frequenting sewers and other insanitary places, the black rat is cleaner in its feeding habits than the brown, and spends much time meticulously grooming its fur, tail and paws.

Left: Jack Black, Her Majesty's Ratcatcher, around 1850.

Below: A black rat with young. Rats have three to five litters a year.

SUCCESS AND THE BROWN RAT

Brown rats arrived in Britain about 250 years ago. Since then they have established themselves as major pests, and still resist man's attempts at control.

The brown rat arrived in Britain late by comparison with most other mammals, yet it is now more widespread than many which have been here far longer. The key to its undoubted success is its versatility. It is small enough to move about unnoticed, and is well camouflaged by its dull greyish brown coat.

Before the arrival of the brown rat the common rat was the black or ship rat, now found only in ports. However, it is unlikely that the brown rat contributed significantly to the decline of the black. Black rats came from the Mediterranean and, in this country, can only survive in a warm, indoor environment. By contrast, the brown rat is a native of the great Russian steppes and finds few climates too inhospitable.

Habitat The brown rat thrives wherever man grows food and stores it for himself and his animals, provided there is enough cover for living and nesting. Rats often make their homes under sheds and other raised buildings. They gain access to the foundations of houses through damaged air bricks or cracked brickwork. Once inside a house, the rats soon have the run of it, especially when there are wooden floors through which they can gnaw. Sometimes, if the cover on a sewer stench pipe is missing, rats may get into a building at roof level. Where property is empty and damaged, broken bathroom fittings may allow rats to invade surface premises from the sewers below.

Rats produce litters rapidly and as a result large numbers soon build up and spread to any suitable habitats nearby. Two unusual environments in which brown rats have been successful are coal mines and sewers. Rats are rare today in mines, but still cause problems in sewers.

Although mainly associated with urban areas and man-made installations, the brown rat also lives in the open countryside in most parts of the British Isles. Many country rats make their way into farm buildings in winter, but some live in the hedgerows throughout the year, using underground burrows for shelter and nesting. Rats are capable of excavating their own burrows, but often move into disused rabbit warrens to save themselves the trouble.

Signs of activity If you look closely along the base of hedges, you may see well-worn runways leading to the entrances of underground burrows. The tracks of the brown rat show up in mud and snow. They are characterised by the deep impression made by the claws. In the fields, brown rats dig up the germinating corn and leave a series of telltale 'scrapes' behind. They also dig up the roots of many wild plants.

In buildings, the presence of rats can be detected by droppings or body smears. The droppings of the brown rat are sausage-shaped, often pointed at one or both ends, and about 12mm ($\frac{1}{2}$in) long. The dark body smears around the edges of rat holes in woodwork or stones, and on places which rats rub against regularly in passing, are produced by the greasy secretions of skin glands.

Harmful carriers Damage to food and the fabric of buildings is one reason why rats are undesirable visitors. Another, perhaps more important, reason is that they carry certain diseases, some of which are serious and even fatal to man and domestic animals.

The urine of many rats carries spirochaete bacteria called leptospires. These can survive in damp surroundings and infect people, cattle and domesticated animals through cuts and abrasions. Once in the new host, the bacteria multiply in the blood stream and invade the liver, causing jaundice, before finally settling in the kidneys. In the most severe cases, they cause death by kidney failure. Known as leptospirosis or Weil's disease, this was once a serious occupational hazard for coal miners, farm workers and sewermen. Although much less common today, because of the reduction in the number of rats, it still occurs occasionally.

Above: Access to a grain store ensures a rat colony plentiful food supplies through even the harshest of winters. In these ideal conditions, breeding is continuous.

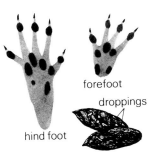

forefoot

droppings

hind foot

BROWN RAT (*Rattus norvegicus*). Also known as common rat, Norway rat, sewer rat
Size of adult Max weight 500g (18oz). Max length (excluding tail) 28cm (11in). Female smaller
Colour Grey-brown on back, paler underneath
Breeding season In a constant environment with plenty of food, breeding may be continuous. Elsewhere, mainly summer and autumn
Gestation 21-24 days
No of young Average 7-8
Lifespan Average 1-2 years
Food Eats almost anything. Feeds on cereals when available
Predators Man. Young: weasels, stoats, mink, foxes, owls
Distribution Throughout British Isles except a few small islands and more exposed mountains

Above: Nests are loosely constructed out of straw, rags, feathers or any other available material. The size of the litter depends on the size of the mother: 16 is normal for a large rat, 6 for a small one. The young rats are born naked and blind. Their eyes open six days after birth, and they are weaned after about three weeks.

Below: As both parasite and scavenger, the brown rat mainly depends on man for food and shelter. It is common around man-made installations such as farm buildings, warehouses and sewers. Even in the open it pilfers the germinating corn from the soil and, later, the ripened grain from the harvest.

Infected farm stock can pass the disease on to humans.

One of the risks of eating underdone pork is that it may contain a rat parasite. This is a small roundworm which lives in rat muscle. Pigs sometimes eat infected rats and, when this happens, the worm encysts in the pig flesh. Thorough cooking will kill the worm, but if infected pork is not properly cooked and is then eaten, the worms may settle in various parts of the human body, including the eye, and cause severe damage.

Battle for control Until the middle of this century, rats were endemic around farms, slaughter houses and food warehouses, and their numbers were far greater than today.

During World War II, extensive research was carried out on rat control, in the hope that losses to precious stocks of imported food could be avoided. In the course of this work, an important behavioural characteristic was noticed.

If a new object was introduced into the rats' familiar environment, they would avoid it – unlike mice, who eagerly explore new materials. This explained why poisons had until then been relatively ineffective. The rats treated newly placed poison bait as a new object and only nibbled tentatively. As a result, they ate only enough poison to feel ill. To make matters worse, they then associated their illness with the poison and its food base.

Following this discovery, the technique of prebaiting was developed. Unpoisoned bait was placed for a few nights to encourage the rats to begin eating with confidence. Poison was then mixed with the bait and the rats ate swiftly enough to take in a lethal dose.

This method of control had the disadvantage of being labour intensive and in the early 1950s a new poison was developed. This was an anticoagulant, called Warfarin, which prevented the blood clotting and caused the poisoned rats to die of haemorrhages. More usefully, however, the rats did not associate their deteriorating health with either the poison or its base. Because the method involved regular daily doses over a week or more, it was economical on manpower.

Brown rats have been successful in most habitats. Because they produce large numbers of offspring rapidly, any genetic changes operate relatively quickly throughout a population. In Scotland and the West Midlands, some rats have become 'Warfarin resistant' and this resistance can be genetically transmitted to the young.

This development has been a blow to rodent control and has meant both a return to the older poisons and a search for new ones. The evidence from the past history of the brown rat seems to indicate that this adaptable species will continue to survive.

FERAL CATS: BACK TO NATURE

Feral cats – cats whose ancestors were domesticated but are themselves living wild – have existed for generations around towns, farms and the wild places of Britain.

A feral cat is one that was once domesticated, or whose ancestors were domesticated, but which has reverted to the wild state. The cat was one of the last animals to be domesticated, and adapts easily to a wild, free-living existence. However, the feral cat does not live only in towns, for, in addition to the marauding alley cats slinking in the shadows of back streets, generations of feral cats have lived on the fells and other wild places of Britain. As we sailed out on voyages of exploration so our cats travelled too, and many islands throughout the world now also have feral cat populations.

Scottish relatives The domestic cat is closely related to the forest wild cat (*Felis sylvestris*) or, as it has become known in Britain, the Scottish wild cat. This relationship is made even closer by the fact that the two varieties can, and do, interbreed.

Feral populations Areas of suburban housing, with their usually large domestic cat populations, are not conducive to the formation of feral colonies. Therefore in towns, feral cat colonies tend to form in non-housing places such as hospital compounds and factories. Here they may use an area such as a square as a communal meeting place. In the countryside, feral cats do not usually encounter the problems of competition for territories, although they may have to compete with domestic or semi-feral cats at prime sites such as farms and factories. Food is normally scarcer than in towns, and this factor alone helps to regulate feral populations in out-of-town areas.

In Britain a large percentage of the cat population is living in a feral condition, usually by their own endeavours. In towns and cities, and particularly in the huge conurbation of London, there is a far higher population of feral cats than the available food could support, were it not for the vast army of auxiliary feeders – usually elderly ladies – who provide food for many of them.

Social graces Feral cats may, on meeting others of their group, raise tails in greeting, and rub heads and flanks in a very social manner – even though cats normally prefer to

Above: Feral cats living in the countryside – like this one with tabby markings discovered on a moorland track – are usually in surprisingly good condition. Feral animals living in such places must rely normally on their own hunting abilities to catch food and, as with any other wild population of animals, the strongest survive.

'keep their distance'. Similarly, during the day when much of their time is spent resting, related cats may sleep side by side. In particular, sub-adults often stay near their mother. As well as reinforcing social group bonds, such contacts also transfer scent, which leads to a group identity.

Most members of the cat family live in forest or woodland, where it is not possible to scan territory visually, and therefore scent marking is important. Toms (males) have a home range approximately ten times greater than the area patrolled by queens (females). Toms mark out their territory with a characteristic strongly smelling spray, but all cats also mark their territory in less obvious ways. They have scent glands under the chin, on the top of the head, along the midline of the back and also along the tail.

The glands that provided the scent during social contact are also used when marking out the territory. Scent is normally transferred to some prominent object so that it serves as a warning to any cats entering the territory. The end of an obstacle such as a low twig or straw projecting into the cat's path is closely investigated by careful sniffing, after which the cat usually rubs the side of its chin against the end of the obstacle, or at least brushes its body against it. In towns, feral cats adopt the same tactics, rubbing themselves against the sides of fences, buildings and other structures. Car hubcaps, too, seem to be favourite sites.

This simple act fulfils a number of functions. The cat is able to determine if it was the last cat to pass that way or, if another cat has passed by, it also enables an 'identikit' to be built up on the cat in question, giving information such as the sex and state of sexual maturity. This explains why a cat will in-

scent stick

Above: Examining a 'scent stick' (left) can tell one cat a great deal about another. Scent can be transmitted from glands on the head, back, tail and under the chin. Females often spend several minutes 'chinning' the ground (right).

Right: The image of a cat as a solitary animal is confounded by feral cats, where strong family ties exist and where a hierarchy with a 'pecking order' is established.

Below: Feral cats frequently use non-territorial areas, such as a town square, as a communal meeting place, especially if they have become accustomed to finding food there.

vestigate such a 'scent stick' even if it can see the other cat walking on ahead.

Hunting The feral cat is an enterprising opportunist. As a member of the cat family it is, among mammals, the supreme solitary hunter, and catching live prey presents no problem. On isolated islands off Scotland where no man is present, generations of feral cats have had to depend on their impressive armoury of keen senses and stiletto-fine teeth and claws to catch prey in order to survive. They prey on nesting seabirds and their young, but nonetheless also readily scavenge carrion. Likewise on the mainland feral cats will as readily devour a road-casualty rabbit as one they have killed themselves. Similarly, the presence of man nearly always means there is a greater variety of scavengable food available – not just for the feral cat but also for other nocturnal opportunists like the fox, hedgehog, rats and mice.

In towns and cities, our waste provides a super-abundance of food, which is largely responsible for the high urban density of the fox as well as the urban feral cat. Changes in the type of refuse to be found in dustbins – less ash due to a reduction in coal fires meaning less contaminated scraps – and the increase in the use of plastic bags to hold refuse, means that these containers are easy and valuable prey to the deft razor-sharp claws of scavenging cats. Certainly the urban feral cat finds this more profitable in terms of energy expenditure than chasing pigeons in the park. Cats are rather inept at catching adult birds, anyway, never seeming to have understood the sneaky escape route of flight.

Producing offspring In towns, feral cats usually seek quiet, undisturbed places within the home territory in which to have their litters. Some unusual places have been recorded, including overturned dustbins and the back seats of cars. In the countryside, anywhere which offers a suitable den may be chosen, haylofts in old farm outbuildings being a particular favourite.

Due to the lack of veterinary care, ailments such as eye infections and the dreaded cat 'flu are common among feral cats. As a result, kitten mortalities tend to reduce litter size to about four, which is more compatible with food availability than the larger litters reared by domestic cats.

There are examples of feral offspring being successfully reared in a domestic situation, although these kittens usually exhibit more aggressive behaviour and are generally less tractable than the offspring of domestic cats.

The offspring of a feral tom cat and a domestic queen (female) can usually be reared successfully as pets. Domestic cats, unlike all other domesticated animals, are free-roaming once they escape the confines of the house. They have their own home ranges and defended territories like any truly wild animal, and a feral tom can compete for a domestic queen in just the same way as a domestic tom.

Above: Family portrait. Hay lofts provide the ideal place for producing and rearing a litter of kittens. Feral cats may also mate with Scottish wild cats and domestic cats.

Above: Despite the alert, crouched hunting techniques adopted by cats, many attempts end in disaster.

Below: Eye sores, like the one from which this feral cat is suffering, are common.

The feral cat's future

Although in the countryside feral cats have been very successful for centuries with little or no harmful effect on the environment, in certain places they are considered, on health grounds, to have been too successful. Hospitals in particular, with underground networks of ducting, surrounding grounds with shrubs, huge bins of waste and often a soft-hearted nurse offering extra food, have become a popular focal point for many feral cats. The health authorities have for many years tried to enforce a policy of eradication, which in urban areas has failed. More recently, it has been realised that biological control through an understanding of the feral cat's way of life is a more acceptable way of dealing with the problem. Instead of trapping and killing the cats, a proportion of the animals are neutered, medically examined and then returned to the site. The presence of these cats tends to stop others straying into their territories, but means that numbers do not increase.

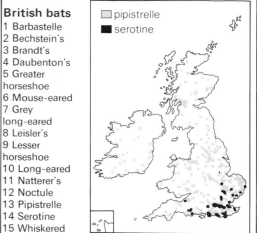

British bats
1 Barbastelle
2 Bechstein's
3 Brandt's
4 Daubenton's
5 Greater
horseshoe
6 Mouse-eared
7 Grey
long-eared
8 Leisler's
9 Lesser
horseshoe
10 Long-eared
11 Natterer's
12 Noctule
13 Pipistrelle
14 Serotine
15 Whiskered

☐ pipistrelle
■ serotine

TOWN BATS: SEROTINE & PIPISTRELLE

The serotine and pipistrelle are urban bats, most often found roosting in buildings in towns and villages.

Above: The pipistrelle is one of the first bats to emerge at dusk, usually beginning flights about 20 minutes after sunset in southern Britain but up to one hour later in the north.

Below: Portrait of a pipistrelle. This species is widespread throughout most of the British Isles, but the serotine is confined to southern Britain.

Both serotine and pipistrelle bats are robust, chunky looking mammals with short, dog-like faces which are covered by many glandular swellings. They have thicker forearms and shorter thumbs than most other species of bats. The lobes on their calcars (the cartilaginous spurs running from the feet towards the tail) are distinctive. Both bats generally have dark red-brown fur but their colour varies more than that of other bats, ranging from pale brown to almost black.

The serotine is usually found in urban areas, where it roosts in the roofs of buildings, but it is also seen in woodland. The pipistrelle – again a typically urban bat – is more widespread, frequenting farmland and open moorland as well as towns and cities.

Food and foraging: pipistrelle The pipistrelle has tiny, very sharp teeth. These are ideally suited to chewing the soft bodies of small insects, such as caddisflies, which form the bulk of its diet. Its flight is fast and rather jerky–it often flies low over the ground, twisting and turning as it searches for flying insects.

Like all bats, pipistrelles are creatures of habit and tend to follow the same routes each night. However, should food become scarce in one area, they quickly change to new hunting grounds.

Pipistrelles leave their daytime roosts at dusk and fly along hedgerows, rivers and streams, catching small flying insects which they usually eat on the wing. However, slightly larger insects may be taken to a perch to be consumed. On summer nights, pipistrelles are often seen flying at a height of only 20cm to 2m (8in to 6½ft) over water, picking up adult caddisflies and other insects as they take flight after emerging from their nymphal or pupal stages.

When the bat's stomach is full it comes to rest on a tree or a bridge, and stays there until digestion has progressed sufficiently to allow further feeding. On warm, humid nights when there is a plentiful supply of insects, pipistrelles will have several feeding bouts, resting between each one.

During their foraging expeditions pipistrelles often travel many kilometres from their daytime roosts and may occupy temporary roosts during the night, only returning to the daytime roost at dawn.

Food and foraging: serotine Serotine bats have powerful jaws and long, strong teeth which enable them to crush the hard cases of even quite large beetles. These, together with large moths, are their usual diet.

Like pipistrelles, serotine bats emerge from their roosts when it is still fairly light. They usually head straight for the cover of trees where they are less visible to predators such as owls. They feed over grassland or in parkland, but always near to trees. Serotines are heavy and slow on the wing, usually flying straight and level but occasionally swooping down to catch an insect.

Many insects are caught as they fly up to the trees for mating, having just emerged from the grass. Many large chafer beetles are caught in May and June in this way. These beetles spend up to four years as larvae in the soil and are caught just after they become airborne but while still flying slowly. Serotines often eat their prey in flight, cruising slowly and dropping the hard wing cases, wings and legs but chewing and swallowing the rest. Chewing sounds are clearly audible from many metres away. Serotines, and another large bat the noctule, can be attracted by an observer who tosses small pebbles slightly ahead of the bats. Mistaking these for insects, they swoop down – sometimes even catching the pebble before realising their mistake.

Roosts for all seasons Bats are heterothermic, which means that their body temperature is not constant but dependent on the temperature of their surroundings and whether they have eaten. Roosts are therefore

Above: A pipistrelle bat at rest hangs upside down, clinging to surfaces by means of its strong, clawed feet. It is the smallest British bat – its head and body together measuring only 4cm (1½in) in length. It has a wing span of 18-23cm (8in). The fine soft fur is normally reddish brown but can vary considerably, ranging from pale brown to nearly black.

Above: Portrait of a serotine bat. Notice its short, doglike face and its powerful jaws with long teeth with which it can crush large beetles.
The ears are large with a short rounded tragus (a prominent lobe of the lower ear).

Left: A serotine bat crawling up a stone wall. It uses its thumbs to pull itself forward while it pushes with its backward-directed hind feet. The serotine's tail extends beyond the membrane.

chosen with great care so as to ensure adequate warmth and a good food supply. During extremes of weather one roost may be abandoned for another. If non-flying young are present they are carried to the new site by their mother.

An individual colony may occupy several different sites in succession during a year. On a modern housing estate every house along the road may be occupied at some time.

Both bats are, typically, urban dwellers usually found in houses in villages and towns. Almost all their known breeding colonies are in buildings, although individuals and small groups sometimes roost in other places, such as in hollow trees or behind loose bark, and sometimes even in exposed positions under leaves or hanging from branches. Contrary to popular belief, the buildings favoured by bats tend to be new rather than old. Colonies have even been known to move into unfinished buildings.

In a recent survey nearly half of several pipistrelle colonies were discovered in houses less than 25 years old. Serotines tend to be found in slightly older buildings, although they do seem to favour new houses with hollow walls into which they crawl to hibernate, gaining access where the roof meets the walls.

Both species tend to roost in confined spaces such as behind barge boards, weather boarding or hanging tiles, above soffits or in hollow walls. Roost temperatures of 59°C (138°F) have been recorded in such places. Under these conditions the bats pant vigorously, sweat and eventually crawl to a cooler place, possible under the eaves.

During the summer the females form nursery roosts, but the adult males are usually solitary. The nursery roosts are generally on the south side of buildings so as to receive heat from the sun during the day. This is particularly important to pipistrelle bats because they are tiny and therefore get cold very quickly. Roosting in warm sites and in large clusters reduces the amount of energy expended on maintaining body temperature and means that more energy is available for the development of the foetus.

A few nursery colonies of more than a 1000 bats have been recorded, but the average colony size is 50 to 100 animals.

The breeding cycle Mating occurs in autumn but fertilisation is not immediate. The female stores the sperm in her uterus during hibernation, and fertilisation eventually takes place in April or May. The length of gestation is dependent upon the weather and as a result births may occur as early as the second week of June but most occur in the last week of that month. Each female gives birth to a single youngster which she immediately suckles. The young bats grow quickly and start to fly at only three weeks old.

Hibernation Little is known about where pipistrelle or serotine bats hibernate as they

are rarely found in winter. However, it appears that, like most bats, the males and females hibernate together. Different species of bats require different temperatures during hibernation; pipistrelle and serotine prefer cool temperatures down to 2°C (36°F).

Pipistrelles hibernate from late November until late March and serotines from late September until the end of April.

Above: A pipistrelle mother with her offspring. Only one baby is born, usually in the last week of June. The young grow quickly and begin to fly at three weeks old. If mother and young become separated the baby calls loudly and the mother collects it.

Left: A young serotine bat —the young are almost completely hairless at birth.

PIPISTRELLE BAT
(*Pipistrellus pipistrellus*)
Size Forearm 28-35mm (1in), head and body 4cm (1½in), weight 5-7gm (⅕oz).
Colour Brown, pale buff, red, chocolate, sometimes blackish. Paler below, often greyish.
Breeding season Autumn and winter.
Gestation 45-70 days.
Number of young One, born in June.
Food Caddisflies and small moths.
Predators Hawks, owls and men.
Distribution Widespread throughout the British Isles.

SEROTINE BAT
(*Eptesicus serotinus*)
Size Forearm 48-55mm (2in), head and body 6cm (2½in), weight 15-30gm (½-1oz).
Colour Usually dark red-brown, but can be almost black. Underparts paler.
Breeding Autumn and winter.
Number of young 1.
Food Large beetles and moths.
Predators See pipistrelle.
Distribution South Wales and southern England south of the Wash.

Where to look for bats

Serotines and pipistrelles are typical house bats, favouring buildings less than 25 years old. Both bats tend to roost between the outer covering and the ceiling of flat roofs (**1**), or behind hanging tiles (**2**). Loose window frames (**3**) where the cement has dropped out are typical points of access. Bats roost in hollow walls (**4**), particularly near the apex of the gable where they get in through a slit between the soffit and the wall.
Loose lead flashing around a chimney (**5**) gives access to the roof space. Bats may be found under ridge tiles (**6**), behind drain pipes (**7**) or between roof felt and tiles (**8**).

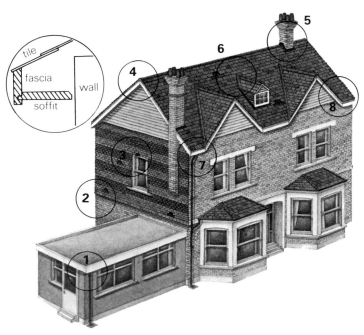

THE BAT WITH LONG EARS

The name of the long-eared bat is an understatement: the ears are huge – almost as long as the rest of the body – and they play a vital role in the detection of prey.

Of all the British bats, the long-eared is the most distinctive. No other mammal has ears that are nearly as long as its body. In fact, the ears of the long-eared bat are so big that they can often be seen even when it is in flight – making identification easy. With its long, soft fur, large eyes (for a bat) and delicate wings, it is a quiet attractive mammal with inoffensive habits.

Echo location A bat finds its way about in the dark by means of echo location. It emits

high intensity, ultrasonic sounds (too high-pitched for us to hear), which are reflected from objects in its path. From the patterns of the remaining echoes the bat can interpret its surroundings and avoid flying into obstacles.

The same mechanism is used to catch insect prey. Echoes bounce off even the smallest midge and alert the bat to the presence of a potential meal. All British bats are capable of intercepting flying insects in this way, and probably compete for similar prey. But this leaves a whole range of suitable food items untouched – the insects, caterpillars and spiders which do not fly but crawl about among tree-top vegetation instead. Most bats fly too fast to notice these creatures, and in any case probably cannot differentiate between the echo of, say, a caterpillar and the leaf on which it is resting.

This is where the long-eared bat comes into its own. Instead of emitting loud echo location sounds which just bounce off foliage indiscriminately, this bat whispers. Its ultrasonic noises are so quiet and sensitive that it can tell the difference between an echo from an insect and what it is sitting on. The huge ears detect these minute echoes, and also

Above: The long-eared bat is a nocturnal mammal, foraging by night. In flight the sensitive ears are held erect, directed forwards so they can detect insect prey by echo location. When the bat is at rest or crawling about, the ears crinkle along their outer edges and are then lowered over the shoulders.

There are two long-eared bats in Britain, the common and the grey. The grey (*Plecotus austriacus*) is very difficult to distinguish from the common and there are no external features which provide positive identification of every specimen. Generally speaking the grey long-eared bat has darker fur than the common, which is browner. The presence of the grey was overlooked in Britain until 1963, and even now little is known about it. So far it has been identified only in southern England, though it may be more widespread.

Naming the parts of a long-eared bat

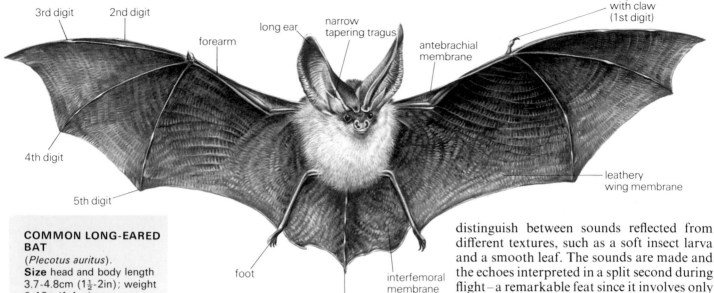

3rd digit
2nd digit
forearm
long ear
narrow tapering tragus
antebrachial membrane
long thumb with claw (1st digit)
4th digit
5th digit
foot
tail
interfemoral membrane
leathery wing membrane

COMMON LONG-EARED BAT
(*Plecotus auritus*).
Size head and body length 3.7-4.8cm (1½-2in); weight 6-12g (⅕-¼oz); on average males weigh 10% less than females.
Colour yellow-buff on top, buff underneath.
Breeding season Summer.
No of young One a year.
Lifespan 20 or more years.
Food Mostly moths, insects.
Predators Owls, cats.
Distribution widespread, except N of Scotland.

Below: A long-eared bat at rest on a tree trunk. Bats are harmless and, even when handled roughly, rarely bite or protest in any way. This bat is most common in southern England, becoming scarcer in the north and even absent from parts of Scotland.

distinguish between sounds reflected from different textures, such as a soft insect larva and a smooth leaf. The sounds are made and the echoes interpreted in a split second during flight – a remarkable feat since it involves only part of the bat's brain, the whole of which is smaller than a pea.

Foraging The task of catching insects is made easier for the long-eared bat by its ability to hover at an angle of 30°. The long-eared bat can pick food delicately and precisely off foliage and bark, and perhaps even from the ground. As well as the usual flying insects, its diet therefore includes a whole range of invertebrates gleaned from trees which other bats do not manage to exploit.

In late summer especially, the long-eared bat takes large numbers of noctuid moths, snapped up on the wing and carried off to a convenient perch to be dismembered and eaten. Usually the moth wings and legs are discarded, and a little heap of such litter accumulates below the perch.

Attic nurseries The long-eared bat's habit of using feeding roosts near human habitation, and its ability to hover and fly in confined spaces make it likely to be one of the species that flies into bedrooms at night through open windows. It is difficult to be more precise since few people favoured by such a visit stop to check the identity of the intruder.

The long-eared bat mostly roosts in attics. Groups of up to two dozen females gather in attics in summer to bear their young. They are usually so quiet that they easily pass unnoticed by the householder, and can raise their young undisturbed. Attics make good bat nurseries because they are warm; higher temperatures mean faster growth and development for the young. On cool days the bats huddle together to warm their offspring. Such a colony does no harm, and may help to keep the roof space clear of moths, spiders and destructive beetles.

The young are born in June and July. Each female never has more than one baby a year, and none at all in some years. The population thus increases only slowly. When a colony is wiped out it may take a decade to recoup.

A low breeding rate is characteristic of bats -probably because their babies are so big. Each weighs nearly a third as much as its mother at birth. Under natural conditions bats do not need to produce large numbers of offspring as they have few predators to fear. The long-eared, for example, is occasionally taken by owls and cats, but is otherwise safe -except from destruction by humans.

Adult males do not usually roost with nursing females, and take no part in rearing the young. They meet up with the females again once the young have been weaned and the nursery colony has dispersed for the winter.

Three-month hibernation Like other insectivorous animals, the long-eared bat faces a critical shortage of food once the colder nights of autumn begin. Two options are open to it: flying south to warmer places, or staying put and drastically reducing energy requirements by hibernating.

It seems that long-eared bats normally hibernate, often staying close to where they have spent the summer months. They usually hibernate in trees and buildings, though sometimes use caves, mines and other similarly cool places. Their preferred hibernating temperature is probably about 0°C (32°F). They would be forced into unnecessary and unwelcome activity if they hibernated somewhere that became too warm on sunny winter days. Winter activity is undesirable because there is little chance of recouping the fat reserves used to provide energy for flight. If the bat finds a suitable place, it may well hibernate for over three months.

During hibernation the large ears pose a problem. Precarious moisture may evaporate from their large surface and, even when this difficulty is avoided by the choice of a cool, humid place to pass the winter, they are still vulnerable to frostbite. The ears could get in the way if the bat wanted to crawl into a more

Above: The long-eared bat favours open woodland with deciduous trees that provide shelter and abundant insects. Below: A nursing colony of long-eared bats in a house roof – there are two grey babies on the left, being kept warm by the females' bodies. Males take no part in rearing young.

sheltered crevice, so the problem is solved by folding the ears backwards.

Hibernation ends in March in the south of England, probably later in the north – though this varies with the prevailing weather. Mating takes place soon after hibernation ends, or perhaps earlier during periods of wakefulness in winter. When they wake up the bats start feeding to recoup the 20% or more of lost weight.

Nocturnal sorties Long-eared bats become active within the day roost at about sunset every night, emerging from the nooks and crannies where they have passed the day. They may spend up to an hour or so making short flights and grooming their silky fur. Cleanliness is important: if the long fine fur becomes matted, it loses its insulation, streamlining and rain-proofing properties.

Once it is fully dark, the bats go out to forage. Sometimes they stay out all night; at other times – especially if there is plenty of food about, or if there are babies to be fed – they may return within the hour, perhaps making another sortie later. Long-eared bats normally manage to find all the food they need without having to fly far from home.

Occasionally, some long-eared bats appear to make extensive journeys out to sea. They have turned up among night-migrating birds attracted to offshore lighthouses. In 1968 one was found dead on a lightship in the North Sea, 31 miles out from Great Yarmouth.

INDEX

The entries listed in **bold** type refer to main subjects. The page numbers in *italics* indicate illustrations. Medium type entries refer to the text.

ACKNOWLEDGEMENTS

Photographers' credits A-Z Collection 45 (top), 65, 66; Allison & Busby 175; Mike Amphlett 27 (middle, bottom), 28 (top); Heather Angel 8, 12, 14 (top), 16 (bottom), 21, 24 (lower middle), 29, 33, 35, 36, 39, 48 (top), 49 (middle), 55, 60, 62 (middle), 73, 78, 81, 83, 84, 97, 106 (top), 107 (bottom), 109, 113, 116, 117, 186 (bottom); Animal Graphics 182 (middle); Aquila Photographics/AW Cundall 14 (bottom); Sister Daniel 41; EA Janes 140 (top); T Leach 139 (top); RA Mather 90 (top); AT Moffett 129 (bottom), 147 (bottom); J Roberts 72 (bottom); CJ Smale 148 (bottom); W Walter 30 (middle); MC Wilkes 127 (top), 131 (bottom), 134 (bottom), 141 (bottom); Ian Beames 19, 41, 68 (top), 89, 96 (top), 145, 148 (middle), 159, 161 (bottom); Biofotos/G Kinns 174; Bob Gibbons Photography/R Fletcher 33 (bottom), 82 (bottom left), 88 (top), 90 (bottom), 119 (top), 121 (top left), 165 (bottom); Bob Gibbons 16 (middle), 63; P Wilson 107 (bottom); Bruce Coleman Ltd/Jane Burton 6-7, 95 (middle left), 103, 172, 176 (top), 180 (top), 185 (top), 189 (top); Bruce Coleman 64; Eric Crichton 58, 62 (bottom); M Dakin 91; S Dalton 122-3; AJ Deave 149; G Langsbury 135; John Markham 176 (bottom), 177 (top, bottom right); Hans Reinhard 13, 164, 166; K Taylor front cover, 34 (top), 94 (top); Norman Tomalin 150; Michael Chinery 24 (bottom), 57; A Cleave 42 (top); David Corke 30 (top), 104; Adrian Davies 100; Department of Transport 40; Martin Dohrn 162; Eric Crichton Photos 56 (bottom); Vaughan Fleming 44 (middle), 59 (top); Dennis Green 20 (bottom), 132 (middle), 147 (middle); S Harris 158 (top), 160 (top), 163 (top), 165 (top right); Harry Smith Photographic Collection 108 (top); Brian Hawkes 92 (middle); George Hyde 37 (bottom), 61, 62 (top), 114, 121 (top right); Institute for Terrestrial Ecology/Michael Way 42 (bottom); EA Janes 79;

Jack Laundon 70, 71; Mike Leach 46 (top), 134 (top), 158 (bottom); Mary Evans Picture Library 177 (bottom left); John Mason 56 (middle), 76, 92 (bottom), 118 (top), 121 (bottom); S & O Mathews 11; Richard T Mills 28 (middle right), 47, 49 (bottom), 125, 126 (bottom), 183 (top); Pat Morris 9 (top), 24 (upper middle), 45 (bottom), 126 (top), 163 (bottom), 168 (bottom), 169, 185 (middle), 186 (middle), 189 (bottom); Natural History Photographic Agency/AM Andrews 44 (bottom); JB Blossom 170; NA Callow 101 (middle), 102 (bottom), 110-11 (bottom), 115, 118 (middle); L Campbell 85 (top, bottom); DN Dalton 128; S Dalton 88 (bottom), 90 (middle), 98 (top), 102 (middle), 107 (top), 108 (bottom), 130, 184 (top); R Fotheringham 94 (bottom), 95 (middle right); JB Free 99; Brian Hawkes 74 (bottom), 96 (bottom), 138, 140-1, 185 (bottom); EA Janes 20 (top), 74 (top), 188; J Jeffery 112; RWS Knightsbridge 155 (bottom); WJC Murray 24 (top), 136 (middle, bottom), 167 (bottom); KG Preston-Mafham 49 (top); Jany Sauvanet 131 (bottom); M Savonius 23; JR Soothill 140 (bottom); MWF Tweedie 30 (bottom); Nature Photographers/SC Bisserot 50-51, 119 (bottom), 184 (bottom); FV Blackburn 75 (bottom), 77; D Bonsall 152 (bottom), 178; N Brown 106 (bottom); B Burbidge 59 (middle), 68 (bottom), 74 (middle); NA Callow 28 (middle left, bottom), 102 (top), 132 (bottom); AK Davies 38 (top), 154; Michael Gore 144 (top); MR Hill 151 (top); JV & GR Harrison 43; EA Janes 10, 146; Owen Newman 33 (middle), 171; WS Paton 152 (top); Don Smith 131 (middle); Paul Sterry 82 (bottom right), 86-7, 98 (bottom), 105; D Swindells 25; Roger Tidman 32 (top), 127 (bottom), 129 (top), 139 (bottom), 148 (top); D Washington 18, 46 (bottom); Keith Porter 32 (bottom); John F Preedy 173 (bottom); Premaphotos Wildlife/KG Preston-Mafham 14 (middle), 16 (top), 34 (middle), 72 (top), 75 (top),

82 (top), 85 (middle), 101 (bottom), 109 (bottom), 110 (top); Press-tige Pictures/D Avon & T Tilford 31 (top), 48 (middle), 156-7, 173 (top), 179, 180, 187; John Robinson 31 (bottom), 34 (bottom), 144 (bottom), 151 (middle, bottom), 155 (top), 160 (bottom), 161 (top); David Sewell 124, 168 (middle); Spectrum 183 (bottom); David Squire 52, 53; Roger Tidman 38 (bottom); 153; BS Turner 142; Michael Tweedie 120; UNHA/A Jollands 9 (bottom); P Morrison 165 (top left); Wildlife Matters/John Feltwell 42 (middle); Gerald Wilkinson 54; S Woodell 26; George Wright 22; Zefa/John Flowerdew 182 (bottom); Simon Warner 181.

Artists' credits Graham Allen/Linden Artists 156, 175 (top), 182, 183, 188; Norman Arlott 125, 126, 135, 136, 137, 143, 145; Craig Austen/The Garden Studio 83; Roger Bampton/The Garden Studio 53; Russell Barnett 141 (line), 167 (bottom); Sarah De'Ath 44; Wayne Ford 122, 128, 131, 133, 141, 147, 150, 153; Hayward Art Group title page, 56, 76, 77, 78, 79, 80, 81, 93, 179; Kristin Jakob/The Garden Studio 50; Felicity Kayes/The Garden Studio 117; Richard Lewington/The Garden Studio 92, 98, 99, 101, 102, 103, 104, 105, 111, 112, 113, 114, 115, 118; Josephine Martin/The Garden Studio 71; David More/Linden Artists 55, 60, 67; Sandra Pond 14, 64, 65, 71 (line), 84, 95, 96, 176; Gordon Riley 86, 89, 120 (colour); Colin Salmon (maps) 17, 70, 120, 128, 133, 139, 153, 175, 184; Helen Senior/Groom & Pickerill 57, 59, 61, 186; Phil Weare/Linden Artists 10-11, 15, 69; Ann Winterbotham 35.

Index compiled by Richard Raper of Indexing Specialists, Hove, East Sussex.

Typesetting PHOTOCOMP LTD, BIRMINGHAM; Printing & Binding PRINTER INDUSTRIA, GRÁFICA S.A. BARCELONA;
Separations YORK HOUSE GRAPHICS, HANWELL; COLOURSCAN OVERSEAS CO PTE LTD, SINGAPORE;
Paper KNP MILL, HOLLAND